THE REFRACTORY CARBIDES

REFRACTORY MATERIALS

A SERIES OF MONOGRAPHS

John L. Margrave, *Editor*

DEPARTMENT OF CHEMISTRY
RICE UNIVERSITY, HOUSTON, TEXAS

VOLUME 1. L. R. McCreight, H. W. Rauch, Sr., W. H. Sutton
Ceramic and Graphite Fibers and Whiskers
A Survey of the Technology

VOLUME 2. Edmund K. Storms
The Refractory Carbides

THE REFRACTORY CARBIDES

Edmund K. Storms

Los Alamos Scientific Laboratory
University of California
Los Alamos, New Mexico

1967

ACADEMIC PRESS NEW YORK AND LONDON

ACADEMIC PRESS INC.
111 Fifth Avenue, New York, New York 10003

United Kingdom Edition published by
ACADEMIC PRESS INC. (LONDON) LTD.
Berkeley Square House, London W.1

LIBRARY OF CONGRESS CATALOG CARD NUMBER: 66-30119

PRINTED IN THE UNITED STATES OF AMERICA

PREFACE

During the last ten years, an increasing interest in the refractory carbide systems has generated a large collection of data, much of which adds little understanding to the subject. It is clear that these systems are a good deal more difficult to investigate than many authors have suspected. This book, therefore, is intended as a guide to the chemist who wishes to undertake a fundamental study of these compounds.

No effort has been made to discuss all of the properties for which information is available. Rather, the selection is intended to give the reader information and some insights which are basic to any measurement. In general, early work which is clearly in error has been ignored except to show the difficulties in these attempts. Some unpublished research done at Los Alamos has been included to give a more complete presentation. In some systems, this work conflicts with accepted, or at least, published notions. In these cases, every effort has been made to present both viewpoints as fairly as possible. Since these measurements have not had the solidifying benefit of publication, minor changes might be made when publication is finally accomplished.

Dr. Melvin Bowman provided the environment wherein this effort could be made and a number of my colleagues at Los Alamos have been most generous with their comments and data. They include Dr. Allen Bowman, Dr. Terry Wallace, Mr. Willard Witteman, Mr. Andrew Yencha, and Mr. Nerses Krikorian. Dr. Allan Bowman and Dr. Aaron Goldman kindly supplied several of the computer programs used. In addition, advantage was taken of the Anifac program created by Dr. A. Larson and Dr. D. Cromer (LA–3335), and of the Herta program developed by Mr. R. E. Vogel and Dr. C. P. Kempter (LA–2317) as modified by Dr. A. Bowman. Mrs. Maxine Lewis and Mrs. Rose Mary Boicourt helped relieve much of the drudgery, which accompanies such an effort, by their good humor and secretarial talents.

E. K. STORMS

July, 1967

TABLE OF CONTENTS

CHAPTER XIII / **Discussion**

INTRODUCTION

This work includes a number of the more important physical and chemical properties of the nine transition elements included in Groups 4, 5, and 6 of the 4th, 5th, and 6th periods. The three actinide systems, Th–C, U–C, and Pu–C, have also been discussed. While this limited selection does not include all of the high melting carbides (many Group 3 and rare earth systems fall into this category), it does include the more refractory and the more useful ones. Besides, only for these systems has sufficient information been generated to make a critical review worthwhile.

These systems offer a unique collection of properties for an understanding of the chemical bond. They have very high melting points, which provide very wide temperature ranges for property measurements; they contain compounds which exist over a wide composition range; and they exhibit an unusual mixture of metallic, ionic, and covalent behavior. A number of theoretical treatments have been attempted but, as yet, a basic understanding has not been achieved. Part of this failure must result because so many measurements have been made on impure materials. For this reason, emphasis has been placed on the effect of impurities and the methods for their removal. Each system is discussed individually in terms of each property. These include phase relationship, lattice parameter and structure, chemical stability, hardness, and thermochemical properties which include vaporization behavior. In addition, the thermal data for the carbides and many of the associated elements have been reevaluated. Following a description of the various measurements, a general discussion is given of each property. Although no effort has been made to include the various theoretical treatments, a number of trends are revealed which might be useful for a future understanding.

The carbide systems are characterized by compounds which have a wide range of single phase composition. This is caused, in most cases, by defects in the carbon sublattice, and, for this reason, they are called defect compounds. Until this behavior was understood, many workers, starting with Hägg, in 1931, had described the phases as an interstitial solution of carbon in the metal lattice. Atom size considerations and experience with alloys added emphasis to this view. Unfortunately, such a model is rather poor in predicting properties in these systems. In addition, it creates unnecessary confusion, for example, when one wishes to indicate the interstitial sites between both the metal and the carbon atoms. If this description were applied to sodium chloride, which shares a common crystal structure with many of the carbides, one would have interstitial sodium atoms within a chlorine lattice. Most will admit this adds little insight from a chemist's viewpoint. Some authors have treated the nonstoichiometric compounds as a solid solution between the stoichiometric composition and the metal. While this leads, on some occasions, to an apparently correct prediction, it cannot be trusted. It is better to handle such compounds on the basis of the measured composition. Thus, equations must be written involving the actual stoichiometry which will not be integral nor will it, in some cases, be fixed. For this reason, it is important that data be obtained as a function of composition. Many of us will miss the Law of Definite Proportions which still simplifies chemistry in a few dwindling areas.

A number of expressions for composition are found in the literature, the most popular being weight percent, atomic percent, and atom ratio. The first is useful only in engineering, the second if solution theory is used, while the last simplifies the writing of chemical equations and emphasizes the defect nature of the compounds. For these reasons, all reported compositions have been converted to atom ratio in the text. Conversion to atomic percent is easily made through the identity: at.% = (C/M)/[1 + (C/M)].

The composition statement does not imply anything about the phases present in the sample. This decision must be based on the phase diagram. Thus, $MC_{0.56}$ might be a mixture of $MC_{0.5}$ and $MC_{0.7}$, both being the respective phase boundary compositions of the adjacent phases. When the general phase, irrespective of composition, must be described, the perfect lattice composition will be used, such as MC, M_2C, MC_2. If the perfect lattice is unknown, the designation MC_{1-x}, for example, will be used. Greek letters will be used only to designate allotropes, beginning with α for the low temperature form.

Thermodynamic quantities are given on the basis of one mole of metal, or, in other words, on the basis of a gram formula weight when written as MC_x.

All lattice parameters are given in angstrom units and the conversion from *kx* units is made by the factor 1.00202. In some cases, when the unit is in doubt, the value which would give the best agreement with later data has been used. In all cases, the original paper was consulted for a clarification of this vexing point.

In addition to the usual journals, an attempt has been made to include information which is found in various reports, both government and private. Many of these can be obtained for a small charge through the Clearinghouse for Federal Scientific and Technical Information, National Bureau of Standards, U.S. Department of Commerce, Springfield, Virginia.

THE REFRACTORY CARBIDES

I

THE TITANIUM–TITANIUM CARBIDE SYSTEM

A. PREPARATION

Early techniques for the preparation of TiC include its isolation from titanium-bearing cast iron (Shimer, 1887) and the reduction of TiO_2 by carbon (Moissan, 1895a, 1897a). The latter method is used today for the industrial production of the carbide; and, because of the technical importance of TiC, the reaction has been studied in some detail.

The oxide reduction starts at 935° (Elyutin *et al.*, 1958) and between 1000° and 1500° it proceeds through the following stages,* according to Samsonov (1956):

$$TiO_2 \rightarrow Ti_3O_5 \rightarrow Ti_2O_3 \rightarrow TiO \rightarrow TiC \text{ or } Ti$$

Kutsev and Ormont (1955) point out that the final product is better represented by the formula TiC_xO_y. At 1200° with a 10°/minute temperature rise, carbon-deficient TiC and/or Ti are produced. Higher temperatures and heating rates favor the formation of a more carbon-rich product (Nakagawa, 1957). The presence of CO is said to favor the formation of the carbide, with a higher temperature needed if the CO pressure is too low. Meerson and Krein (1952) conclude that a carbide closest to the 1 : 1 ratio is obtained under 1–10 torr of CO at 1600°–1700°. Krainer and Konopicky (1947), after heating various proportions of TiO_2 and carbon at 2100° for an unspecified time, obtained a carbide which contained at least 2% oxygen.

The preparation of TiC from TiS_2 and C, heated at 2000° for 3 minutes, has been reported by Schuler (1952).

* Temperatures are given in degrees Centigrade throughout this volume, except where degrees Kelvin are specified or in the sections on Thermochemical Properties. In these sections the temperatures are given in degrees Kelvin unless otherwise noted.

Titanium hydride and C begin to react in vacuum at 900° and result in the stoichiometric carbide after 1 hour at 1200° (Ogawa and Bando, 1959).

Campbell *et al.* (1949) formed the carbide by heating a tungsten wire in an atmosphere of $TiCl_4$, H_2, and hydrocarbon vapor. A carbon filament can also be used with similar results (Burgers and Basart, 1934). This method is useful for placing a protective layer on graphite.

The carbide has also been prepared according to the reaction

$$CaC_2 + 2TiCl_4 + 3H_2 \xrightarrow{800^\circ} 2TiC + CaCl_2 + 6HCl$$

A water wash easily frees the TiC of the CaC_2 and $CaCl_2$ (Imai *et al.*, 1957). Of course, unless the CaC_2 is free of hydroxide and oxide, pure TiC will not result.

Although a few percent oxygen may be satisfactory from a commercial point of view, attempts to measure the basic properties of such material have resulted in considerable disagreement. The last trace of oxygen is very difficult to remove, and it can cause a considerable change in the physical properties. Recently, the direct reaction of the elements, either in an arc furnace or as sintered powders, has been used to obtain oxygen-free carbide. Even by this method, considerable care must be taken to exclude oxygen or nitrogen from the environment. In addition, equilibrium conditions are difficult to realize because of the slow rate with which carbon diffuses through TiC. For example, the metal can be held above the melting point in a graphite crucible for a considerable time before it will be converted to the carbide. Some difficulty has been experienced even when arc melting was employed (Cadoff and Nielsen, 1953). Even if a pure carbide is obtained, subsequent heating can quickly contaminate the sample unless a very good vacuum is used.

B. PHASE RELATIONSHIP

The Ti–C system consists of one cubic compound having the general formula TiC. A probable phase diagram based on various measurements is shown in Fig. 1. Because of the great affinity this system has for oxygen and nitrogen and the marked influence these impurities have on the various physical and chemical properties, the accuracy of most measurements is considerably poorer than would be suspected.

The melting point of pure Ti metal is well established at 1668° $\pm$ 8° (Rudy *et al.*, 1965a; Deardorff and Hayes, 1956; Bickerdike and Hughes, 1959; Schofield and Bacon, 1953) and the α–β transition at 882.2° $\pm$ 0.5°

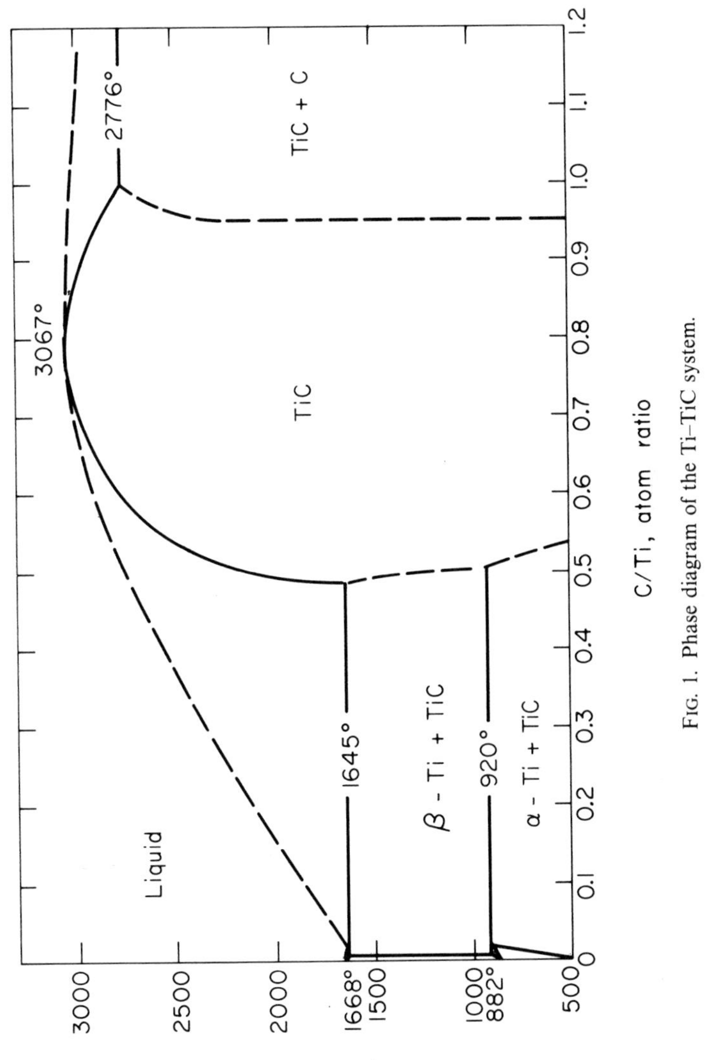

FIG. 1. Phase diagram of the Ti–TiC system.

(McQuillan, 1951; Duwez, 1951; Maykuth *et al.*, 1953). Both temperatures are raised by the dissolution of oxygen (Bumps *et al.*, 1953), thus accounting for the various higher values.

The addition of carbon lowers the melting point to a eutectic at 1645° ± 5° (Rudy *et al.*, 1965a; Bickerdike and Hughes, 1959). Samples containing between 0.5 and 2.5 wt % oxygen have been observed to melt at 1770° (L. Stone and Margolin, 1953). Apparently, peritectic melting reported by Cadoff and Nielsen (1953) and Kurnakov and Troneva (1962) was caused by the presence of oxygen in their samples.

Bickerdike and Hughes (1959) extrapolated the liquidus (see Fig. 2) to a eutectic composition of $TiC_{0.046}$. Rudy *et al.* (1965a) give a value below $TiC_{0.02}$ but point out the difficulty in obtaining this composition metallographically as they did.

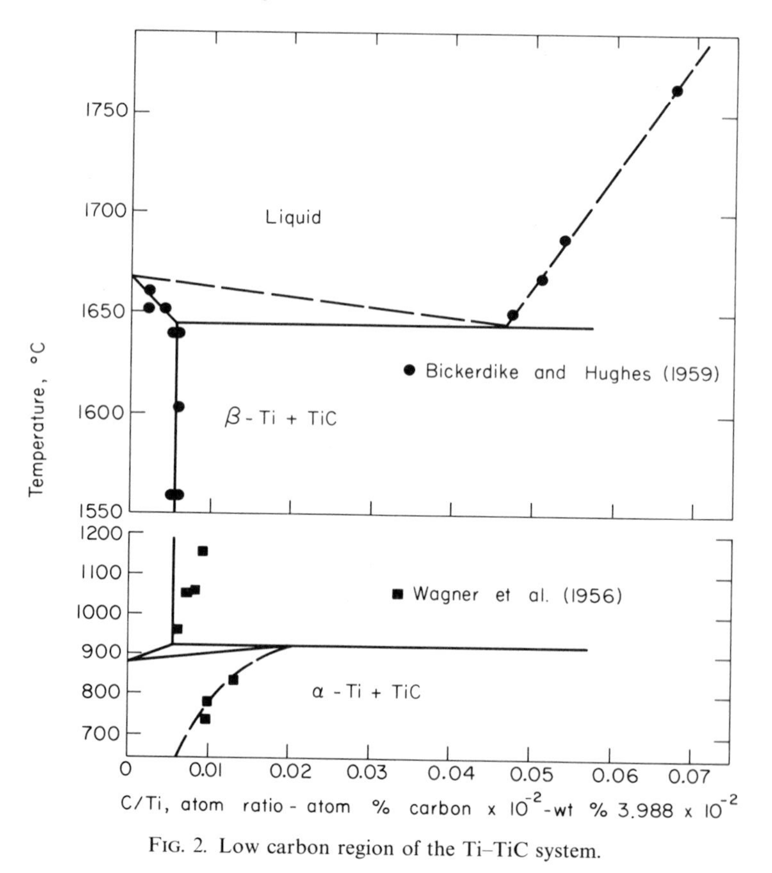

FIG. 2. Low carbon region of the Ti–TiC system.

The α–β transition is raised to a peritectoid near 920° (Rudy *et al.*, 1965a; Jaffee *et al.*, 1950; Cadoff and Nielson, 1953).

Although there is no doubt that titanium has a low solubility for carbon, the reported values show a wide variation. This is caused by the increased solubility of carbon in the presence of oxygen and nitrogen (L. Stone and Margolin, 1953). Therefore, most measurements give only an upper limit to the value. The two studies shown in Fig. 2 are in satisfactory agreement and they are consistent with the limits set by Jaffee *et al.* (1950). However, the values of Cadoff and Nielsen (1953) are much higher.

TiC has an extraordinarily wide composition range. At the Ti–TiC eutectic temperature the composition lies between $TiC_{0.47}$ (Rudy *et al.*, 1965a) and $TiC_{0.49}$ (Cadoff and Nielsen, 1953). Lower values reported by Ehrlich (1949), Rengstorff (1947), and Ragone (1951) were no doubt caused by oxygen contamination. Norton and Lewis (1963) give $TiC_{0.95}$ as the upper-phase boundary at 1950°. Rudy *et al.* (1965a) found a little free carbon in $TiC_{0.96}$ after cooling from 2750°, but this could have precipitated during cooling. Their value is the lower limit to the boundary at this temperature. After arc melting Ti + C ($TiC_{1.8}$) Storms (1966b) obtained a combined carbon content of $TiC_{0.988}$, thus setting a lower limit at the eutectic temperature. The melting point values determined by Rudy *et al.* (1965a) also suggest a composition near $TiC_{1.0}$ at the eutectic. Apparently, unlike the other Group 4 and 5 carbides, the stoichiometry of TiC in contact with graphite increases as the temperature is raised.

Between these composition limits the melting point of the phase rises from 1645° to a maximum of 3067° $\pm$ 15° near $TiC_{0.80}$ (Rudy *et al.*, 1965a) and then drops to the TiC + C eutectic at 2776° $\pm$ 6° (Rudy *et al.*, 1965a; Storms 1964). Other reported melting temperatures for TiC fall in the range from 2940° (Engelke *et al.*, 1960) to 3250° (Schwarzkopf and Kieffer, 1953). The general lack of analytical data, both for carbon and oxygen in the melted material, makes an interpretation of these latter measurements very difficult. Rudy *et al.* (1965a) find the eutectic composition near $TiC_{1.8}$, Kendall *et al.* (1965) give $TiC_{1.4}$, while Portnoĭ *et al.* (1961) are clearly in error with a value of $TiC_{5.7}$.

Two additional phases have been observed, but neither is part of the pure Ti–TiC system. A Ti_2C phase with a W_2C-type structure was claimed by Jacobson and Westgren (1933). Hydrogen has been found to dissolve in carbon-deficient TiC to produce a hexagonal Ti_2CH compound (Goretzki *et al.*, 1964; Rexer and Peterson, 1964) which accounts for this early observation. Raman and Ramachandran (1962) found a simple cubic lattice to result when ethylene was reacted with $TiCl_4$. A formula of TiC_2 was suggested on the basis of the lattice parameter although no analytical data were given. Efforts by Farr (1965) to reproduce this result were unsuccessful.

C. LATTICE PARAMETER AND STRUCTURE

The lattice parameters for Ti and TiC are shown in Table 1. Values are given for the quenched-in phase boundary composition at room temperature. The cubic β–Ti cannot be retained upon cooling. Calculated powder patterns for Ti and $TiC_{1.0}$ are listed in Tables 2 and 3, respectively.

The various studies of lattice parameter as a function of composition are compared in Fig. 3. Below $TiC_{0.65}$ there is good agreement between recent measurements but at higher compositions the scatter becomes pronounced. Rudy *et al.* (1965a) suggest that the parameter depends on the quenching temperature. There is, however, no consistent pattern in the various studies to support this suggestion. On the other hand, the difficulties in preparing TiC which is oxygen- and nitrogen-free are well known and these impurities lower the lattice parameter. With this in mind, a curve was drawn favoring the highest points. Where oxygen contents were given, the purest samples tend to fall closest to the curve

TABLE 1

STRUCTURE AND LATTICE PARAMETER OF Ti AND TiC

Phases in equilibrium	Composition of first phase	Structure type	Lattice parameter (Å)	Investigator
α-Ti	Pure	hcp (*A*3)	$a = 2.95111 \pm 0.00006$ $c = 4.68433 \pm 0.00010$	Wood (1962)
β-Ti	Pure at 25° (extrapolated from quenched alloys)	bcc (*A*2)	$a = 3.287 \pm 0.004$	Donohue (1963)
α-Ti + TiC	α-$TiC_{0.016}$	hcp (*A*3)	$a = 2.9550$ $c = 4.7025$	Cadoff and Nielsen (1953)
TiC + α-Ti	$TiC_{0.47}$ (quenched from 1650°C)	fcc (*B*1)	$a = 4.285$	Rudy *et al.* (1965a)
TiC	$TiC_{0.86}$ (maximum)	fcc (*B*1)	$a = 4.3305$	Norton and Lewis (1963)
TiC + C	$TiC_{1.0}$	fcc (*B*1)	$a = 4.3280$	See Fig. 3

TABLE 2

COPPER RADIATION, POWDER PATTERN FOR α-Ti[a]

2θ	$\sin^2\theta$	d spacing	Intensity	$h\ k\ l$
35.08	0.0908	2.5557	25	1 0 0
38.40	0.1082	2.3422	25	0 0 2
40.16	0.1179	2.2435	100	1 0 1
52.98	0.1990	1.7267	10	1 0 2
62.94	0.2725	1.4755	15	1 1 0
70.63	0.3342	1.3324	15	1 0 3
74.14	0.3633	1.2779	1	2 0 0
76.19	0.3807	1.2484	15	1 1 2
77.33	0.3904	1.2328	10	2 0 1
82.25	0.4326	1.1711	1	0 0 4
86.73	0.4715	1.1218	5	2 0 2
92.69	0.5234	1.0646	5	1 0 4
102.32	0.6067	0.9889	5	2 0 3
105.76	0.6358	0.9660	1	2 1 0
109.01	0.6629	0.9461	10	2 1 1
114.22	0.7051	0.9173	10	1 1 4
119.21	0.7440	0.8930	5	2 1 2
122.25	0.7668	0.8796	5	1 0 5
126.29	0.7959	0.8634	1	2 0 4
129.42	0.8175	0.8519	5	3 0 0
139.32	0.8792	0.8215	15	2 1 3
148.35	0.9257	0.8006	15	3 0 2
161.22	0.9734	0.7807	5	0 0 6

[a] $a_0 = 2.95111$ Å; $c_0 = 4.68433$ Å; $\mu r = 2.0$; structure type $A3$, space group No. 194; $\lambda(K\alpha_1) = 1.54051$ Å.

TABLE 3

COPPER RADIATION, POWDER PATTERN FOR $TiC_{1.0}$[a]

2θ	$\sin^2\theta$	d spacing	Intensity	$h\ k\ l$
35.91	0.0950	2.4988	75	1 1 1
41.70	0.1267	2.1640	100	2 0 0
60.45	0.2534	1.5302	80	2 2 0
72.35	0.3484	1.3049	50	3 1 1
76.12	0.3801	1.2494	30	2 2 2
90.78	0.5068	1.0820	20	4 0 0
101.75	0.6018	0.9929	35	3 3 1
105.48	0.6335	0.9678	70	4 2 0
121.35	0.7602	0.8834	85	4 2 2
135.26	0.8552	0.8329	65	5 1 1, 3 3 3

[a] $a_0 = 4.3280$ Å; $\mu r = 4.0$; structure type $B1$, space group No. 225; $\lambda(K\alpha_1) = 1.54051$ Å.

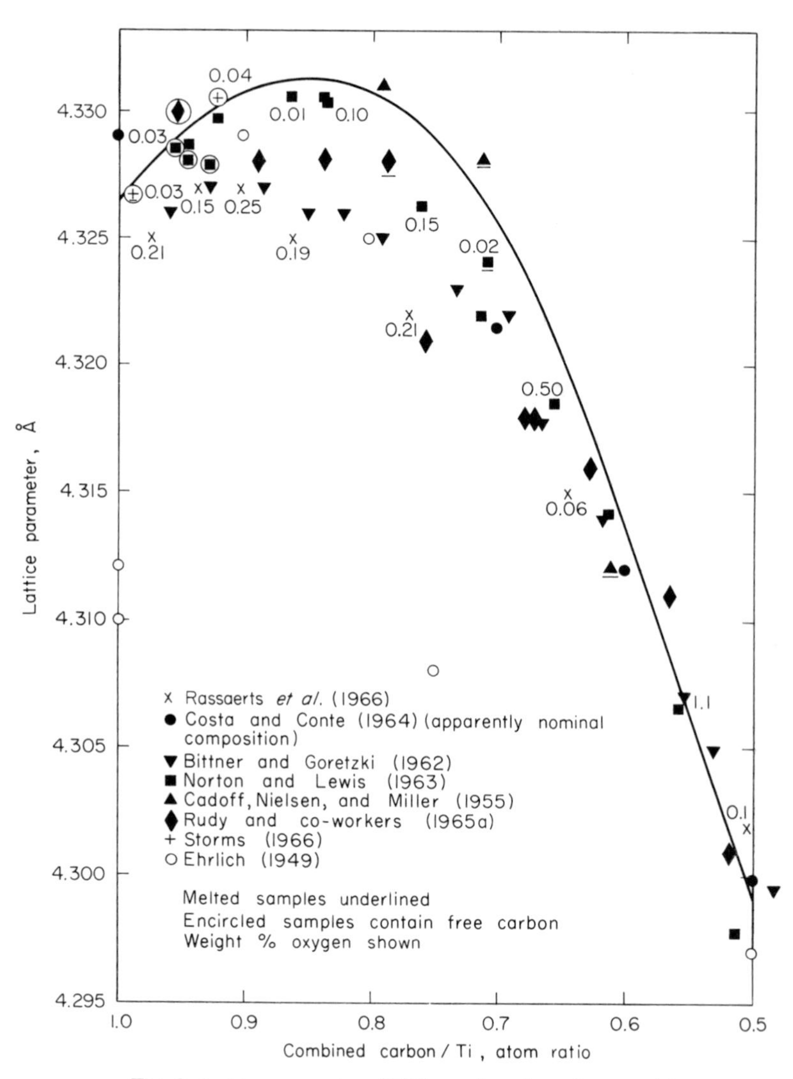

FIG. 3. Lattice parameter of TiC as a function of composition.

although the pattern is not perfect. It is important to realize that a quench from a higher temperature may result in a higher parameter simply because the treatment would produce a purer sample. It cannot be too strongly emphasized that any measurement using TiC should be accompanied by an oxygen as well as a carbon analysis.

The maximum in this curve, first observed by Norton and Lewis (1963), is similar to the one found in the Zr–C system. Later measurements of density by these authors show that it is not caused by a variable metal vacancy concentration. Precision density measurements by Storms (1966b) support this conclusion and place the number of metal atom vacancies at less than 0.5% of the total metal positions. In addition, Gorbunov *et al.* (1961), using neutron diffraction, found the carbon atoms statistically distributed in the octahedral voids and all the metal positions filled by Ti atoms.

Based on the curve in Fig. 3, the density decreases from 4.91 g/cm^3 at $TiC_{1.0}$ to 4.51 g/cm^3 at $TiC_{0.5}$.

D. APPEARANCE

TiC is metallic with no color. There is no noticeable change in its appearance with composition.

E. CHEMICAL REACTIVITY

1. Aqueous Solutions

$TiC_{0.95}$ is not attacked by hot or cold HCl, H_3PO_4, 20% NaOH, acetic acid, $H_2SO_4 + H_3PO_4$, or $H_2SO_4 + H_2C_2O_4$. The acids HNO_3, $HCl + HNO_3$, and $H_2SO_4 + HNO_3$ cause complete dissolution in less than 24 hours at room temperature, and $HClO_3$ only when heated. A mixture of $4HNO_3 + HF$ is very corrosive at all temperatures (Kopyleva, 1961). Although TiC is resistant to aqueous alkali, the presence of oxidizing agents (Br_2, H_2O_2, or potassium ferricyanide) will result in a gradual attack (Kopyleva, 1961; Moissan, 1895a; Friedrich and Sittig, 1925; Ehrlich, 1949; Schwarzkopf and Kieffer, 1953).

2. Hydrogen

TiC is considered structurally stable in static H_2 up to 2400°C (May and Hoekstra, 1961; Ohlinger, 1959a). However, the action of H_2 is complicated by the rapid change in carbon and titanium activity with composition. As carbon is removed from $TiC_{1.0}$ by the formation of hydrocarbons, the carbon activity will be reduced, and in a static system further reaction will cease. In flowing H_2, extensive decarbonization can result and can lead to additional sample loss by the increased evaporation rate for Ti. Competition between these two processes can result in a solid composition considerably below $TiC_{1.0}$. In addition, the carbon-deficient lattice can dissolve hydrogen.

3. Nitrogen

Almost complete nitriding will occur between 1000° and 1300° in 1 atm of N_2. At lower pressures or higher temperatures, the carbide will form a solution with variable nitrogen content depending on the conditions. For example, at 1500° and 45 torr, TiC contains 7.3% nitrogen while between 1800° and 2500° at 1 torr the nitrogen content probably does not exceed 0.01% (Zelikman and Govorit, 1950).

4. Oxygen

In the vicinity of 450°, oxidation produces a nonadherent anatase (TiO_2) layer which is nonprotecting (Macdonald and Ransley, 1959). From 700°, where a minimum in the oxidation rate occurs, to at least 1000° a protective rutile film forms and a parabolic oxidation rate results (Nikolaiski, 1960; Münster, 1959; Samsonov and Golubeva, 1956). Since the oxidation rate of TiC and its temperature dependence is essentially the same as that for pure titanium, a similar rate-controlling mechanism is probably operating in both cases, i.e., the diffusion of oxygen through the oxide layer (Berkowitz-Mattuck *et al.*, 1963; Nikolaiski, 1960; Webb *et al.*, 1956). Both the Ti and C are oxidized at the same rate at 1000° (Webb *et al.*, 1956) even though the pressure of CO at the TiC–TiO_2 interface is very low. In addition, the presence of carbon in the TiO_2 phase has been observed (Webb *et al.*, 1956; Nikolaiski, 1960). These observations have led various workers to suggest that carbon also diffuses through the TiO_2 layer to be oxidized at the outer surface. Observations by Webb *et al.* (1956) indicate that $TiC_{0.63}$ is oxidized more rapidly than is $TiC_{1.0}$, although this has not been confirmed.

5. Carbon Monoxide

CO reacts with TiC to give an oxide, carbon, and an oxygen-saturated carbide. The final equilibrium can be written as

$$TiO_{1.7} + (1.7 - y + x)C = TiC_xO_y + (1.7 - y)CO$$

where $x + y \leqq 1$. The TiC phase can not only dissolve a variable amount of oxygen but can contain nonmetal vacancies (Kutsev and Ormont, 1955; Meerson and Krein, 1952). Nishimura and Kimura (1954) observed a number of fixed compositions of the oxycarbide depending on the starting materials and the reaction conditions. These variables make a meaningful measurement of the equilibrium CO pressure difficult and has led to considerable variation in reported measurements, as shown in Fig. 4. For this reason, the pressure of CO should not be used for thermochemical calculations.

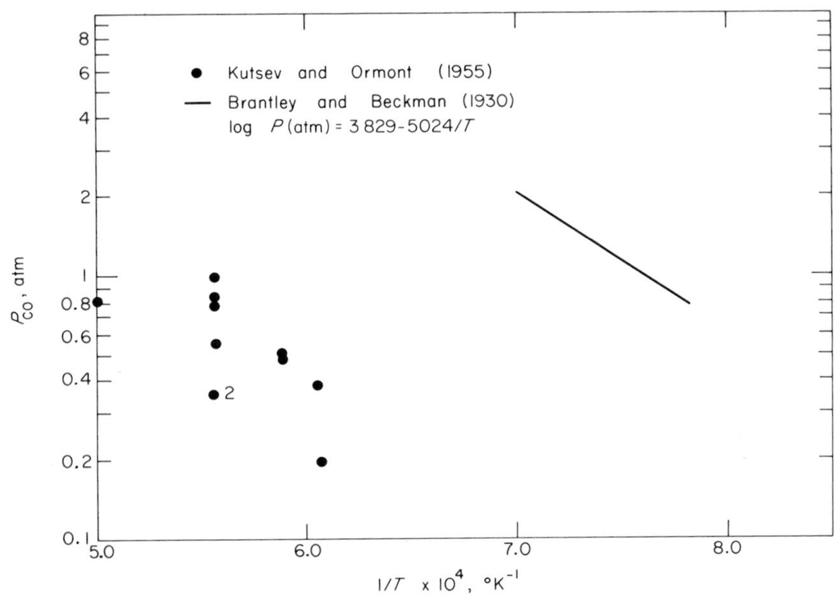

FIG. 4. CO pressure over TiC_xO_y as a function of temperature.

6. CARBON DIOXIDE

CO_2 reacts readily with TiC at 1200° according to the reaction $3CO_2 + TiC = 4CO + TiO_2$ (Pollard and Woodward, 1950).

7. METALS

At 1800°, liquid Fe and Ni penetrate the TiC and surround each grain without reacting, Si forms a black interface, Zr shows a slight reaction, and Mo does not react (Kingery and Halden, 1955).

F. HARDNESS

Cadoff *et al.* (1955) obtained, with a 300-g load, a Vickers hardness with values between 1600 and 2800 and an S-shaped variation with composition. With a 35-kg load the Vickers hardness increased linearly from 225 to 400 across the composition range (Cadoff and Palty, 1952).

The presence of oxygen raised the hardness and caused brittleness. Koval'skii and Makarenko (1953) also found a linear variation which extrapolated to 2900 kg/mm^2 at $TiC_{1.0}$. This agrees with a complete study by W. S. Williams and Lye (1964) where a linear variation from 1900 kg/mm^2 at $TiC_{0.8}$ to 2900 kg/mm^2 (extrapolation) at $TiC_{1.0}$ (50-g load) was found. In addition, the hardness measured on the [100] cleavage planes is orientation-dependent, resulting in a sinusoidal change between 2550 kg/mm^2 and 2850 kg/mm^2. This phenomenon is probably typical of the other refractory carbides. Jones (1956) reported 3100 DPH (diamond pyramid hardness) when graphite was present. Meerson and Umanskii (1953) cite a value of 2850 kg/mm^2 without giving a composition. Gilman and Roberts (1961) give 3200 kg/mm^2, which agrees with the value found by Kieffer and Kölbl (1949). W. S. Williams (1961) obtained 2300 kg/mm^2 from a large single crystal of TiC containing graphite precipitated along the [111] plane. TiC appears to be one of the hardest pure carbides known.

G. THERMOCHEMICAL PROPERTIES

1. Heat of Formation

A determination of ΔH°_{298} by combustion calorimetry gave -43.9 ± 0.4 kcal/mole for a composition near $TiC_{1.0}$ (Humphrey, 1951). The carbide was $TiC_{0.996}$ (total carbon) with 0.60% impurities and was the same material used by Naylor (1946) for his heat capacity measurement. This becomes -44.1 kcal/mole when a more recent value for the heat of formation of TiO_2 is used (Mah *et al.*, 1957). The heat produced by the direct reaction between the elements above 1320° has been used to calculate a standard heat of formation of -45.5 ± 4.6 kcal/mole for an unstated composition (Lowell and Williams, 1961).

2. Heat Content and Heat Capacity

The high temperature heat content measurements of Naylor (1946) and those of Levinson (1965), shown in Fig. 5, are in excellent agreement with each other although slightly different compositions were used. Osment (1963) gives values which not only show a good deal of scatter but which are much higher than the other studies. Using data from Naylor (1946) and Levinson (1965) and fixing C_p(298.15°) at 8.08 cal/mole-deg and the equation to zero at 298.15°, a least-squares fit was made which resulted in the curves in Fig. 5. The resulting heat capacity is compared

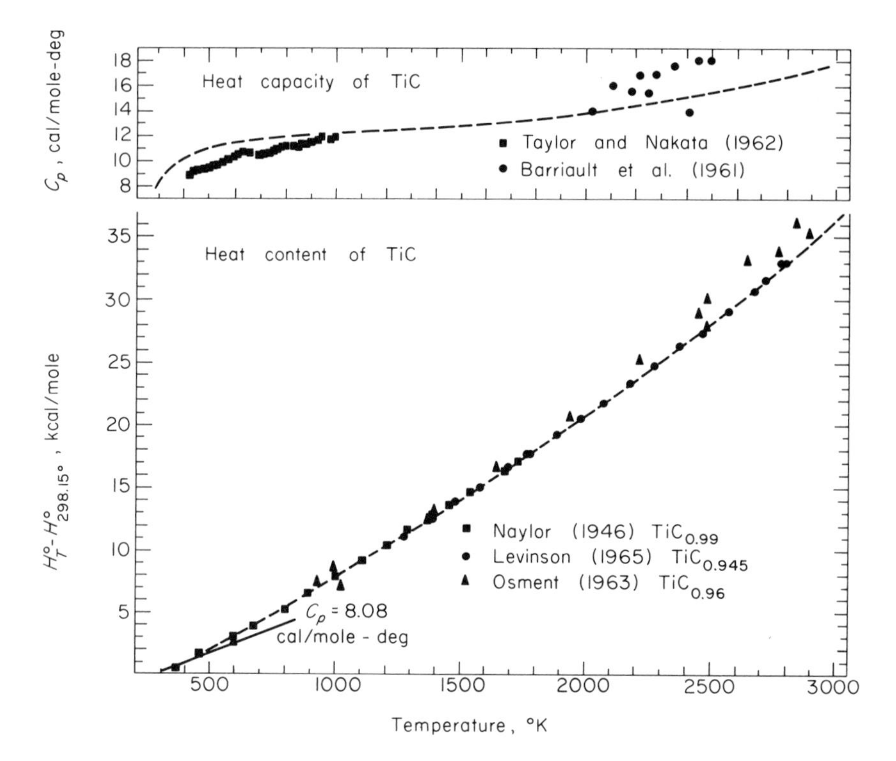

FIG. 5. High temperature heat capacity and enthalpy of $TiC_{1.0}$.

in the figure to several direct measurements obtained from pulsed heating techniques. It is interesting to notice that C_p begins to increase with an increasing rate after about 1500°.

Using this equation and the low temperature measurements of Kelly (1944), as revised by Kelley and King (1961), values for the thermal functions were calculated for $TiC_{\sim 1.0}$ up to 3000° and are listed in Table 4.

3. VAPORIZATION

Chupka *et al.* (1958) were unable to obtain mass spectrometric evidence for the molecular species, TiC. In spite of this, Bolgar *et al.* (1961) have concluded from Langmuir experiments that there is a molecular species which decomposes just after leaving the surface. Their values for the evaporation rate are so unreasonably high and their conclusion (see Nb–NbC system) is so unlikely that their results should be viewed with doubt. In a later work Fesenko and Bolgar (1963) report values which

TABLE 4
THERMAL FUNCTIONS OF $TiC_{\sim 1.0}$[a]

T, (°K)	$H^\circ_T - H^\circ_{298}$ (cal/mole)	C°_p (cal/mole-deg)	S°_T (cal/mole-deg)	$-(F^\circ_T - H^\circ_{298})/T$ (cal/mole-deg)
298.15	0	8.080	5.790	5.790
300	15.00	8.136	5.840	5.790
400	939.7	10.07	8.487	6.138
500	1995	10.93	10.84	6.848
600	3112	11.38	12.87	7.687
700	4264	11.64	14.65	8.557
800	5437	11.82	16.22	9.419
900	6626	11.96	17.62	10.25
1000	7829	12.08	18.88	11.05
1100	9043	12.21	20.04	11.82
1200	10270	12.33	21.11	12.55
1300	11510	12.47	22.10	13.25
1400	12760	12.62	23.03	13.91
1500	14030	12.79	23.91	14.55
1600	15320	12.97	24.74	15.16
1700	16630	13.18	25.53	15.75
1800	17960	13.40	26.29	16.31
1900	19310	13.65	27.02	16.86
2000	20690	13.92	27.73	17.38
2100	22100	14.21	28.41	17.89
2200	23530	14.52	29.08	18.38
2300	25000	14.85	29.73	18.86
2400	26500	15.20	30.37	19.33
2500	28040	15.58	31.00	19.78
2600	29620	15.98	31.62	20.23
2700	31240	16.40	32.23	20.66
2800	32900	16.84	32.83	21.09
2900	34610	17.31	33.43	21.50
3000	36360	17.80	34.03	21.91

[a] $H^\circ_T - H^\circ_{298.15} = -5.3007 \times 10^3 + 13.296T - 9.7189 \times 10^{-4}T^2 + 3.8451 \times 10^{-7}T^3 + 4.2124 \times 10^5/T$ (298.15°–3000°, cal/mole, ± 0.5%), M.W. = 59.91.

are much lower, as shown in Fig. 6. Fujishiro and Gokcen (1961b) obtained the pressure of Ti over TiC, from the weight lost by a graphite Knudsen effusion cell, but the calculated pressures were much higher than would be predicted from the measured thermodynamic functions. This discrepancy was pointed out, but no reason was suggested. Vidale

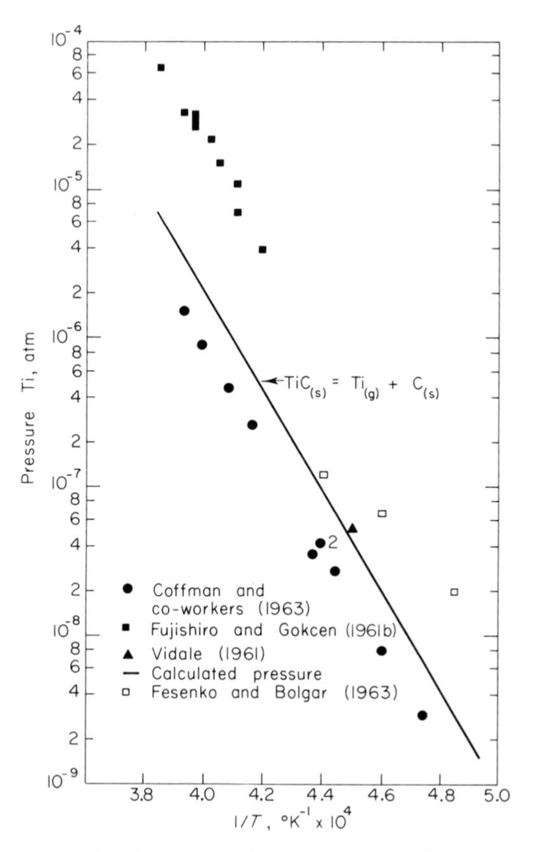

FIG. 6. Pressure of $Ti_{(g)}$ over TiC + C.

(1961) finds a pressure of Ti over the metal at 1666°K which is equal to the metal pressure over $TiC_{(s)} + C_{(s)}$ at 2220°, according to measurements by resonance line absorption. Langmuir experiments, done at the General Electric Company, have been summarized in a report by Kibler *et al.* (1963). Since a significant fraction of the lost weight is carbon, it is necessary to know the vapor composition to obtain the Ti pressure. These workers assumed C_1 as the only carbon species with an evaporation rate equal to that of Ti.

The various measurements are compared in Fig. 6 to the Ti pressure calculated from thermochemical measurements. This was based on $\Delta H°(\text{formation})_{298.15} = -44.1$ kcal/mole, a heat of vaporization for titanium of 113.2 kcal/mole [from a recalculation of the data of Edwards *et al.* (1953) using thermal functions in the JANAF Tables] the free energy functions listed in Table 4 for TiC and those adopted by the JANAF Thermochemical Panel (1960) for $Ti_{(g)}$ and $C_{(s)}$. This gives

$$\log P(\text{atm}) = 7.652 - 3.360 \times 10^4/T$$

as the pressure of Ti over TiC + C. Thus, the system loses Ti preferentially at all temperatures below 2500°.

Using a mass spectrometer, Storms (1966b) measured the Ti pressure over various compositions in this system. When the machine calibration factor is adjusted to make the measured pressure over the metal equal to the Langmuir pressure obtained by Edwards *et al.* (1953), the values for TiC + C agree well with the absolute measurements. In fact, the calculated

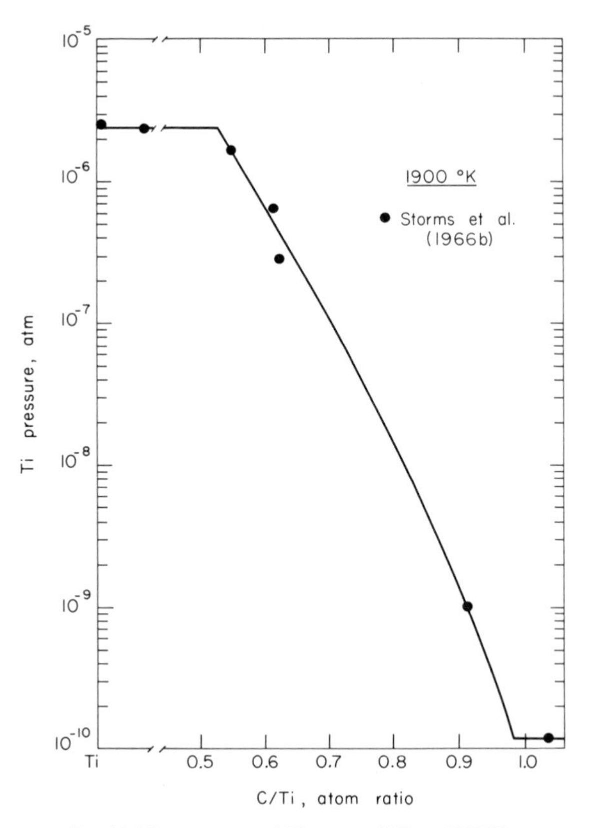

FIG. 7. The pressure of $Ti_{(g)}$ over TiC at 1900°K.

and measured heat of vaporization agree within 0.8 kcal/mole. Most of this difference probably is due to an error in the heat of formation (Humphrey, 1951). The change in pressure with composition at 1900° is shown in Fig. 7, and the partial molar heat of vaporization for Ti in Fig. 8. Additional work will be needed before these relationships will be

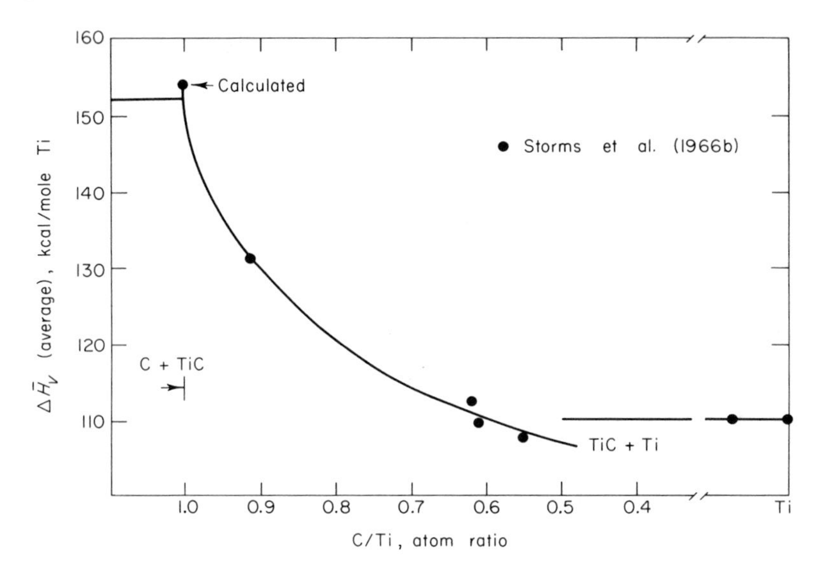

FIG. 8. Average partial heat of vaporization for $Ti_{(g)}$ as a function of composition.

fully defined, but they are consistent with the discussion in Chapter XIII and with similar measurements in the Zr–C and U–C systems.

II

THE ZIRCONIUM–ZIRCONIUM CARBIDE SYSTEM

A. PREPARATION

As early as 1865, ZrC was prepared from zirconia and carbon by Troost. Somewhat later, Moissan (1893a) prepared the carbide by the same reaction in the electric arc. Almost all early measurements were based on material made by heating ZrO_2 and graphite, usually in an evacuated furnace.

The reduction of ZrO_2 proceeds in three steps with the formation of Zr_2O_3, then ZrO, and finally the carbide. The Zr_2O_3 begins to form at 940°–960°, and ZrO is produced above 1240° (Meerson and Samsonov, 1952; Samsonov, 1956). The overall reaction is best written as

$$ZrO_2 + 2.63C = ZrC_{0.71}O_{0.08} + 1.92CO$$

according to Kutsev *et al.* (1955). On the other hand, Henney and Jones (1964) claimed to have obtained two fcc oxycarbides with the approximate formulas $ZrC_{0.45}O_{0.55}$ and $ZrC_{0.5}O_{0.5}$ by heating ZrO_2–C mixtures. Attempts to remove this oxygen by heating under various conditions are summarized in Table 5. Only melting lowered the oxygen impurity to acceptable levels. A similar experience was reported by Norton and Lewis (1963). In their case, samples of ZrH + C heated for 3 hours as high as 2200° in vacuum still retained sufficient oxygen to lower the lattice parameter significantly. As a general rule, pure ZrC heated below ~1800° will getter oxygen until its oxygen content reaches several percent. Only by first melting, then annealing in a good vacuum at the temperature of interest, can the final purity be assured.

Although arc melting the elements together will result in a pure carbide, composition homogeneity and reproducibility are difficult to obtain. This is due to a combination of rapid evaporation which moves the surface to the congruent composition ($ZrC_{<0.85}$); the density difference between

TABLE 5
RESULTS OF HEATING ZrO_2 + C UNDER VARIOUS CONDITIONS

Temp. (°C)	Time (hr)	Initial composition		Final composition		a_0 of fcc phase	Conditions
		Wt % ZrO_2	Wt % C	Wt % O	Wt % C		
1600	24	60	40	0.74[b]	34	4.699	Vacuum
2000	1	77	23	>0.2	11.5	4.700	Vacuum
2100	½	77	23	0.85[b]	14.6	4.698	Argon
2500	¼	77	23	~0.3	12.7	4.700	Argon
2000	¼	84	16	9	6.1	4.675[c]	Flowing Ar
2000	¼	86	14	15	4.4	4.675[c]	Flowing Ar
2500[a]	¼	—	—	8.3	5.0	4.645	Flowing Ar
				<0.1	6.8	4.692	Arc-melted
				<0.2	8.4	4.698	Arc-melted
				<0.1	9.2	4.701	Arc-melted
				<0.4	14.0	4.699	Arc-melted

[a] Portion of previously tabulated sample.
[b] Vacuum fusion—others obtained by (100 − wt % Zr − wt % C).
[c] Contains ZrO_2.

the reactants and the carbide; and the slow diffusion rate of carbon through the carbide coat which initially surrounds the graphite. If a graphite electrode is used, carbon can be picked up from it.

The reaction between ZrH and C has been used to prepare the carbide. Since ZrH is very reactive, its potentially high oxygen content can carry over into the carbide.

Crystalline deposits of ZrC can be formed from the gas phase containing $ZrCl_4 + H_2$ and a hydrocarbon vapor. The reaction goes between 1730° and 2430° (Campbell *et al.*, 1949).

Unfortunately, the correct oxygen content of ZrC is difficult to obtain by analysis. Platinum fusion has been used but unusually high temperatures must be resorted to if all the oxygen is to be extracted.

B. PHASE RELATIONSHIP

Like the other members of this group, the Zr–C system contains one cubic compound. A phase diagram based on a number of studies is shown in Fig. 9. Although the position of the various boundaries is fairly well established, the influence of an unrecognized oxygen, and, to a lesser

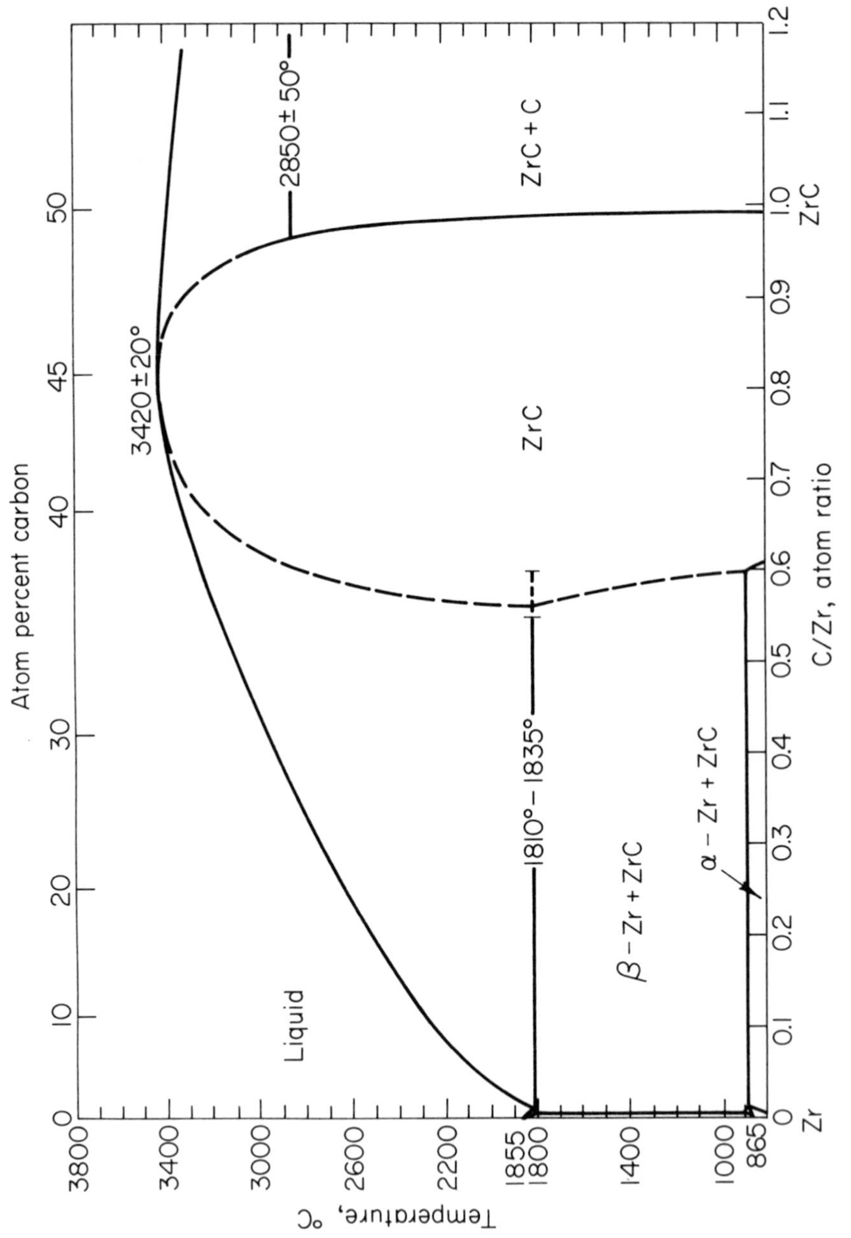

FIG. 9. Phase diagram of the Zr–ZrC system.

extent, nitrogen, impurity has caused much disagreement between the various investigations. All experimental values for which an oxygen content was not given should be considered as approximations.

The melting point of Zr metal is 1855° ± 15° (Deardorff and Hayes, 1956; J. T. Williams, 1955; Domagala and McPherson, 1954; deBoer and Fast, 1930). Higher values have been observed (Sara, 1965a; Rudy *et al.*, 1965a), but since the presence of oxygen raises the melting point (Domagala and McPherson, 1954), the lower value is preferred. The α–β transition occurs at 865° (Duwez, 1951; Domagala and McPherson, 1954), and it also is raised by dissolved oxygen.

Carbon lowers the melting point to a eutectic which has been found at 1810° (Farr, 1962), 1850° (Sara, 1965a), 1830° (Benesovsky and Rudy, 1960), and 1835° ± 15° (Rudy *et al.*, 1965a). Since one would expect oxygen to raise this temperature, 1810° should be considered as a lower limit with 1835° as the upper limit. The α–β transition is raised slightly by carbon to a peritectic which has been reported to lie at 885° (Sara, 1965a) and at 872° ± 15° (Rudy *et al.*, 1965a).

A rather wide range of values has been claimed for the lower composition limit of the ZrC phase. Most workers neither determined the oxygen content nor demonstrated that the ZrC composition existed at the temperature from which the sample was quenched. Sara (1965a) gives $ZrC_{0.63}$ by extrapolating the rather vertical solidus to the eutectic temperature. A metallographic examination by Rudy *et al.* (1965a) of Zr + ZrC which had been quenched from the eutectic temperature places the terminal composition no higher than $ZrC_{0.60}$. Farr (1962) obtained a lower limit of $ZrC_{0.55}$ by chemically removing free zirconium from melted material and determining the combined carbon content of the residue. Metallographic examination has consistently shown no secondary Zr precipitated within the ZrC after cooling. This leads to the conclusion that either the Zr–ZrC boundary is essentially vertical or that the precipitation rate is slow compared to the cooling rate. Which of these conclusions is correct is not yet clear. The upper-phase limit apparently changes from $ZrC_{0.965}$ at the ZrC + C eutectic temperature to $ZrC_{0.98}$ at 2400° (Farr, 1962).

From the Zr–ZrC eutectic, the melting point increases rapidly to a maximum of 3420° ± 20° (Farr, 1962; Rudy *et al.*, 1965a; Sara, 1965a) and then drops to a eutectic with carbon. Recent values for the eutectic temperature are 2800° ± 50° (Anderson *et al.*, 1950), 2850° ± 50° (Farr, 1962), 2850° (Sara, 1965a), 2870° ± 30° (Wallace *et al.*, 1963), 2920° ± 50° (Portnoĭ *et al.*, 1961), and 2911° ± 12° (Rudy *et al.*, 1965a).

Rudy *et al.* (1965a) place the ZrC–C eutectic composition at $ZrC_{1.82}$; Sara (1965a) gives $ZrC_{1.86}$; Anderson *et al.* (1950) find $ZrC_{1.80}$; and Kendall *et al.* (1965) report $ZrC_{1.90}$, all in surprisingly good agreement.

Although no other phases in this system have been confirmed, it has been suggested by Shaffer (1963) and in a later paper by Miccioli and Shaffer (1964) that ZrC has a phase transition between 2000° and 2200°. This conclusion was based on the behavior of the emissivity, resistivity, and thermal expansion of $ZrC_{0.98}$. However, efforts to find this transition by D. K. Smith and Cline (1963) using a high temperature x-ray diffractometer were unsuccessful up to 2680°. The study by Sara (1965a) showed no evidence for this phase when thermal analysis and metallographic techniques were used. In addition, a redetermination of the emissivity and electrical conductivity of very pure ZrC by Grossman (1965) gave no indication of the phenomenon reported by Shaffer (1963). He did, however, observe an increase in the spectral emittance of ZrC with time as it was held in a vacuum of 5×10^{-7} torr at 1400°K. Flashing at 2400°K returned the emittance to its initial low value. He suggested that a reaction product layer forms (probably an oxycarbide) at low temperatures and attributed Shaffer's results to this. The phenomenon is discussed further in the chapter on TaC (Chapter VI, Section B).

If Zr dissolves in graphite, its solubility is less than 0.01 wt % (Godin *et al.*, 1961).

TABLE 6

STRUCTURE AND LATTICE PARAMETER OF Zr AND ZrC

Phases in equilibrium	Composition of first phase	Structure type	Lattice parameter (Å)	Investigator
α-Zr	Pure at 29°C	hcp (*A*3)	$a = 3.23168 \pm 0.0001$ $c = 5.14764 \pm 0.0003$	Lichter (1960)
β-Zr	Pure at 25° (extrapolated from quenched alloys)	bcc (*A*2)	$a = 3.587$	Donohue (1963)
ZrC + Zr	$ZrC_{0.58}$	fcc (*B*1)	$a = 4.691 \pm 0.003$	See Fig. 10
ZrC	$ZrC_{0.83}$	(Maximum)	$a = 4.7017 \pm 0.0005$	See Fig. 10
ZrC + C	$ZnC_{0.97}$	fcc (*B*1)	$a = 4.6983 \pm 0.0003$	Sara *et al.* (1963)

C. LATTICE PARAMETER AND STRUCTURE

The probable lattice parameters for the pure Zr and ZrC phases are listed in Table 6. Values are given for the quenched-in phase boundary compositions at room temperature. The cubic β-Zr cannot be retained upon cooling. Calculated powder patterns for α-Zr and $ZrC_{0.96}$ are shown in Tables 7 and 8, respectively.

Various recent studies of the lattice parameter variation of ZrC are compared in Fig. 10. Except for the upper cluster of points, there is an

TABLE 7

COPPER RADIATION, POWDER PATTERN FOR α–Zr[a]

2θ	$\sin^2 \theta$	*d* spacing	Intensity	*h k l*
31.94	0.0757	2.7992	25	1 0 0
34.83	0.0896	2.5738	25	0 0 2
36.51	0.0981	2.4592	100	1 0 1
47.98	0.1653	1.8947	15	1 0 2
56.93	0.2272	1.6161	15	1 1 0
63.54	0.2772	1.4629	20	1 0 3
66.78	0.3029	1.3996	5	2 0 0
68.50	0.3167	1.3687	20	1 1 2
69.54	0.3253	1.3506	15	2 0 1
73.53	0.3582	1.2869	5	0 0 4
77.58	0.3924	1.2296	5	2 0 2
82.41	0.4339	1.1693	5	1 0 4
90.50	0.5044	1.0846	10	2 0 3
93.44	0.5300	1.0580	5	2 1 0
96.02	0.5524	1.0363	15	2 1 1
99.83	0.5854	1.0067	10	1 1 4
103.84	0.6196	0.9786	5	2 1 2
105.72	0.6355	0.9663	5	1 0 5
108.80	0.6611	0.9473	1	2 0 4
111.28	0.6815	0.9331	5	3 0 0
117.58	0.7315	0.9006	15	2 1 3
122.82	0.7710	0.8772	10	3 0 2
127.74	0.8060	0.8580	1	0 0 6
136.49	0.8626	0.8293	10	2 0 5
139.77	0.8817	0.8203	5	1 0 6
140.94	0.8883	0.8173	5	2 1 4
144.81	0.9086	0.8081	5	2 2 0
165.62	0.9843	0.7764	10	3 1 0

[a] $a_0 = 3.2323$ Å; $c_0 = 5.1477$ Å; $\mu r = 2.0$; structure type *A*3, space group No. 194; $\lambda(K\alpha_1) = 1.54051$ Å.

TABLE 8

COPPER RADIATION, POWDER PATTERN FOR $ZrC_{0.96}$[a]

2θ	$\sin^2\theta$	*d* spacing	Intensity	*h k l*
32.99	0.0806	2.7126	100	1 1 1
38.28	0.1075	2.3491	80	2 0 0
55.25	0.2150	1.6611	45	2 2 0
65.88	0.2957	1.4166	40	3 1 1
69.21	0.3225	1.3563	15	2 2 2
81.96	0.4300	1.1746	10	4 0 0
91.22	0.5107	1.0779	20	3 3 1
94.31	0.5375	1.0506	25	4 2 0
106.86	0.6451	0.9590	20	4 2 2
116.83	0.7257	0.9042	25	5 1 1, 3 3 3
136.07	0.8601	0.8305	15	4 4 0
151.81	0.9407	0.7942	55	5 3 1
159.26	0.9676	0.7830	60	6 0 0, 4 4 2

[a] $a_0 = 4.6983$ Å; $\mu r = 2.0$; structure type *B*1, space group No. 225; $\lambda(K\alpha_1) = 1.54051$ Å.

enormous variation in the measurement. Many of the older studies, which are not shown, give much lower values. The technique for measuring lattice parameters is too precise and the possible variation in stoichiometry is too small to account for this wide scatter. It is clear that an unsuspected and variable impurity is causing this effect. The few reported oxygen contents show that 100 ppm has little effect, and ten times this amount is noticeable. Most studies in this system were apparently based on very impure material, if the reported lattice parameters are an indication. If this is indeed the case, many properties must be remeasured before this system can be understood.

The curve leads to a density of 6.59 g/cm^3 and 6.33 g/cm^3 at $ZrC_{0.97}$ and $ZrC_{0.58}$, respectively.

D. CHEMICAL REACTIVITY

1. AQUEOUS SOLUTIONS

The chemical reactivity of ZrC is somewhat greater than that of TiC. It is essentially inert to cold concentrated HCl, H_2SO_4, H_3PO_4, $H_2C_2O_4$, $HClO_4$, and $H_2SO_4 + H_3PO_4$. However, cold HNO_3, HCl + HNO_3, or dilute $H_2SO_4 + H_3PO_4$ and the oxidizing acids when heated dissolve the carbide. A mixture of HNO_3 + HF is very corrosive at all temperatures. Although alkali solutions have no effect, the presence of Br_2, H_2O_2,

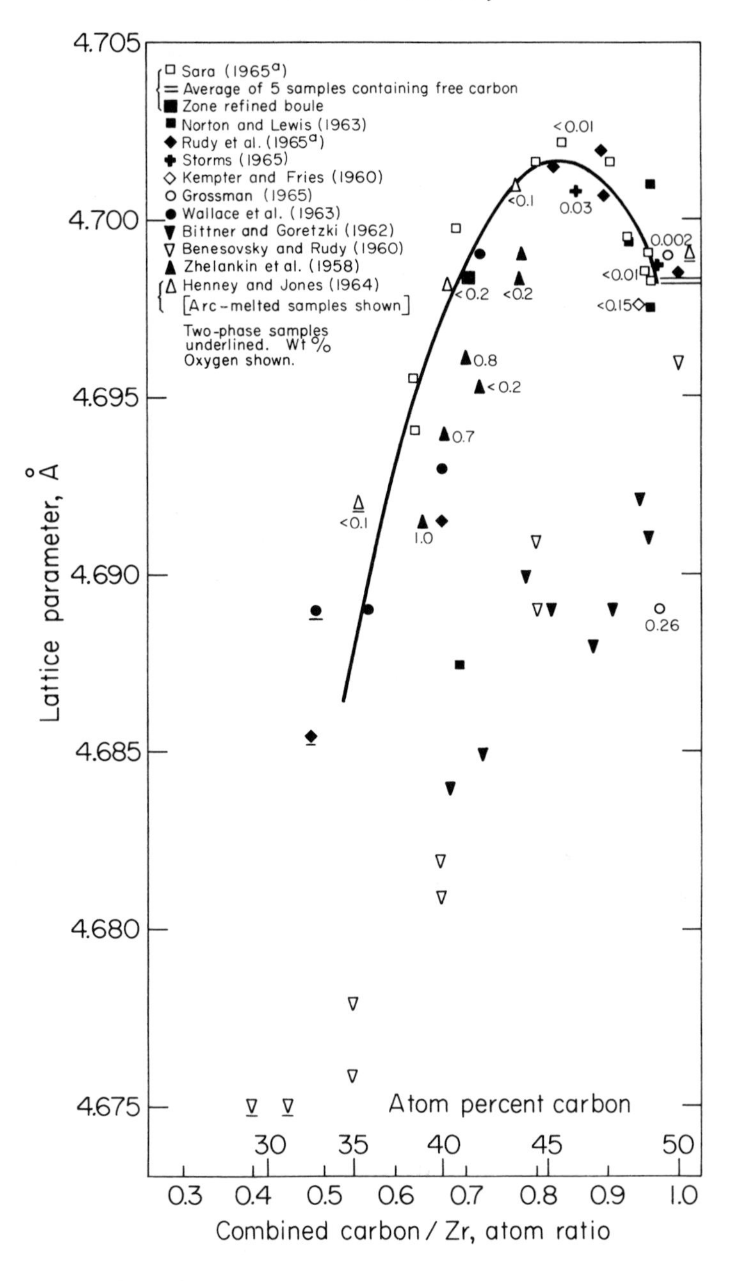

FIG. 10. Lattice parameter of ZrC as a function of composition.

or $K_3Fe(CN)_4$, when warmed, cause a gradual attack (Kopyleva, 1961). Carbon-deficient ZrC is more reactive to water at 315° than is carbon-saturated Zr (Coriou *et al.*, 1959).

2. Oxygen

ZrC oxidizes rapidly above 500°. Unlike TiC, a protective film of oxide is not formed, and the resulting oxidation rates follow a linear law. Between 450° and 580°, and in oxygen pressures below 1 atm, Bartlett (1963) found mostly cubic ZrO_2 in the oxide layer. He suggests that at pressures above 5×10^{-3} atm, where the oxidation rates become pressure-independent, the formation of the oxycarbide and ZrO_2 take place concurrently. Below this pressure, only ZrO_2 forms. In the temperature interval 853°–1927°, Berkowitz-Mattuck (1963) found mostly the monoclinic ZrO_2. In addition, Zr and C were shown to oxidize at the same rate. Part of the high oxidation rate exhibited by ZrC at low temperatures is probably due to the way the oxygen attacks the structure. Photomicrographs published in a subsequent report (McClaine, 1963) show an oxide layer which follows the grain boundaries and mechanically separates these grains from the bulk material, thus increasing the oxidizing area. However, above 1300° there is apparently enough plasticity to keep the sample intact.

3. Nitrogen

Heating in nitrogen will convert the carbide to the carbonitride and eventually to the nitride.

4. Carbon Monoxide

As with TiC, the reaction between CO and ZrC leads to an oxycarbide of uncertain composition. Prescott (1926) measured the pressure of CO over what he thought was a mixture of ZrO_2, C, and ZrC. This data was represented by the equation: $\log P(CO) = 8.592 - 16{,}580/T$ (1880°–2016°K). A similar study by Hollahan and Gregory (1964) using torsion effusion gave the equation $\log P(CO) = 6.55 - 16{,}100/T$ (1422°–1520°K). They found a pressure drop with time when a large orifice was used, and powdered samples gave a lower pressure than did pelletized material. Kutsev *et al.* (1955) have reported a few CO pressure measurements between 1814° and 2020°K, giving the equation $\Delta F = 138{,}000 - 69.0T$ for the reaction $ZrO_2 + 2.63C = Zr_{0.71}O_{0.08} + 1.92CO$. The use of an oxycarbide containing different oxygen and vacancy concentrations is no doubt the reason for the marked difference between the studies.

E. HARDNESS

The hardness of ZrC is in some doubt. Meerson and Umanskii (1953) cite a value of 2836 kg/mm^2 obtained by Soviet investigators, Kieffer and Kölbl (1949) give 2600 kg/mm^2, Jones (1956) obtained 2200 DPH. The variation of hardness with composition was found to be linear by Koval'skii and Makarenko (1951). Their curve extrapolates to 2700 kg/mm^2 at $ZrC_{1.0}$, while at $ZrC_{0.52}$ 1850 kg/mm^2 was measured. A similar result by Samsonov and Rozinova (1956) leads to 2900 kg/mm^2 and 2000 kg/mm^2 as the limits. However, because of the very low lattice parameters (4.582–4.683 Å) and the wide homogeneity range ($ZrC_{0.27}$–$ZrC_{1.0}$) reported by the latter workers, the presence of considerable oxygen and/or nitrogen can be inferred.

F. THERMOCHEMICAL PROPERTIES

1. Heat of Formation

An early combustion determination of $\Delta H_f^\circ(298.15^\circ)$ by Mah and Boyle (1955) led to -44.1 ± 1.5 kcal/mole for a possibly impure sample. A recent redetermination by Mah (1964) gave -47.0 ± 0.6 kcal/mole for two samples; one analyzing $ZrC_{0.93}$ with 0.11% free carbon, 0.18% N, and 0.17% O, and the other of $ZrC_{0.99}$ containing 0.12% Ti, 0.07% N, 0.05% O, and an unstated amount of free carbon. When $ZrC_{0.71}$ containing 0.5% O, 0.22% N, and 0.12% Ti was burned, a heat of formation of -33.1 ± 0.8 kcal/mole was obtained. The impurity content of the latter sample is sufficiently high to make a knowledge of its chemical form important. Mah assumed the oxygen was present as ZrO_2, and the Ti and B were both uncombined. If, on the other hand, the oxygen were dissolved as $ZrO_{0.7}$, the boron as $ZrB_{0.7}$, and the titanium as $TiC_{0.7}$, a heat of formation of -30.8 kcal/mole for $ZrC_{0.73}$ results. Thus, the reported value could be in error by a good deal more than indicated.

2. Low Temperature Heat Capacity

The low temperature properties of $ZrC_{0.96}$ were determined between 5.59° and 345.16° by Westrum and Feick (1963). Unfortunately, the final calculations were based on a composition of $ZrC_{1.0}$ with corrections for the hypothetical free Zr content. Based on the actual composition, their data give the following values at 298.15°: $C_p = 9.016$ cal/mole-deg, $S^\circ = 7.927$ eu, $H_{298.15}^\circ - H_0^\circ = 1394$ cal/mole.

3. High Temperature Heat Content

The various high temperature thermal studies are compared in Fig. 11. There is excellent agreement between the two studies using carbon-

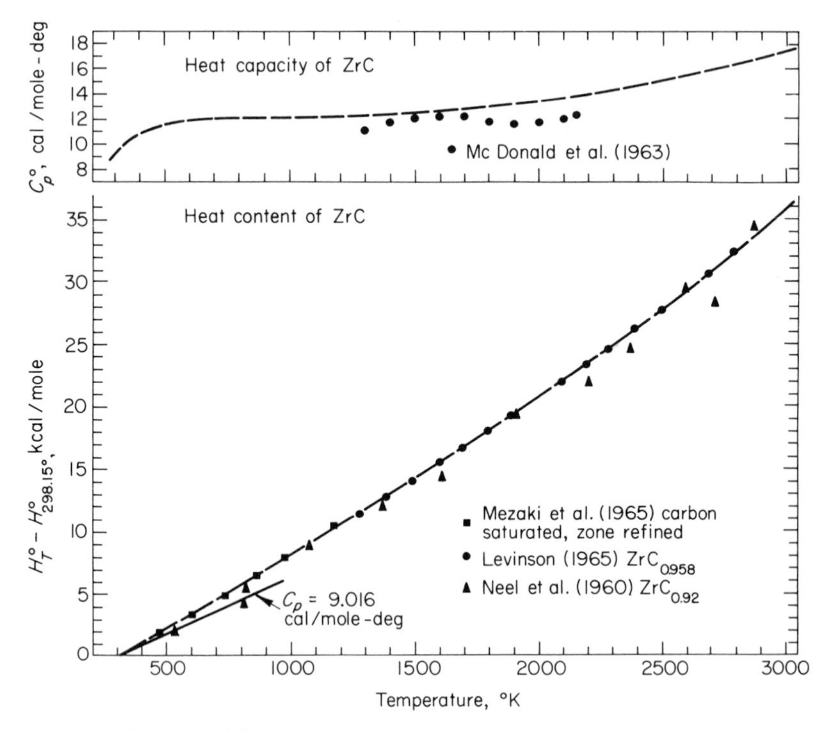

Fig. 11. High temperature heat capacity and enthalpy of $ZrC_{0.96}$.

saturated ZrC ($ZrC_{0.96}$). The low values obtained by Neel *et al.* (1960) may be due to the low carbon content of their sample. Using the results of Levinson (1965) and Mezaki *et al.* (1965), a least-squares curve was fit which gave the curve in Fig. 11 and the equation in Table 9. For this fit, C_p° and $H_T^\circ - H_{298.15^\circ}^\circ$ at 298.15° were fixed at 9.016 cal/mole-deg and zero, respectively. The resulting heat capacity curve, also shown in Fig. 11, is compared to a direct measurement using pulse heating techniques. Such a study (not shown) by Barriault *et al.* (1961), at AVCO, gave a constant value of 20 cal/mole-deg between 1600° and 2500°. This high value, as they suggest, was probably due to the high impurity content of their sample.

Using the adjusted low temperature measurements of Westrum and Feick (1963) and the above equation, thermal functions were calculated and are listed in Table 9, from 298.15° to 3000° for $ZrC_{0.96}$.

TABLE 9

THERMAL FUNCTIONS OF $ZrC_{0.96}$[a]

T (°K)	$H_T^\circ - H_{298.15}^\circ$ (cal/mole)	C_p° (cal/mole-deg)	S_T° (cal/mole-deg)	$-(F_T^\circ - H_{298.15}^\circ)/T$ (cal/mole-deg)
298.15	0	9.016	7.927	7.927
300	16.73	9.066	7.983	7.927
400	1021	10.76	10.86	8.308
500	2136	11.45	13.35	9.074
600	3299	11.77	15.47	9.967
700	4485	11.93	17.29	10.89
800	5683	12.01	18.89	11.79
900	6887	12.07	20.31	12.66
1000	8095	12.11	21.58	13.49
1100	9309	12.16	22.74	14.28
1200	10530	12.22	23.80	15.03
1300	11750	12.30	24.78	15.74
1400	12990	12.39	25.70	16.42
1500	14230	12.51	26.56	17.07
1600	15490	12.65	27.37	17.69
1700	16760	12.81	28.14	18.28
1800	18050	13.00	28.88	18.85
1900	19360	13.22	29.59	19.39
2000	20700	13.46	30.27	19.92
2100	22060	13.73	30.93	20.43
2200	23450	14.02	31.58	20.92
2300	24860	14.34	32.21	21.40
2400	26310	14.69	32.83	21.86
2500	27800	15.07	33.43	22.31
2600	29330	15.47	34.03	22.75
2700	30900	15.90	34.62	23.18
2800	32510	16.36	35.21	23.60
2900	34170	16.84	35.79	24.01
3000	35880	17.35	36.37	24.41

[a] $H_T^\circ - H_{298.15}^\circ = -5.4298 \times 10^3 + 14.228T - 1.5583 \times 10^{-3}T^2 + 4.6364 \times 10^{-7}T^3 + 3.9173 \times 10^5/T$ (298.15°–3000°, cal/mole, ±0.2%); M.W. = 102.75; $H_{298.15}^\circ - H_0^\circ = 1394$ cal/mole.

4. VAPORIZATION

A calculation of the Zr pressure over $ZrC_{1.0}$ + C, based on the thermal values in Table 9 for $ZrC_{0.96}$, the JANAF tables (1963) for $Zr_{(g)}$ and $C_{(s)}$, a heat of formation of −47.0 kcal/mole for the carbide, and a heat of vaporization of 145.4 kcal/mole for the metal, leads to the equation

$$\log P(\text{atm}) = -4.161 \times 10^4/T + 7.586$$

As can be seen in Fig. 12, the Knudsen measurements of Pollock (1961) and the optical absorption work of Vidale (1961), both done in a graphite environment, show excellent agreement with this calculation. However, the various Langmuir experiments, although they are internally consistent, give much higher pressures. Pollock (1961) noted a higher lattice parameter on the surface of evaporated plugs than in the interior. Coffman

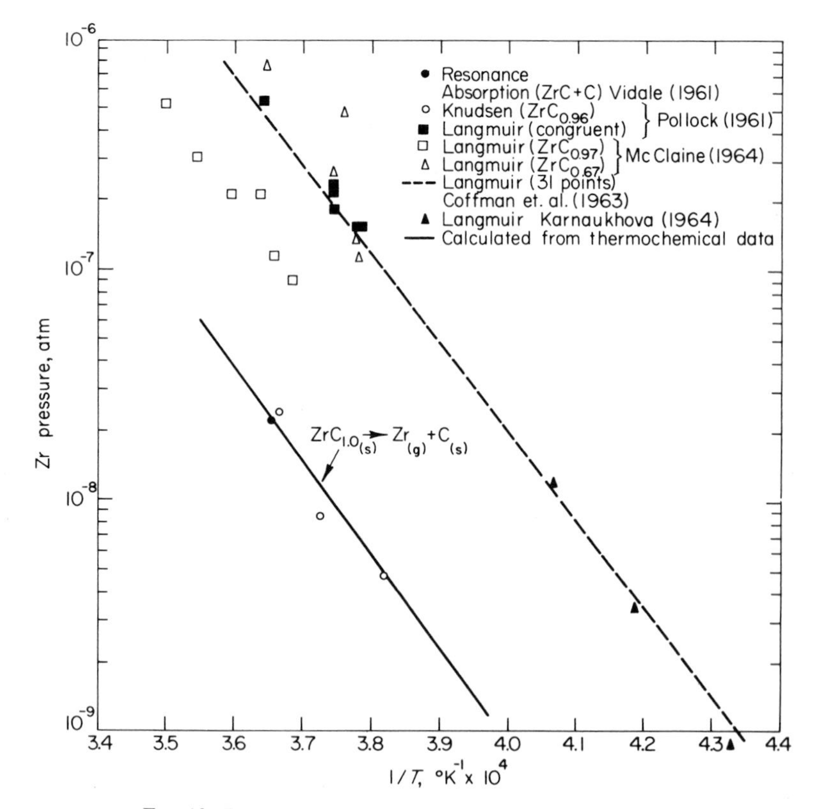

FIG. 12. Pressure of $Zr_{(g)}$ over ZrC as a function of temperature.

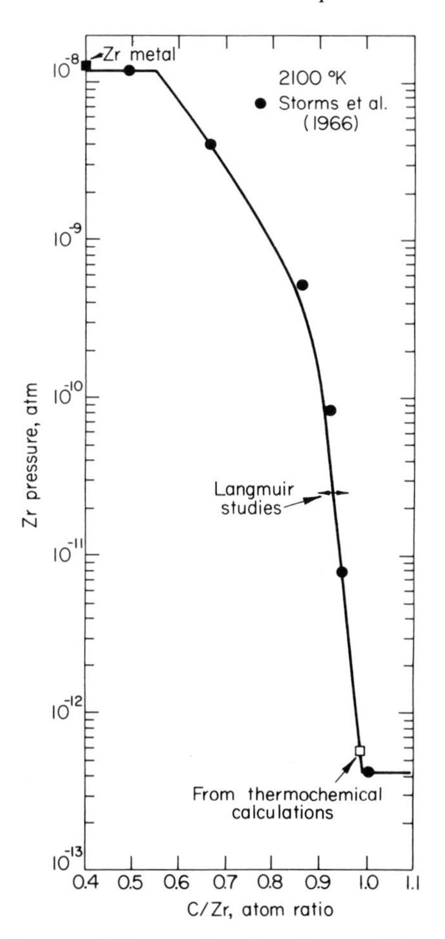

FIG. 13. Pressure of $Zr_{(g)}$ as a function of composition at 2100°K.

et al. (1963) also found that free evaporation of carbon-saturated ZrC resulted in a parameter increasing to $a_0 = 4.700$. In both cases, the congruent composition was assumed to lie very near $ZrC_{1.0}$. The increasing lattice parameter was thought to result from an increase in the combined carbon content. Both of these assumptions are false. The carbide is congruently vaporizing between $ZrC_{0.82}$ (Farr, 1965) and $ZrC_{0.87}$ (Sara, 1965a) near 3000°C. Also, coincidentally, the maximum lattice parameter occurs near this composition. Thus, any noncongruent sample heated in vacuum will show an increasing parameter as material is lost. Of course, part of this increase may result from purification. Since

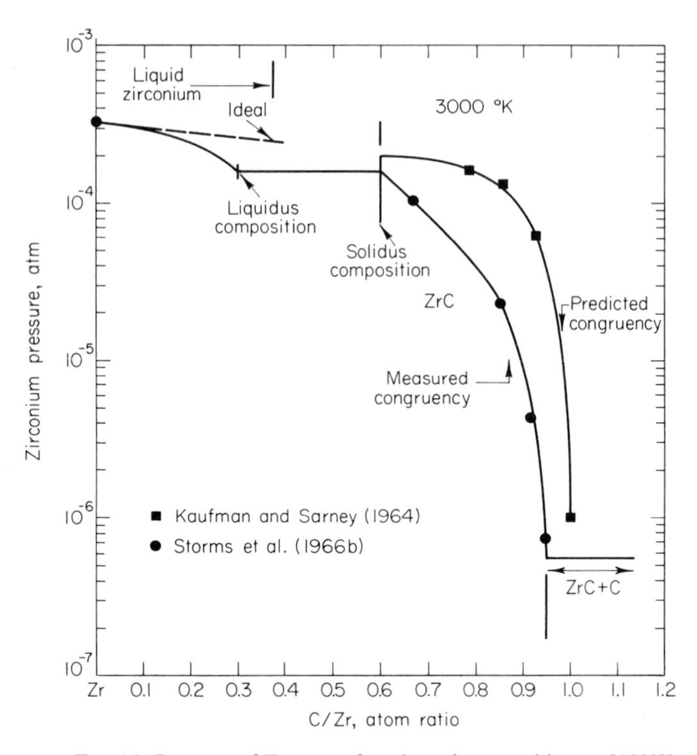

FIG. 14. Pressure of $Zr_{(g)}$ as a function of composition at 3000°K.

none of the Langmuir studies started at the congruent composition, a concentration gradient in the plug might have influenced the evaporation rate. However, when a starting composition of $ZrC_{0.67}$ (McClaine, 1964) was used, the evaporation rate eventually equaled that of the other studies. Apparently, the composition gradient has little effect on the evaporation rates. Thus, the Langmuir pressures are indeed characteristic of the congruent composition. Since the congruent composition will change with temperature, the slope of the Langmuir pressure curve has little thermodynamic importance.

Recently, Storms (1966b) made a study of the zirconium pressure both as a function of composition and temperature, using a mass spectrometer. If the instrument calibration is adjusted to make the pressure over pure Zr metal consistent with the Langmuir measurements of Skinner *et al.* (1951), the resulting pressure over ZrC + C agrees very well with the absolute measurements of Pollock (1961) and Vidale (1961). Between these extremes, the pressure changes at 2100° as shown in Fig. 13. It is easy to see why there is a large difference between the pressures over ZrC + C and those over the congruent composition even though there is only a small composition difference. Attempts by Kaufman and Sarney (1964) to predict this behavior show rather poor agreement with the measurements at 3000°, as shown in Fig. 14, and their calculated congruent composition is not only inconsistent with direct measurements, but it apparently falls within the two-phase region at this temperature. The second law partial heat of vaporization, Fig. 15, also shows a rapid

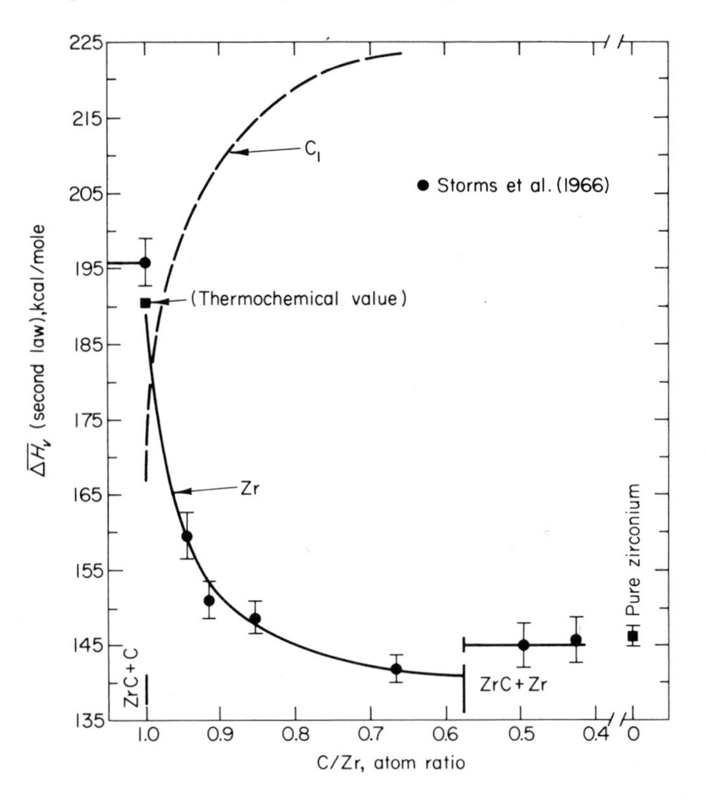

FIG. 15. Average partial heat of vaporization of $C_{1(g)}$ and $Zr_{(g)}$ from ZrC as a function of composition.

change as the stoichiometric composition is approached. Agreement with the calculated value at $ZrC_{0.98}$ is excellent, and the single-phase and two-phase slopes show a relationship which is consistent with the phase diagram (see Chapter XIII, Section G). The partial heat of vaporization of C_1, calculated from the relationship

$$\Delta H_f = \Delta H^\circ_{Zr} - \Delta \bar{H}_{Zr} + C/Zr(\Delta H^\circ_C - \Delta \bar{H}_C),$$

is also shown in the figure. At the congruent composition, the partial heat of carbon is much higher than that of Zr. Hence, congruent vaporization will move down in composition as the temperature is raised. In fact, it should become very temperature sensitive near the melting point.

III

THE HAFNIUM–HAFNIUM CARBIDE SYSTEM

A. PREPARATION

As with the other carbides, HfC is often prepared by the reduction of the oxide by graphite. The reaction

$$HfO_2 + 2.9C = HfC_{0.95}O_{0.05} + 1.95CO$$

has been studied between 1743° and 2033°K by Zhelankin *et al.* (1961), for which they obtain a ΔH_T of -132.3 kcal/mole. In this temperature interval and under 70–1000 torr of CO, an oxycarbide of constant composition was formed. Samsonov and Paderno (1961) reported that at 1000°–1200° this reduction proceeded through Hf_2O_3; at 1300°–1800° the HfC–HfO solid solution formed; and, finally, between 1800° and 2000° HfC formed with a carbon-deficient lattice. Repeated 1-hour heatings at 1900° resulted in a product near $HfC_{1.0}$.

Moers (1931) pioneered the technique whereby HfC is produced from the reaction $HfCl_4 + CH_4 + (H_2) = HfC + 4HCl + (H_2)$. Campbell *et al.* (1949) have used this reaction to form a coating of HfC on a heated tungsten filament.

The purest HfC can be produced by reacting the elemental powders either by arc melting or by powder metallurgy. Like the other elements in this group, Hf does not react quickly with carbon. Therefore, some patience is needed to obtain a uniform product when starting with the elements. Also, like the other members, HfC is very difficult to obtain in an oxygen-free state. In fact, experience would suggest that, of all the carbides, this one is the most difficult to purify. Only by melting or heating in a good vacuum above ~2500° can the oxygen content be reduced to acceptable levels. The reaction between hafnium hydride and C goes much more quickly and also can produce an oxygen-free product if precautions are taken to purify the resulting carbide at a high temperature (Nowotny *et al.*, 1959).

B. PHASE RELATIONSHIP

With few exceptions there have been no studies of the effect of oxygen and nitrogen impurities on the Hf–C system. It is not unreasonable, however, to expect this system to behave like the other members of Group 4 in this regard. An additional difficulty is created by the frequent presence of zirconium, which generally depresses the various properties. When the zirconium content is given, the reported measurements have been corrected assuming the mixed system to have a linear variation of the property between end members of equal carbon content.

The results of various melting point studies of hafnium metal are listed in Table 10. After correcting for the zirconium content, a value between 2222° and 2233° seems to be favored. Since oxygen raises the melting point, the lower value obtained by Deardorff and Hayes (1956) is preferred. However, in view of the basic agreement, the error on this measurement can be reduced to ±10°. A similar problem occurs in choosing a value for the α–β transition temperature. A complete study by N. H. Krikorian and Wallace (1964a) has shown that Zr lowers the temperature by

TABLE 10
MELTING POINT DETERMINATIONS FOR HAFNIUM METAL

Observed melting point (°C)	Atomic % zirconium	Corrected melting point (°C)	Oxygen (ppm)	Investigator
2222 ± 30	0.015	2222	120	Deardorff and Hayes (1956)
2230 ± 20	<0.04	2230	<1900	N. H. Krikorian and Wallace (1964a)
2218 ± 6	4.0	2233	680	Rudy (1965)
2208	4.8	2226	~2000	Sara (1965b)
2207	4.8	2225	?	deBoer and Fast (1930)
2157	36.3	2329	?	deBoer and Fast (1930)
2190	4.4	2206	?	A. Taylor *et al.* (1963)
2130[a]	1.6	2155[b]	?	Litton (1951)
1975[c]	1.3	—	—	Adenstedt (1952)

[a] Based on a surface temperature and an emissivity of 0.43 ($\lambda = 0.65\ \mu$).
[b] Corrected using an emissivity of 0.40 (N. H. Krikorian and Wallace, 1964a).
[c] Probably the Hf–W eutectic, as suggested by Deardorff and Hayes (1956).

$11.2° \pm 11.1°$/at. %, and oxygen and nitrogen raise it by $16.1° \pm 5.0°$/at. % and $83.6° \pm 101°$/at. %, respectively. The final extrapolated temperature was reported as $1740° \pm 20°$. This is in good agreement with measurements by Deardorff and Kato (1959) both with respect to the transition temperature ($1750° \pm 20°$) and the effect of Zr (13.5°/at. %). The measurements of Gibson *et al.* (1958) (1735°); Geissen *et al.* (1962) ($1755° \pm 20°$), Siemens *et al.* (1964) ($1750° \pm 20°$); and Bedford (1964) ($1757° \pm 30°$) also agree, but the values of Rudy (1965) ($1795° \pm 35°$); Fast (1952) (1950°); A. Taylor and Doyle (1964) (1950°); and Ross and Hume-Rothery (1963) ($1995° \pm 70°$) are significantly higher. In view of the effect of oxygen and nitrogen and the general absence of a final analysis for these impurities in the latter works, the higher values should be discounted. As an example of the great care which is needed in this measurement, Romans *et al.* (1965) observed an increase from 1777° to 1950° 5 minutes after the vacuum had been worsened from 5×10^{-6} to 5×10^{-5} torr. Even at 1×10^{-6} torr, the transition temperature slowly increased.

Recent efforts to determine the phase relationship in the low carbon region of the system have resulted in considerable disagreement, as can be seen in Fig. 16. Avarbe *et al.* (1962) proposed that the α form of Hf melts peritectically in contact with the β form and this in turn melts peritectically in contact with HfC at 2820°. Sara and Lowell (1964) found only the β form to melt peritectically, and this occurred in contact with HfC at 2240°. On the other hand, Rudy (1965) observed a narrow eutectic region between the α- and β-Hf at $2180° \pm 10°$ and a peritectic between the β structure and HfC at $2360° \pm 30°$. If this system is indeed as complicated as it would appear, many of the subtle features could have been easily overlooked in the various studies, so some disagreement is understandable. However, the reported melting temperatures differ greatly. Rudy (1965) suggests, as a possible explanation, that these differences are caused by the difficulty in observing incipient melting in this region. It is more probable, as proposed by Sara and Lowell (1964), that the spread in values owes, mainly, to an oxygen impurity. Oxygen is known to increase the melting temperature in this region in the other Group 4 carbide systems. Whether this can have an effect sufficient to explain the very high values of Avarbe *et al.* (1962) is not known.

The low carbon limit to the HfC phase is $HfC_{0.52 \pm 0.01}$ at the invariant temperature (Sara, 1965b; Rudy, 1965). This boundary moves to higher carbon contents as the temperature is lowered with the appearance of a Widmanstätten structure. Below 1900° the boundary is near $HfC_{0.6}$ (Rudy, 1965; Benesovsky and Rudy, 1960). The high carbon phase

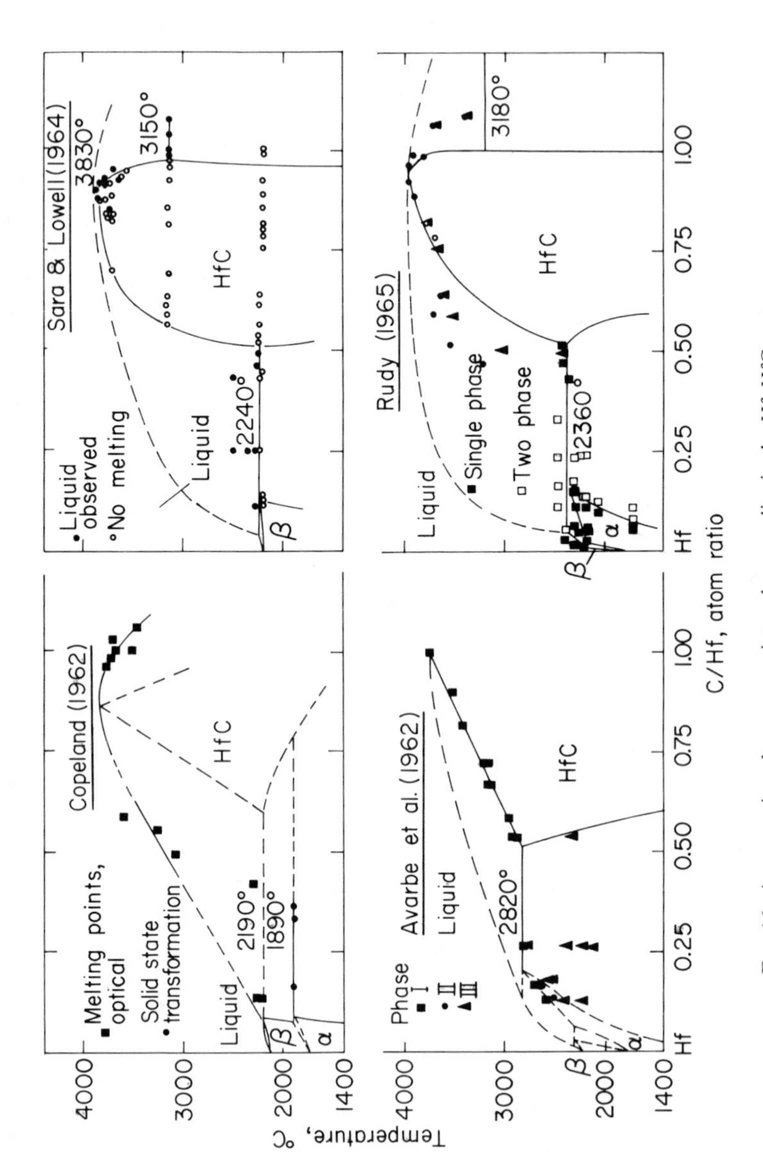

FIG. 16. A comparison between various phase studies in the Hf–HfC system.

boundary is near $HfC_{1.0}$, but no detailed study has been made. Based on metallographic examination and melting point data, Sara and Lowell (1964) find the limit at $HfC_{0.97}$ at the eutectic temperature. From the variation of the lattice parameter at 1600°, Rudy (1965) indicates a terminal composition of $HfC_{0.98}$.

As the carbon content of HfC is changed, the melting point goes through a maximum and finally forms a eutectic with carbon. The temperatures in this region are so high few measurements have been made. An often-quoted value of 3887° for the maximum is due to the early efforts of Agte and Alterthum (1930). Recently Rudy (1965) obtained 3928° ± 20° at $HfC_{0.94}$, Sara and Lowell (1964) suggested, from rather sparse data, a maximum at 3830° and $HfC_{0.91}$, and the data of Adams and Beall (1963) would place the maximum between 3800° and 3900°. Since most experimental difficulties would lead to a lower temperature, the measurement of Rudy (1965) is preferred. This gives 3950° after a correction for the zirconium content is applied. Values for the HfC–C eutectic temperature have also been rather scattered. The lowest value of 2800° (Cotter and Kohn, 1954) was obtained using potentially impure material prepared from the oxide. Higher melting points at 3260° (Portnoĭ *et al.*, 1961); 3276° ± 120° (average) (Adams and Beall, 1963); 3150° (Sara, 1965b); and 3180° ± 20° (Rudy, 1965) were found when apparently purer samples were used. A temperature of 3180° ± 50° is suggested as the probable value for zirconium-free material.

TABLE 11

STRUCTURE AND LATTICE PARAMETER OF Hf AND HfC

Phases in equilibrium	Composition of first phase	Structure type	Lattice parameter (Å)	Investigator
α-Hf	4.0 at. % Zr (at 25°)	hcp (*A*3)	*a* = 3.196 *c* = 5.057	Rudy (1965)
β-Hf	2.3 at. % Zr (extrapolated to 25°)	bcc (*A*2)	*a* = 3.545	A. Taylor *et al.* (1963)
	2.9 at. %Zr (at 1800°)	bcc (*A*2)	*a* = 3.615	Romans *et al.*, (1965)
α-Hf + HfC	α-$HfC_{\sim 0.06}$ (slow cooling)	hcp (*A*3)	*a* = 3.202 *c* = 5.100	Rudy (1965)
HfC + α-Hf	$HfC_{0.61}$	fcc (*B*1)	*a* = 4.619	Rudy (1965)
HfC + C	$HfC_{0.99}$	fcc (*B*1)	*a* = 4.6402 ± 0.0005	See Fig. 17

The following eutectic compositions have been reported: $HfC_{1.86}$ (Rudy, 1965); $HfC_{<2.13}$ (Adams and Beall, 1963); $HfC_{1.94}$ (Sara, 1965b); and $HfC_{\sim 5.7}$ (Portnoĭ *et al.*, 1961).

C. LATTICE PARAMETER AND STRUCTURE

The lattice parameters for pure Hf and HfC are listed in Table 11 for the quenched-in phase boundary composition. Cubic β-Hf cannot be retained upon cooling. The calculated powder patterns of α-Hf and $HfC_{0.98}$ are listed in Tables 12 and 13, respectively.

TABLE 12
COPPER RADIATION, POWDER PATTERN FOR α-Hf[a]

2θ	$\sin^2\theta$	d spacing	Intensity	$h\ k\ l$
32.32	0.0774	2.7678	20	1 0 0
35.47	0.0928	2.5285	25	0 0 2
36.99	0.1006	2.4279	100	1 0 1
48.74	0.1702	1.8668	20	1 0 2
57.63	0.2323	1.5980	30	1 1 0
64.69	0.2862	1.4397	35	1 0 3
67.64	0.3098	1.3839	5	2 0 0
69.53	0.3251	1.3508	40	1 1 2
70.49	0.3330	1.3348	30	2 0 1
75.07	0.3712	1.2642	5	0 0 4
78.77	0.4026	1.2140	10	2 0 2
84.10	0.4486	1.1500	5	1 0 4
92.13	0.5186	1.0696	20	2 0 3
94.83	0.5421	1.0461	5	2 1 0
97.51	0.5653	1.0244	40	2 1 1
101.95	0.6035	0.9915	25	1 1 4
105.66	0.6349	0.9667	15	2 1 2
108.35	0.6574	0.9500	20	1 0 5
111.22	0.6810	0.9334	5	2 0 4
113.21	0.6970	0.9226	15	3 0 0
120.12	0.7509	0.8889	45	2 1 3
125.43	0.7898	0.8667	30	3 0 2
132.10	0.8352	0.8428	5	0 0 6
141.22	0.8898	0.8166	35	2 0 5
145.62	0.9126	0.8063	15	1 0 6
145.76	0.9133	0.8060	25	2 1 4
149.18	0.9294	0.7990	30	2 2 0

[a] $a_0 = 3.196$; $c_0 = 5.057$; $\mu r = 5$; structure type *A*3, space group No. 194; $\lambda(K\alpha_1) = 1.54051$ Å.

TABLE 13
COPPER RADIATION, POWDER FOR $HfC_{0.99}$[a]

2θ	$\sin^2\theta$	d spacing	Intensity	$h\ k\ l$
33.42	0.0827	2.6790	20	1 1 1
38.78	0.1102	2.3201	15	2 0 0
56.00	0.2204	1.6406	15	2 2 0
66.81	0.3031	1.3991	15	3 1 1
70.20	0.3307	1.3395	5	2 2 2
83.21	0.4409	1.1600	5	4 0 0
92.70	0.5235	1.0645	10	3 3 1
95.87	0.5511	1.0376	10	4 2 0
108.82	0.6613	0.9472	10	4 2 2
119.21	0.7440	0.8930	15	5 1 1, 3 3 3
139.77	0.8818	0.8203	10	4 4 0
158.25	0.9644	0.7843	60	5 3 1
169.72	0.9920	0.7734	100	4 4 2, 6 0 0

[a] $a_0 = 4.6402$ Å; $\mu r = 5.0$; structure type $B1$, space group No. 225; $\lambda(K\alpha_1) = 1.54051$ Å.

Some recent measurements of the HfC lattice parameter are compared in Fig. 17. The plotted values have been corrected for the reported zirconium impurity by assuming a linear relationship between HfC and ZrC of the same composition. Like the other Group 4 carbides, HfC shows a wide scatter of lattice parameter values. It is clear that here again the presence of oxygen or nitrogen is having a marked effect. Until a study is made which clearly demonstrates the absence of these impurities, a description of the lattice parameter behavior in this system will remain very uncertain. If a comparison between the parameters of Norton and Lewis (1964) for relatively pure material, and the results from other studies gives any indication, the effect of impurity can become very severe as the carbon content is reduced. At the other extreme, material prepared from the oxide at 2000°–2200° by Meerson and Krein (1960a) give the very low values of 4.63 Å for $HfC_{0.99}$, 4.62 Å for $HfC_{0.96}$, and 4.61 Å for $HfC_{0.95}$. It is not unreasonable to suggest a lattice parameter maximum in view of the behavior of TiC and ZrC.

D. HARDNESS

The following hardness values have been reported: 2600 kg/mm^2 (100 g Knoop) for HfC + C (Cotter and Kohn, 1954); 2913 $\pm$ 300 (Vickers) (Curtis *et al.*, 1954); 1675 DPH for $HfC_{0.95}$ (Jones, 1956); and the formula $H = 2000 + 52C$, where C is at. % carbon and H is kg/mm^2

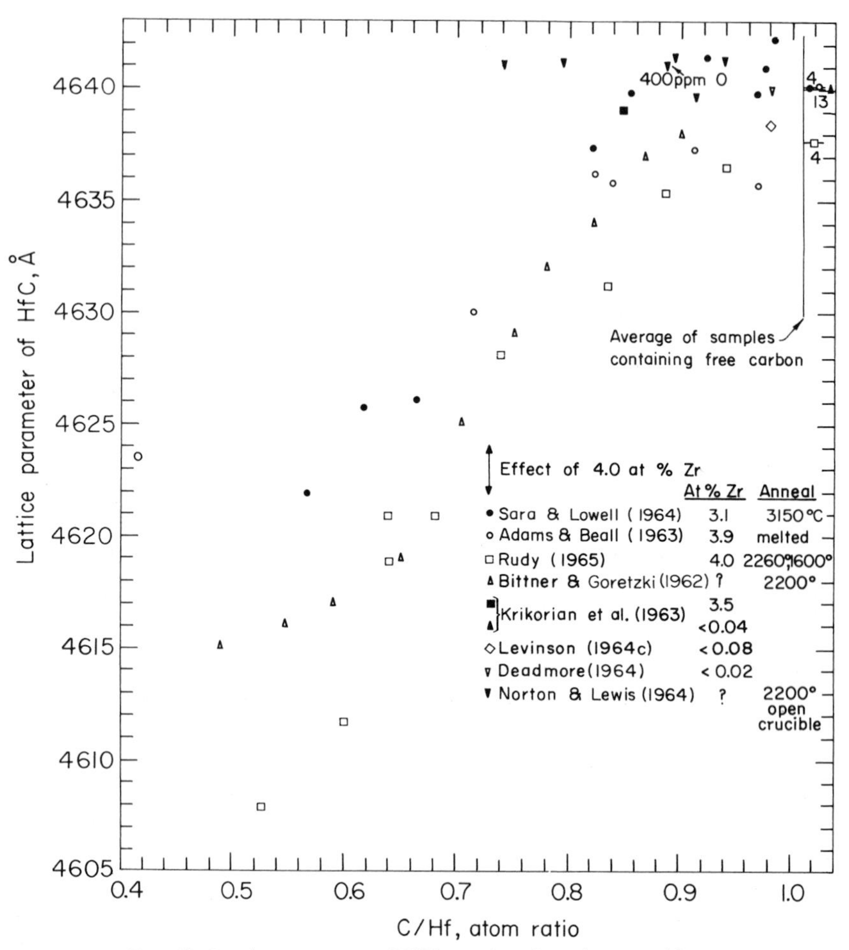

FIG. 17. Lattice parameter of HfC as a function of composition.

(Avarbe *et al.*, 1962). The material used by the latter workers probably contained considerable dissolved oxygen. Using a 100-g load, Adams and Beall (1963) found the Knoop hardness to vary between 1815 kg/mm^2 at $HfC_{0.42}$ and 2276 kg/mm^2 at $HfC_{1.00}$.

E. THERMOCHEMICAL PROPERTIES

1. HEAT OF FORMATION

The work of Zhelankin and Kutzev (1964) has been recalculated using Humphrey's (1953) value of the heat of formation of HfO_2 and is plotted in Fig. 18. A single determination by Mah (1964) differs from the Russian

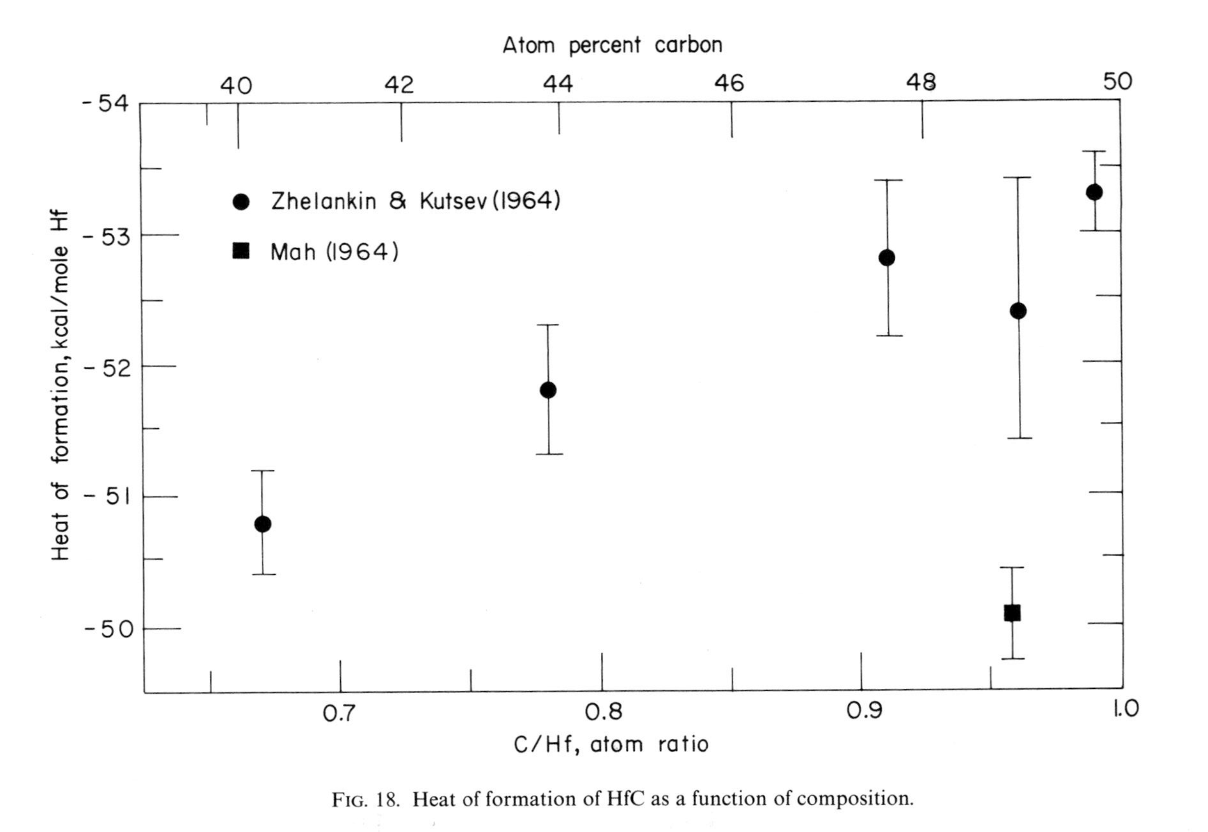

FIG. 18. Heat of formation of HfC as a function of composition.

work by more than the errors in the technique would warrant. Since the material used by Mah was demonstrated to be pure, her value of -50.08 ± 0.35 kcal/mole (298.15°) for $HfC_{0.958}$ is recommended.

2. Low Temperature Heat Capacity

Tentative measurements of Westrum have been reported by McClaine (1964). Using pure $HfC_{0.968}$ containing 350 ppm Zr, the following uncorrected values were obtained at 298.15°: $C_p^\circ = 8.955$ cal/mole, $S^\circ = 9.431$ cal/mole-deg, $H_{298}^\circ - H_0^\circ = 1523.2$ cal/mole.

3. High Temperature Heat Content and Heat Capacity

The various heat content measurements are compared in Fig. 19. A least-squares fit was made using the data of Levinson (1965) and Coffman *et al.* (1963) which resulted in the curve shown in Fig. 19 and the equation given in Table 14. For this fit, C_p° was forced to equal 8.995 cal/mole-deg and $H_T^\circ - H_{298.15}^\circ$ to equal zero, both at 298.15°. The resulting C_p values show excellent agreement with the direct measurements by McDonald *et al.* (1964). The thermal properties based on the above data are tabulated in Table 14 for $HfC_{\sim 0.98}$.

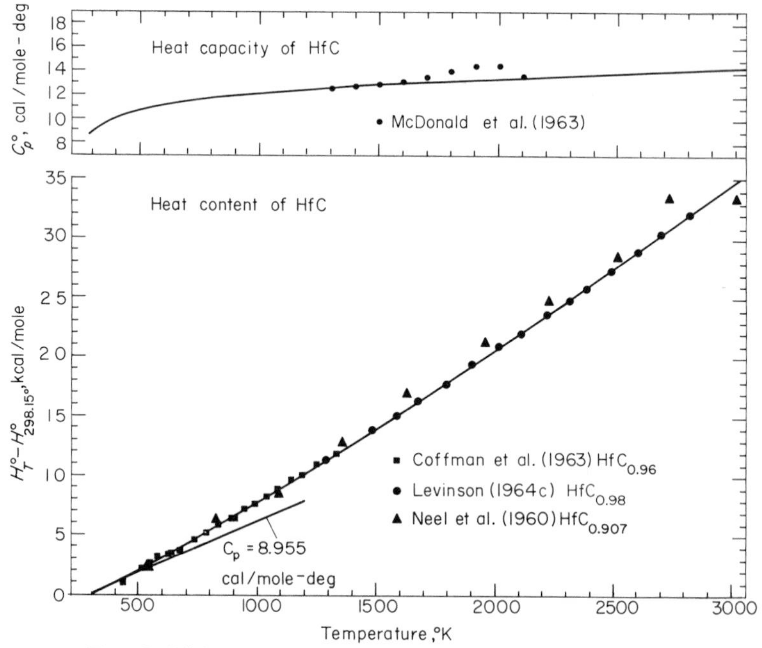

FIG. 19. High temperature heat capacity and enthalpy of $HfC_{0.98}$.

TABLE 14
THERMAL FUNCTIONS OF $HfC_{0.98}$[a]

T (°K)	$H_T^\circ - H_{298}^\circ$ (cal/mole)	C_p° (cal/mole-deg)	S_T° (cal/mole-deg)	$-(F_T^\circ - H_{298}^\circ)/T$ (cal/mole-deg)
298.15	0.00	8.955	9.431	9.431
300	16.60	8.986	9.486	9.431
400	979.4	10.13	12.25	9.800
500	2027	10.77	14.58	10.53
600	3126	11.19	16.59	11.38
700	4261	11.51	18.34	12.25
800	5426	11.78	19.89	13.11
900	6616	12.01	21.29	13.94
1000	7828	12.22	22.57	14.74
1100	9060	12.41	23.74	15.51
1200	10310	12.58	24.83	16.24
1300	11580	12.75	25.84	16.94
1400	12860	12.90	26.79	17.61
1500	14160	13.04	27.69	18.25
1600	15470	13.18	28.53	18.87
1700	16790	13.31	29.34	19.46
1800	18130	13.43	30.10	20.03
1900	19480	13.54	30.83	20.58
2000	20840	13.65	31.53	21.11
2100	22200	13.74	32.20	21.62
2200	23580	13.84	32.84	22.12
2300	24970	13.92	33.45	22.60
2400	26370	14.00	34.05	23.06
2500	27770	14.07	34.62	23.51
2600	29180	14.14	35.17	23.95
2700	30600	14.20	35.71	24.38
2800	32020	14.25	36.23	24.79
2900	33450	14.30	36.73	25.19
3000	34880	14.34	37.21	25.59

[a] $H_T^\circ - H_{298.15}^\circ = -3.8886 \times 10^3 + 10.526T + 1.0963 \times 10^{-3}T^2 - 1.0149 \times 10^{-7}T^3 + 1.9539 \times 10^5/T$ (298.15°–3000°; cal/mole ± 0.7%); M.W. = 190.26; $H_{298.15}^\circ - H_0^\circ =$ 1523.2 cal/mole.

4. VAPORIZATION

Hansler (1965) has concluded from the behavior of the electrical resistivity that nearly stoichiometric HfC loses carbon preferentially. This is not inconsistent with the direct measurements of N. H. Krikorian (1965) who found the congruently vaporizing composition near $HfC_{0.94}$

at 2900°K, with a trend to lower carbon contents as the temperature was raised. Consequently, Langmuir measurements should give pressures which are much higher than an equilibrium measurement using HfC + C. This is indeed the case.

The Langmuir studies by various investigators are compared in Fig. 20 to the pressure over $HfC_{0.98}$ + C. This is based on a calculation using the

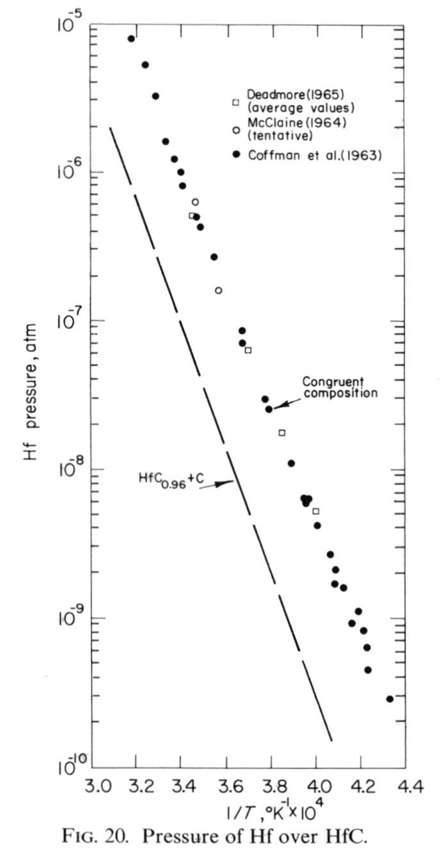

FIG. 20. Pressure of Hf over HfC.

thermodynamic information found in Table 14 for $HfC_{0.98}$, the JANAF Tables (1963) for $C_{(s)}$, the tables prepared by Barriault *et al.* (1961) for $Hf_{(g)}$, a heat of formation for $HfC_{0.96}$ of −50.08 kcal/mole, and a heat of vaporization for the metal of 144.9 kcal/mole. Until measurements are made in equilibrium with carbon, the following equation can be used to describe the pressure of Hf over HfC + C:

$$\log P(\text{atm}) = 8.300 - 4.206 \times 10^4/T$$

IV

THE VANADIUM–VANADIUM CARBIDE SYSTEM

A. PREPARATION

Vanadium carbide was first prepared by Moissan in 1893 during his comprehensive studies with the electric arc furnace. By heating a mixture of V_2O_5 and sugar charcoal in the absence of air, a carbide near $VC_{1.0}$ was obtained. Since that time, most work has been based on a carbide prepared in essentially the same manner, from the reaction of carbon with V_2O_5 or V_2O_3. These results are highly compromised because there is always doubt whether all of the oxygen was removed. This is especially true when low temperatures and short heating times are employed, as was generally the case. Meerson and Krein (1960b) studied the reduction of V_2O_3 with carbon to determine conditions which would produce oxygen-free VC. They found it necessary to heat for more than 2 hours between 1700° and 1800° in a CO pressure of 1–10 torr to reduce the oxygen content to below the limit of detection. Because they did not analyze for oxygen directly, but relied on the relationship 100% − (%V + $\%C_{total}$) = wt % oxygen, the limit of detection was about 0.8%. Zhelankin *et al.* (1958), while observing the same reaction, found that a temperature of 2300° held for about 2 hours with a pressure of 1–1.5 torr would reduce the oxygen content below 0.2 wt %. In this case, the oxygen was determined directly by activation analysis using the reaction $0^{16}(\gamma, n)0^{15}$. Details about the formation of oxycarbides from this reaction can be found in the paper by Gurevich and Ormont (1958). The lowest temperature at which V_2O_5 will react with carbon is 435° (Elyutin *et al.*, 1958).

The stoichiometry also determines how easily oxygen can be eliminated. This can be inferred from data obtained by heating V_2O_5 (Krainer and Konopicky, 1947) with various amounts of carbon at 1500° in a hydrogen atmosphere. These results show a lower oxygen level when the carbon content was high. Gurevich and Ormont (1957) also show this in their work, but, because they did not analyze for oxygen directly, the indicated oxygen contents should not be taken too seriously. The amount of deviation to the left of the curve in Fig. 22 is a better indication of the impurity content.

Vanadium carbide has been obtained from alloy steel after a suitable solvent for the iron has been applied. On the basis of this method the discredited phases V_5C (Ôsawa and Ôya, 1930), V_4C_3 (Arnold and Read, 1912), and V_2C_3 (Pütz, 1906) were reported. The V_5C phase is actually the hexagonal V_2C, as first suggested by Westgren (1930), and the V_4C_3 phase is cubic VC with a composition near the low carbon phase boundary. According to many authors, this is the usual composition occurring in vanadium-alloy steels.

Moers (1931) deposited the carbide onto a tungsten wire by heating it at 1500°–2000° in an atmosphere of VCl_4, H_2, and a hydrocarbon. Campbell *et al.* (1949) also investigated this reaction. Although the method might be used to obtain single crystals, it does not give a product of uniform and predictable chemical composition.

Pure carbide of uniform composition can be obtained conveniently by starting with powdered vanadium metal or hydride, and carbon. Because the carbide will react avidly with oxygen and less rapidly with N_2 and CO at high temperatures, it is necessary, when seeking the purest carbide, to heat in a good vacuum (better than 10^{-5} torr). When carbon-saturated material is needed, purification can be facilitated by heating as high as 2000° without excessive loss of vanadium. At lower carbon contents the loss of vanadium can exceed that for oxygen unless low temperatures are used, in which case, purification can be very slow. Consequently, it is difficult to have purity and homogeneity at the same time in this region. This is discussed in more detail at the end of the next section.

The carbide can also be prepared by arc melting. However, subsequent powdering of the hard button can recontaminate the sample.

B. PHASE RELATIONSHIP

In 1930, Ôsawa and Ôya presented a phase diagram which contained the phases V_5C and V_4C_3. Later Goldschmidt (1948) combined his data with the melting point determinations of Ruff and Martin (1912) and proposed a diagram showing eutectic melting between vanadium and V_4C_3. Finally, with confirmation of the hexagonal V_2C phase by a number of workers (Hardy and Hulm, 1954; Schönberg, 1954; Rostoker and

Yamamoto, 1954), Hansen and Anderko (1958) drew a partial diagram. A more complete phase diagram, shown in Fig. 21, was reported by Storms and McNeal (1962).

Values for the melting point of vanadium metal have ranged from 1860° (Wilhelm *et al.*, 1954) to 1919° (Oriani and Jones, 1954). All of these measurements were made using material of variable purity, for which corrections were not made. The use of proper corrections leads to good agreement with the corrected value of 1888° ± 10°, given by Storms and McNeal (1962).

At the eutectic temperature the solubility of carbon in V is near $VC_{0.096}$ (Storms and McNeal, 1962), but as the temperature is reduced the

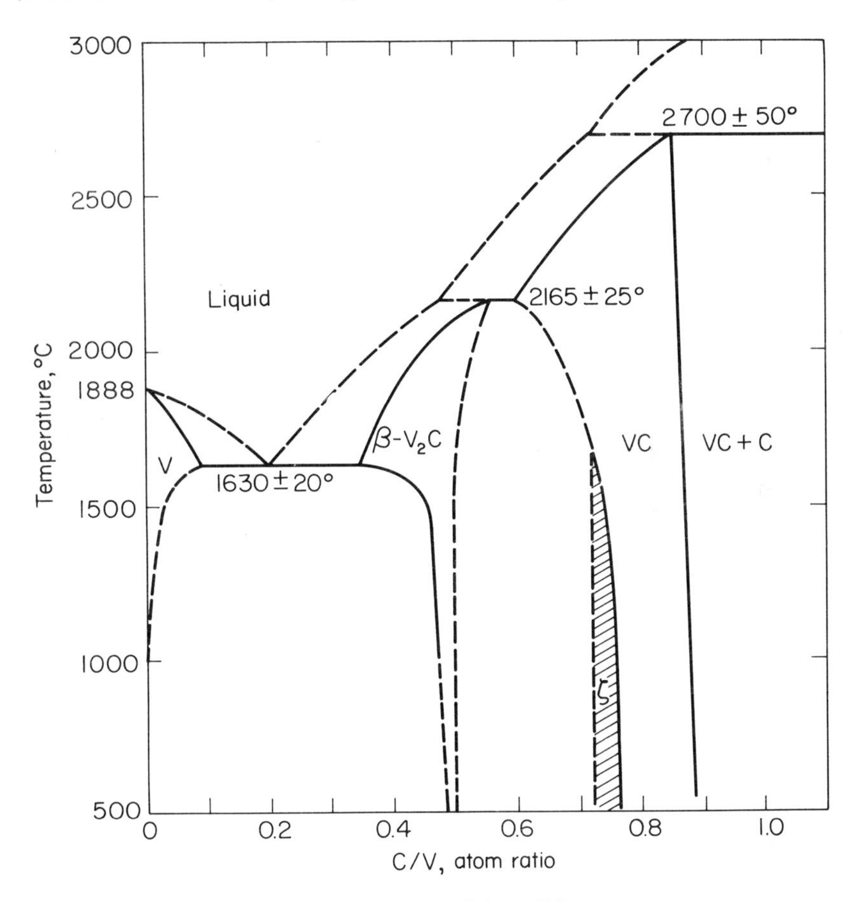

Fig. 21. Phase diagram of the V–VC system.

solubility drops rapidly Schönberg (1954) and Gurevich and Ormont (1957) found vanadium to contain approximately 2000 ppm ($VC_{0.008}$) carbon at 1000°.

The carbon-saturated metal melts in contact with $VC_{0.33}$ (V_2C) at 1630° ± 20° (Storms and McNeal, 1962). This is in good agreement with 1650°, reported by Rostoker and Yamamoto (1954). As the carbon content is increased the melting temperature rises to a peritectic between $VC_{0.56}$ (V_2C) and $VC_{0.60}$ (VC) at 2165°, and finally the VC phase melts peritectically at 2650° in contact with graphite according to Storms and McNeal (1962). This value for the VC–C peritectic temperature is somewhat lower than previous measurements: 2830° (Friederich and Sittig, 1925); 2750° (Ruff and Martin, 1912); and 2780° (Engelke *et al.*, 1960). A temperature of 2700° ± 50° is recommended. (See page 60.)

Below the solidus, the phase relationship is similar to the other Group 5 carbides. Single-phase β-V_2C is found in quenched material between $VC_{0.44}$ and $VC_{0.50}$ (Storms and McNeal, 1962). Other reported ranges are $VC_{0.37}$–$VC_{0.50}$ (Schönberg, 1954); $VC_{0.41}$–$VC_{0.59}$ (Gurevich and Ormont, 1957); and $VC_{0.45}$–$VC_{0.47}$ (Grdina and Lykhin, 1965). Slow cooling of material in the vanadium-rich region results in an ordered α-V_2C phase (Yvon *et al.*, 1966).

The lower-phase boundary of the VC phase is usually found near $VC_{0.75}$ after quenching, while the upper boundary is quite a bit below the stoichiometric composition. This has led early workers (Ôsawa and Ôya, 1930; Morette, 1938) to think of the phase as V_4C_3. The extent to which the upper-phase limit deviates from the 1:1 ratio is rather unusual, although this behavior is not unique among the carbides. Schönberg (1954) was unable to form compositions above $VC_{\sim 0.8}$ without the presence of free carbon, but he assumed this was due to a slow reaction rate. Meerson and Krein (1960b) also could not produce VC with a composition higher than $VC_{0.92}$. Brauer and Schnell (1964), working with pure materials, placed the boundary at $VC_{0.92}$. Rudy *et al.* (1962b) found free carbon in most of their samples at $VC_{0.85}$ and Grdina and Lykhin (1965) report $VC_{0.92}$ + C below 1000°. As can be seen from Fig. 21, Storms and McNeal (1962) give $VC_{0.88}$ as the limit at 1000° with a trend to lower carbon contents at higher temperatures. Most other authors either mention that all of the free carbon had not quite reacted or assumed they were working with single-phase $VC_{1.0}$.

Various Russian workers have consistently found extra lines in the powder patterns which they attributed to additional phases in this system. Beginning with Gurevich and Ormont (1954, 1957, 1958), two cubic

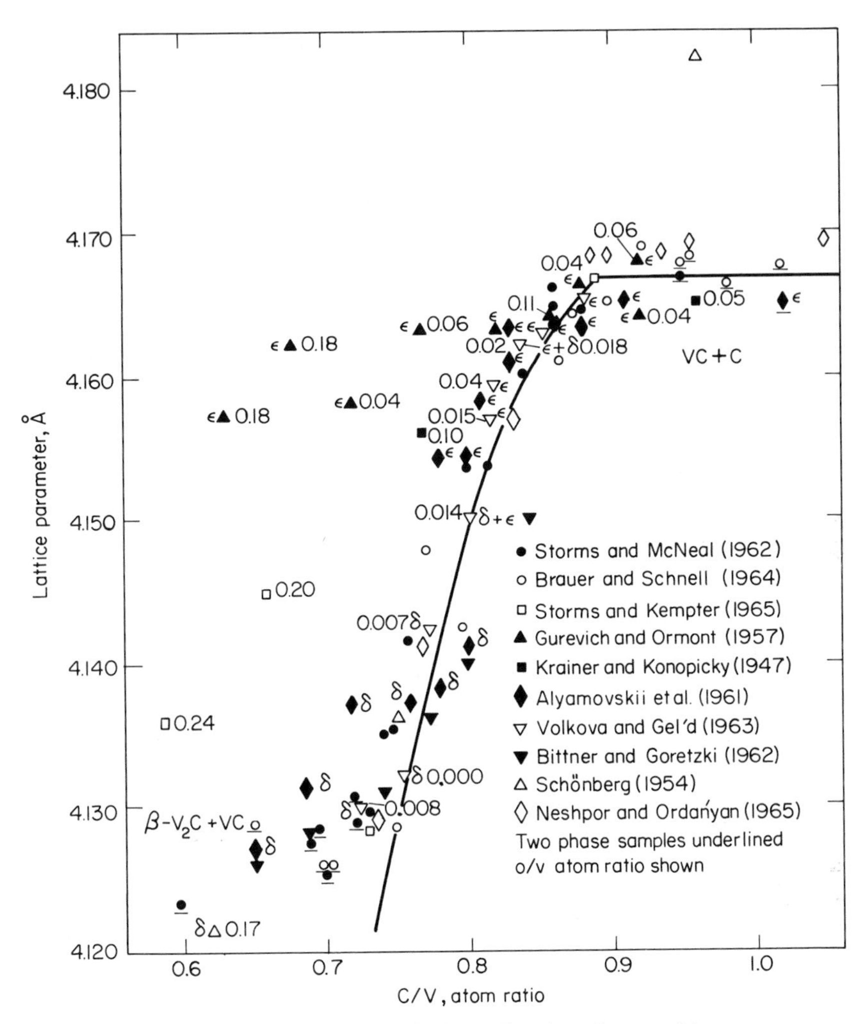

FIG. 22. Lattice parameter of VC as a function of composition.

phases were found, one below $VC_{0.69}$ containing a high oxygen level (δ phase) and the other at higher carbon contents and containing less oxygen (ε phase).* The regions were distinguished by a break in the lattice parameter vs. composition curve. Alyamovskii *et al.* (1961) and later Volkova and Gel'd (1963) observed the break but placed the upper limit

* Ôsawa and Ôya (1930) use ε to designate the pure carbide phase, while Brauer and Schnell (1964) prefer to call it the δ phase.

TABLE 15
STRUCTURE AND LATTICE PARAMETER OF V, β-V_2C, AND VC

Phases in equilibrium	Composition first phase	Structure type	Lattice parameter, (Å)	Investigator
V	Pure	bcc($A2$)	$a = 3.0240 \pm 0.0003$	James and Straumanis (1961)
α-V_2C	$VC_{\sim 0.45}$	D_{2h}^{14}	$a = 4.575$ $b = 5.760$ $c = 5.02$	Yvon *et al.* (1966)
β-V_2C + V	$VC_{0.47}$	hcp($L'3$)	$a = 2.8855 \pm 0.0005$ $c = 4.5705 \pm 0.0005$	Storms and McNeal (1962)
β-V_2C + VC	$VC_{0.50}$	hcp($L'3$)	$a = 2.9020 \pm 0.0005$ $c = 4.577 \pm 0.001$	Storms and McNeal (1962)
VC + β-V_2C	$VC_{0.73}$	fcc($B1$)	$a = 4.1310 \pm 0.0005$	Storms and McNeal (1962)
VC + C	$VC_{0.87}$	fcc($B1$)	$a = 4.1655 \pm 0.0003$	Storms and McNeal (1962)

of the δ phase near $VC_{0.8}$. In general, most of this material was prepared from the oxide. On the other hand, Volkova *et al.* (1963) found 12–14 extra lines in patterns of $VC_{0.884}$ and $VC_{1.483}$ which could not be indexed as cubic. Recently these workers (Volkova *et al.*, 1965) observed a break in the enthalpy curve of $VC_{0.91}$ near 1393°K (Fig. 23) as well as extra lines in the powder pattern. This was attributed to a δ' phase. Any attempt to resolve this problem must include the effect of dissolved oxygen. Gurevich and Ormont (1958) describe the δ phase as an intermediate oxycarbide which eventually converts to the ε phase as oxygen is replaced by carbon. However, both phases are shown in their diagram as belonging to the binary V–C system. Apparently, subsequent Russian workers have accepted the latter view. Another interpretation is more probable. When the oxide is used as the starting material, the last bit of oxygen is very difficult to remove from the resulting carbide. If purification is done much above 1500° in vacuum, the preferential loss of vanadium from substoichiometric material can lead to a concentration gradient. If an inert atmosphere is used to suppress the evaporation, purification rate will suffer. Besides causing additional diffraction lines, the presence of oxygen can raise the lattice parameter, as shown in Fig. 22. Consequently, the material will appear to contain two cubic lattices of different parameters. The higher parameter will be characteristic of material at the surface. As the composition nears the upper-phase limit this effect should

TABLE 16

COPPER RADIATION, POWDER PATTERN FOR V[a]

2θ	$\sin^2\theta$	d spacing	Intensity	$h\ k\ l$
42.23	0.1298	2.1383	100	1 1 0
61.25	0.2595	1.5120	20	2 0 0
77.21	0.3893	1.2345	40	2 1 1
92.18	0.5190	1.0691	15	2 2 0
107.31	0.6488	0.9563	25	3 1 0
123.86	0.7786	0.8730	10	2 2 2
144.75	0.9083	0.8082	80	3 2 1

[a] $a_0 = 3.0240$ Å; $\mu r = 3.0$; structure type $A2$, space group No. 229; $\lambda(K\alpha_1) = 1.54051$ Å.

disappear, as indeed it does, as the solubility of oxygen and the extent of the carbon gradient are reduced.

Some samples of V_2C, used by Volkova and Gel'd (1965) for combustion studies, showed a line splitting which they interpreted as indicating a rhombohedral distortion to the lattice. This splitting also has been seen by Yvon *et al.* (1966) and attributed to the ordered α form.

Storms and McNeal (1962) reported a zeta phase, very similar to the one found in the TaC and NbC systems (Lesser and Brauer, 1958; Brauer and Lesser, 1959a).

C. LATTICE PARAMETER AND STRUCTURE

The structure and lattice parameters for the established phases V, β-V_2C, and VC are shown in Table 15 and the calculated powder patterns are listed in Tables 16, 17, and 18, respectively. Because of the fairly wide composition range exhibited by the compounds, the lattice parameters are given for the composition at the phase boundary after a quench from 1300°. Between these extremes the parameters will change with composition.

Of the M_2C carbides, only V_2C, containing VC, normally has the $L'3$ structure at room temperature (A. L. Bowman *et al.*, 1965). Apparently the α–β transition is sufficiently slow and/or low in temperature to allow retention of the high temperature form. Rudy and Harmon (1965) estimated a transition temperature below 800°. However, thermal expansion studies by Storms and Kempter (1965) show no abnormality below 600°. On the other hand, carbon-deficient samples have given a line splitting which is characteristic of the ordered phase (Yvon *et al.*, 1966). This

TABLE 17
COPPER RADIATION, POWDER PATTERN FOR β-V_2C[a]

2θ	$\sin^2\theta$	d spacing	Intensity	$h\ k\ l$
35.70	0.0939	2.5132	10	1 0 0
39.34	0.1133	2.2885	15	0 0 2
40.93	0.1223	2.2029	100	1 0 1
54.16	0.2072	1.6921	30	1 0 2
64.13	0.2818	1.4510	30	1 1 0
72.40	0.3488	1.3042	20	1 0 3
75.61	0.3757	1.2566	1	2 0 0
77.89	0.3951	1.2254	15	1 1 2
78.94	0.4041	1.2117	15	2 0 1
84.62	0.4531	1.1443	5	0 0 4
88.74	0.4890	1.1015	10	2 0 2
95.40	0.5471	1.0414	1	1 0 4
105.14	0.6306	0.9699	10	2 0 3
108.37	0.6575	0.9499	1	2 1 0
111.82	0.6859	0.9301	20	2 1 1
118.03	0.7349	0.8985	20	1 1 4
122.80	0.7708	0.8773	15	2 1 2
127.15	0.8020	0.8601	15	1 0 5
131.13	0.8289	0.8460	1	2 0 4
133.69	0.8454	0.8377	15	3 0 0
145.57	0.9124	0.8064	40	2 1 3
156.55	0.9587	0.7867	25	3 0 2

[a] $a_0 = 2.902$ Å; $c_0 = 4.577$ Å; $\mu r = 3.0$; structure type $L'3$, space group No. 194; $\lambda(K\alpha_1) = 1.54051$ Å.

splitting was absent under similar conditions in samples studied by Storms and McNeal (1962). Apparently the cooling rate is an important factor in this observation. V_2C has a x-ray density of 5.665 g/cm^3 at $VC_{0.50}$.

The various lattice parameter measurements of VC are compared in Fig. 22. The ε phase, reported by various Russian workers, behaves in every respect like the δ phase. As described previously, there is no reason to believe that two separate phases exist, although, in their case, the material is better described as an oxycarbide. The lattice parameter of VC at the VC–V_2C boundary is strongly influenced by the heating temperature between 1348° and 1430°. Quenching in vacuum from above 1430° produces $VC_{0.73}$ with a parameter of 4.125 Å; below 1348° the composition and lattice parameter are $VC_{0.738}$ and 4.131 Å, independent of temperature (Storms and McNeal, 1962). The x-ray density of VC is

TABLE 18

COPPER RADIATION, POWDER PATTERN FOR $VC_{0.88}$[a]

2θ	$\sin^2\theta$	d spacing	Intensity	$h\ k\ l$
37.36	0.1026	2.4050	100	1 1 1
43.41	0.1368	2.0827	100	2 0 0
63.07	0.2735	1.4727	60	2 2 0
75.66	0.3761	1.2559	35	3 1 1
79.67	0.4103	1.2025	20	2 2 2
95.40	0.5471	1.0414	10	4 0 0
107.42	0.6497	0.9556	15	3 3 1
111.57	0.6839	0.9314	30	4 2 0
129.89	0.8206	0.8503	40	4 2 2
147.82	0.9232	0.8017	30	5 1 1, 3 3 3

[a] $a_0 = 4.1655$ Å; $\mu r = 2.0$; structure type $B1$, space group No. 225; $\lambda(K\alpha_1) = 1.54051$ Å.

5.649 g/cm^3 at both phase boundaries with a minimum of 5.607 g/cm^3 at $VC_{0.78}$. NbC also shows a minimum near this composition (Kempter *et al.*, 1960).

D. CHEMICAL REACTIVITY

V_2C is dissolved slowly by hot 1:1 HCl, leaving a carbon residue. VC is inert under these conditions (Storms and McNeal, 1962). Both carbides are attacked by concentrated HNO_3, H_2SO_4, and $HClO_4$, slowly at room temperature and vigorously when heated. Hot aqueous NaOH has no effect. Powdered V_2C reacts slowly with air at room temperature.

VC will react with dry HCl gas at 750° to produce CH_4, H_2, VCl_2, and VCl_3 (Oldham and Fishel, 1932). It has a high rate of oxidation in air at 800° (Cockett and Watt, 1950) and will burn in oxygen to produce an oxide of variable oxygen content. VC, when heated in nitrogen, will gradually convert to the nitride, but it is considered structurally stable up to 2400° (Bradshaw and Matthews, 1959). Powdered VC (325 mesh) is slowly attacked by air at room temperature.

E. HARDNESS

A range of hardness values have been reported from 2094 kg/mm^2 (Meerson and Umanskii, 1953) to about 3000 kg/mm^2 (Gaev, 1953; Kieffer and Kölbl, 1949). As Gurevich and Ormont (1957) point out, the hardness will change with composition. With this in mind, they obtained

2140 kg/mm^2 for V_2C and values between 2850 and 3000 kg/mm^2 across the range of the VC phase. In addition they found the abrading ability of high carbon VC to equal that of SiC. Jones (1956), during a study of the Group 4a, 5a, and 6a carbides, found VC (containing free carbon) equal in hardness to WC (2250 DPH) and exceeded only by TiC (3100 DPH). The work of Kieffer and Kölbl (1949) is also consistent with this observation. VC($VC_{0.88}$) would appear to be one of the hardest pure carbides known.

F. THERMOCHEMICAL PROPERTIES

1. Heat of Formation

Volkova and Gel'd (1965) have measured the heat of formation of V_2C as a function of composition and fit their data by the equation* $\Delta H_f^\circ(298.15°) = -(10.1 + 12.8\ C/V) \pm 0.6$ kcal/mole. This can only be compared to equilibrium measurements using CH_4 and H_2 reported by Alekseev and Shvartsman (1961, 1960). They give the equation $\log K_p(\text{atm}^{-1}) = 2720/T - 6.20$ for the equilibrium $VC_{0.76}$–H_2–V_2C–CH_4, and $\log K(\text{atm}^{-1}) = 2201.9/T - 5.825$ for V_2C–H_2–V–CH_4, both in very poor agreement with the combustion data.

VC was studied as a function of composition by Volkova and Gel'd (1963), and in a later paper (1965) the work was extended and fitted by the equation $\Delta H_f^\circ(298.15°) = -(11.5 + 15.8\ C/V) \pm 1.6$ kcal/mole. Unfortunately, several of their samples contained two cubic lattices. They interpreted this as a mixture of $\delta + \varepsilon$ phases while single-phase samples were designated as pure δ phase or pure ε phase, apparently on the basis of the lattice parameter. However, there appears to be no correlation between this problem and the combustion measurements. Their data agree with a value of -24.35 ± 0.40 kcal/mole obtained by Mah (1963a) using material of questionable purity and stoichiometry. Gurevich (1963) reports obtaining -43 kcal/mole for $VC_{0.91}O_{0.04}$ and -40 kcal/mole for $VC_{1.03}O_{0.05}$ by combustion. Accurate combustion measurements of vanadium compounds are especially difficult to make. Not only is incomplete combustion frequent, but the form of the resulting oxides is uncertain. Vanadium has a number of oxides each of which exhibits a range of composition. This also accounts for the difficulty in obtaining an accurate analysis for vanadium by combustion.

By measuring the CO pressure over $VC_{0.88} + V_2O_5 + C$ between 1200° and 1350°, Worrell and Chipman (1964) calculate -24.1 ± 0.7

* The reference temperature must be inferred since it was not stated in the paper.

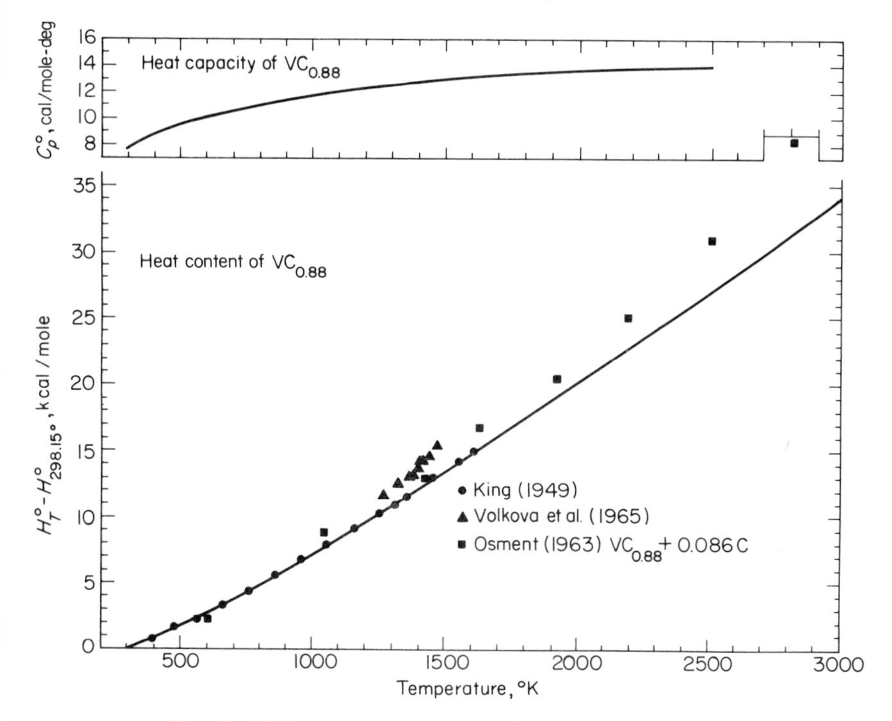

FIG. 23. High temperature heat capacity and enthalpy of $VC_{0.88}$.

kcal/mole as the heat of formation of the carbide. Limits were placed on the effect of dissolved oxygen and the result was included in the uncertainty. Additional studies involving CO have been made by Slade and Higson (1919), Samsonov (1956), and Gurevich (1963a).

2. Low Temperature Heat Capacity

Measurements have been made by Shomate and Kelley (1949) using material which analyzed as $VC_{1.0}$. Although they could detect no free carbon, there must have been at least 2.3 wt % present (Storms and McNeal, 1962). With this in mind, the corrected values become 6.61 ± 0.03 cal/mole-deg for $S^\circ_{298.15}$ and 7.722 cal/mole-deg for $C_p^\circ(298.15°)$.

3. High Temperature Heat Content

Using the same material as Shomate and Kelley (1949), King (1949) measured the heat content between 397.2° and 1611°. After correcting for free carbon, these values were fitted by the equation shown in Table 19. This

TABLE 19

THERMAL FUNCTIONS OF $VC_{0.88}$[a]

T (°K)	$H_T^\circ - H_{298}^\circ$ (cal/mole)	C_p° (cal/mole-deg)	S_T°[b] (cal/mole-deg)	$-(F_T^\circ - H_{298}^\circ)/T$[b] (cal/mole-deg)
298.15	0	7.722	6.610	6.610
300	14.31	7.749	6.658	6.610
400	849.7	8.858	9.053	6.929
500	1774	9.581	11.11	7.565
600	2761	10.14	12.91	8.309
700	3799	10.61	14.51	9.083
800	4882	11.03	15.96	9.853
900	6004	11.41	17.28	10.61
1000	7162	11.75	18.50	11.33
1100	8352	12.06	19.63	12.04
1200	9573	12.35	20.69	12.72
1300	10820	12.61	21.69	13.37
1400	12100	12.86	22.64	14.00
1500	13390	13.07	23.53	14.60
1600	14710	13.27	24.38	15.19
1700	16050	13.45	25.19	15.75
1800	17400	13.60	25.96	16.30
1900	18770	13.74	26.70	16.83
2000	20150	13.85	27.41	17.34
2100	21530	13.94	28.09	17.83
2200	22930	14.02	28.74	18.31
2300	24340	14.07	29.36	18.78
2400	25750	14.10	29.96	19.24
2500	27160	14.11	30.54	19.68

[a] $H_T^\circ - H_{298.15}^\circ = -3.0347 \times 10^3 + 7.8928T + 2.4967 \times 10^{-3}T^2 - 3.3282 \times 10^{-7}T^3 + 1.3964 \times 10^5/T$; (298.15°–2500°K, ±1.0%); M.W. = 61.51.

[b] A randomization entropy of 0.73 eu is not included.

equation was also based on $C_p = 7.722$ cal/mole-deg and $H_T^\circ - H_{298.15}^\circ = 0.0$, both at 298.15°. A comparison is made with the data in Fig. 23 and the resulting thermal functions are listed in Table 19. Because of the long extrapolation and the correction for free carbon, the equation is not considered accurate above 2500°.

Osment (1963) also measured this property using material which was stated to be $VC_{0.97}$, but which contained more than 0.3% N. His values are higher than those of King (1949) even after a correction for the free carbon is applied. Although this more recent work might, in this case, be

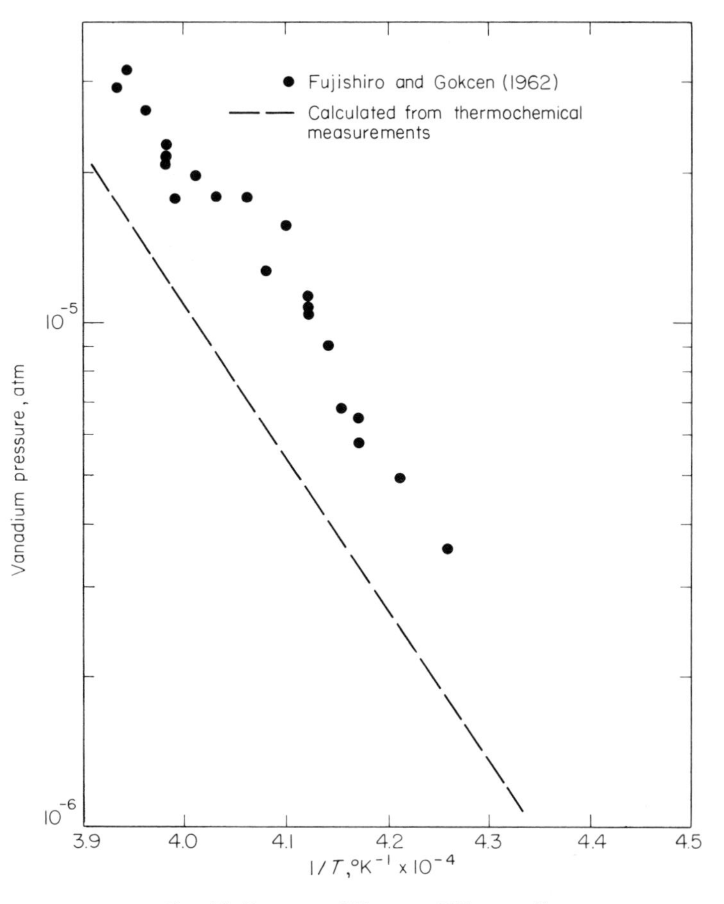

FIG. 24. Pressure of $V_{(g)}$ over $VC_{0.88}$ + C.

closer to the truth, other measurements made by this laboratory have generally given high values when compared to other studies.

The measurements of Volkova *et al.* (1965) also are high and the resulting heat capacity of >16 cal/mole-deg would be greater than other transition metal carbides. In addition, there is some doubt concerning the purity of the sample used.

4. VAPORIZATION

All compositions studied by Storms and McNeal (1962) were found to lose vanadium preferentially when heated in vacuum. Evaporation became noticeable above 1800°, and an inert atmosphere was needed to suppress the pronounced loss above 2100°.

Using Knudsen effusion techniques, Fujishiro and Gokcen (1962) studied the pressure of $V_{(g)}$ over VC + C between 2482° and 2513° and fit the measurements by the equation $\log P(\text{atm}) = -30{,}700/T + 7.63$. From weight-loss experiments, they found atomic vanadium as the only species. These results are compared in Fig. 24 to pressures calculated using the following values: $\Delta H_f^\circ(298.15°) = -24.0$ kcal/mole; a heat of vaporization for the metal of 122.8 kcal/mole (Stull and Sinke, 1956), based on the work of Edwards *et al.* (1951a); the free energy functions in Table 19,* the JANAF tables (1963) for $C_{(s)}$, and Stull and Sinke (1956) for $V_{(g)}$. This results in the equation

$$\log P(\text{atm}) = -3.121 \times 10^4/T + 7.56$$

* A randomization entropy of 0.73 eu is included. See Chapter XIII, Section G.

Note Added in Proof: Rudy and Windisch (1967) find eutectic melting at 2625 ± 6° between $VC_{0.85}$ and carbon, and a melting point maximum at 2648 ± 8° and $VC_{0.75}$.

V

THE NIOBIUM–NIOBIUM CARBIDE SYSTEM

A. PREPARATION

Niobium carbide with a composition near $NbC_{1.0}$ was first prepared by Joly (1877) from the reaction of $K_2O \cdot 3Nb_2O_5$ with carbon. Nb_2O_5 has been used as a starting material by most early workers and is presently used in the industrial preparation of the carbide.

The reaction between Nb_2O_5 and carbon begins at 675° (Elyutin *et al.*, 1958). Below 1200°, NbO_2 and NbC_x are the main products, and these react between 1450° and 1500° to give a NbC_xO_y solid solution (Shveikin, 1958). Shveikin, in a series of papers, has studied this reaction in some detail. A continual rise in temperature at first favors formation of the carbide, but at higher temperatures and correct stoichiometry, Nb metal is formed (Kusenko and Gel'd, 1961). In fact, ductile metal can be produced in this way (Kolchin and Cheveluva, 1959; Downing *et al.*, 1961). The form of the carbon determines the ease with which the reduction will proceed (Shveikin and Gel'd, 1961).

Pure NbC can be easily obtained either from the above reaction or by heating the elemental powders together, provided a sufficiently high final temperature is used. This is necessary to eliminate oxygen and nitrogen, and to bring about a complete reaction with the carbon. For example, both oxygen and nitrogen can be essentially eliminated from a commercial sample of NbC containing 0.28 wt % oxygen and 0.66 wt % nitrogen if the material is heated in vacuum above 1900° for about 30 minutes, but temperatures below 1400° have little effect on the purity (Storms and Krikorian, 1960). Considerably longer times are needed to react all of the carbon. More than 38 hours at 1800° were found necessary to bring a mixture of graphite and niobium powders at $NbC_{0.74}$ to equilibrium. A H_2 atmosphere or a higher temperature can shorten this time considerably (Storms and Krikorian, 1960).

Pure materials can also be produced by arc-melting, but composition inhomogeneity often results instead.

It is possible to deposit the carbide from the gas phase onto a hot object. By heating a tungsten wire to 900°–1000° in a gas containing $NbCl_5$, H_2, and hydrocarbons, Moers (1931) was able to deposit NbC containing some free metal. The metal can be easily converted to the carbide by heating it in a hydrocarbon + H_2 mixture as was demonstrated by Campbell *et al.* (1949). Protective coatings have been applied to graphite by exposing the surface to $NbCl_5$ vapor while at high temperature.

B. PHASE RELATIONSHIP

Two compounds are formed in the Nb–NbC system: Nb_2C with two crystal forms and the cubic NbC. A phase diagram, based primarily on the work of Storms and Krikorian (1960), is shown in Fig. 25.

The melting point of the pure metal at 2467° (Schofield, 1957; Pemsler, 1961) drops to a eutectic as carbon is added. A number of measurements of the eutectic temperature are in excellent agreement, namely, 2335° reported both by Pochon *et al.* (1959) and Storms and Krikorian (1960), 2328° obtained by Nadler and Kempter (1960), and 2340° ± 20° measured by Kimura and Sasaki (1961). It is difficult to account for the low value of 2230° ± 10° obtained by Elliott (1959). Pochon *et al.* (1959) and Elliott (1959) both find the eutectic composition at $NbC_{0.12}$. Kimura and Sasaki (1961) place it between $NbC_{0.152}$ and $NbC_{0.167}$.

At $NbC_{0.39}$ the melting point rises to 3090°, whereupon Nb_2C decomposes according to the reaction $NbC_{0.52} = NbC_{0.56}$ + liquid, according to Storms and Krikorian (1960). Nadler and Kempter (1960) and Kimura and Sasaki (1961) both obtained 3080° for the peritectic temperature. From the peritectic, the melting point rises to a maximum of 3600°, reported by both Rudy and Harmon (1965) and Kimura and Sasaki (1961), then drops to a eutectic with carbon. These workers are also in agreement with 3300° as the NbC–C eutectic temperature. These temperatures are somewhat higher than those of Nadler and Kempter (1960), who gave 3480° as the maximum and 3220° for the NbC–C eutectic temperature; Storms and Krikorian (1960), who measured 3500° and 3250° as the respective temperatures; and Elliott (1959) who also found eutectic melting near 3250°. Engelke *et al.* (1960) obtained 3420° by arc-melting a material which, according to the lattice parameter, had a composition of $NbC_{0.92}$. A paper by Portnoĭ *et al.* (1961) claims a eutectic temperature of 3150° for a material of unknown purity, and

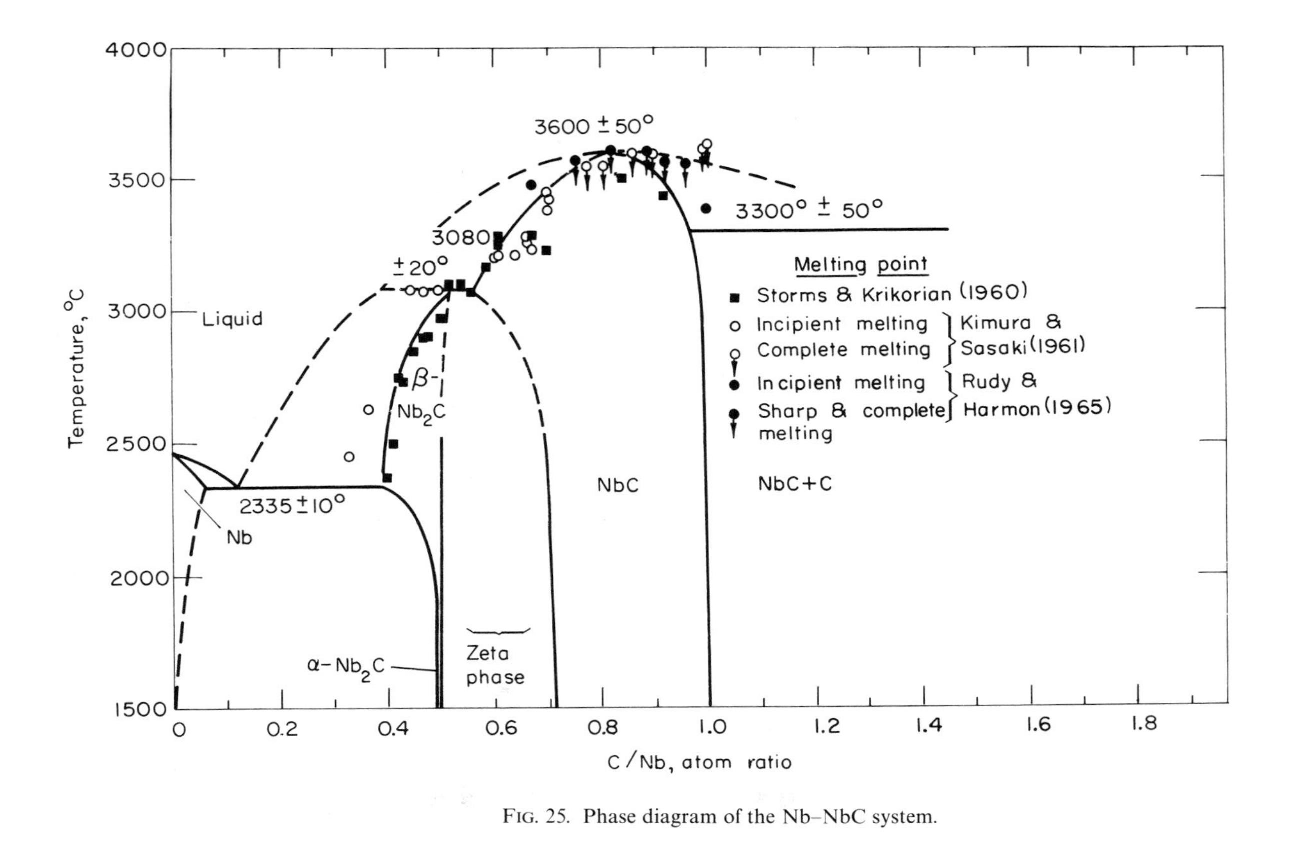

FIG. 25. Phase diagram of the Nb–NbC system.

Kovalchenko and Samsonov (1961) place the value between 2950° and 3000°C. Probable values for the melting temperatures are shown in Fig. 25.

The solubility curve for niobium metal, according to Elliott (1959), shows only 100 ppm dissolved carbon at 1500° and, even at the eutectic temperature, $NbC_{0.06}$ (0.8 wt %) is the phase limit. Although this work is in good agreement at 2000° with the measurement of Brauer and Lesser (1959a), Elliott's (1959) low value for the eutectic temperature suggests a temperature error of nearly 100°.

Likewise, the Nb_2C phase has a rather narrow range of existence at low temperatures. There is, however, some disagreement over this observation. Brauer and Lesser (1959a) reported $NbC_{0.36}$ as being the lower limit, but their data are consistent with any value up to $NbC_{0.42}$. Elliott (1959) places the homogeneity range between $NbC_{0.44}$ and $NbC_{0.48}$. Until this region of the phase diagram is better understood, none of the studies can be completely discounted. On the other hand, Kimura and Sasaki (1961) found, as did Storms and Krikorian (1960), a very narrow composition range, as shown in Fig. 25, with the upper boundary at $NbC_{0.5}$.

The NbC phase exists from about $NbC_{0.70}$ to near $NbC_{0.99}$. The lower compositions reported by other workers at the upper boundary (Elliott, 1959; Brauer and Lesser, 1959a) result from the increasingly slow reaction rates as the 1:1 ratio is approached. In fact, heating times in excess of 60 hours at 1900° are needed to obtain a fully saturated material (Storms and Krikorian, 1960), $NbC_{0.97}$ is the phase limit at the eutectic temperature (Storms, 1964).

If Nb is soluble in graphite, the limit is less than 0.01% after being cooled rapidly from the melt (Godin *et al.*, 1961).

Recently, two other phases have been reported in this system. Pochon *et al.* (1959) found what they suggested was a tetragonally distorted form of NbC in arc-cast alloys containing about 0.066% carbon. This was designated as a delta phase. Because it converted to Nb_2C upon annealing at 1200°, it was dismissed as being metastable.

On the basis of one weak powder pattern line at $\theta = 19.70°$, Brauer and Lesser (1959a) suggested a ζ phase, similar to their finding in the Ta–TaC system (Lesser and Brauer, 1958). Although neither Elliott (1959), Storms and Krikorian (1960), nor Kimura and Sasaki (1961) found evidence of this phase, subsequent work by Storms (1964) has confirmed its existence, but at a lower temperature. Recent evidence for a similar phase in the V–VC system gives additional support to this observation.

Recently Rudy and Harmon (1965) have suggested a more complicated relationship for the Nb_2C phase than had been supposed. They interpret DTA (differential thermal analysis) studies as showing a β–γ transition between 2450° and 2550° across the homogeneity region of Nb_2C and an α–β transition near 1200°. The phase diagram (Fig. 25) has not been modified in this region pending confirmation.

C. LATTICE PARAMETER AND STRUCTURE

The structure, lattice parameter and calculated powder pattern of the established phases (Nb, Nb_2C, and NbC) are shown in Tables 20 through 24. Lattice parameters are given for the phase boundaries quenched from 2000°.

Until recently, the structure of Nb_2C has been reported as hexagonal closest-packed ($L'3$). Storms and Krikorian (1960), during their study of the Nb–C system, noticed a line splitting in many of the Nb_2C patterns, although this was not reported at the time. From a neutron diffraction study, A. L. Bowman (1966) proposed an orthorhombic structure, which generates the calculated pattern shown in Table 22. Based on thermal effects noted at ~1200° and ~2500°, and the electron diffraction studies by Terao (1964), Rudy and Harmon (1965) propose the following scheme:

$$\alpha\text{-}Nb_2C(\zeta\text{-}Fe_2N) \underset{}{\overset{\sim 1200°}{\rightleftarrows}} \beta\text{-}Nb_2C(\varepsilon\text{-}Fe_2N) \underset{}{\overset{\sim 2500°}{\rightleftarrows}} \gamma\text{-}Nb_2C(L'3\text{-type})$$

Terao (1964), however, prepared the Nb_2C by oxidizing NbC in low pressure air above 1600°. This is hardly the way to obtain pure materials. Alyamovskii *et al.* (1963) also observed additional lines in the pattern after oxidizing Nb_2C in air at 300°. An orthorhombic structure was proposed. The patterns observed by Storms and Krikorian (1960) and that reported by Rudy and Brukl (1966), except for two lines at low angles in the latter case, agree very well with the pattern given in Table 22.

The lattice parameter of pure NbC varies with composition according to the equation

$$a_0 = 4.09847 + 0.71820(C/Nb) - 0.34570(C/Nb)^2$$

where C/Nb is the atom ratio (Kempter *et al.*, 1960). A refraction correction is included. This equation is based on 41 data points and was used to generate the curve in Fig. 26. As pointed out by Storms and Krikorian (1960), the lattice parameter of alloys containing an appreciable quantity of oxygen and nitrogen will lie above this curve if the points are plotted as if the impurity content were unknown. This is shown in Fig. 26, where the black circles represent material containing various amounts of these impurities. A few carbonitrides, prepared by Brauer and Lesser (1959b),

TABLE 20

STRUCTURE AND LATTICE PARAMETER OF Nb, α-Nb_2C, AND NbC

Phases in equilibrium	Composition of first phase	Structure type	Lattice parameter, (Å)	Investigator
Nb	Pure	bcc($A2$)	$a = 3.3000 \pm 0.0003$	Seybolt (1954)
Nb + Nb_2C	Carbon-saturated, quenched from 2000°	—	$a = 3.3012$	Brauer and Lesser (1959a)
α-Nb_2C + Nb	$NbC_{0.49}$	Based on $L'3$ indexing	$a = 3.127 \pm 0.001$ $c = 4.965 \pm 0.001$	Storms and Krikorian (1960)
α-Nb_2C + NbC	$NbC_{0.50}$	Based on $L'3$ indexing	$a = 3.127 \pm 0.001$ $c = 4.972 \pm 0.001$	Storms and Krikorian (1960)
α-Nb_2C + Nb	$NbC_{0.49}$	Orthorhombic	$a = 10.9042 \pm 0.0008$ $b = 3.0958 \pm 0.0004$ $c = 4.9700 \pm 0.0003$	Storms (1966b)
NbC + Nb_2C	$NbC_{0.70}$	fcc ($B1$)	$a = 4.4318 \pm 0.0005$[a]	Kempter *et al.* (1960)
NbC + C	$NbC_{0.99}$	fcc ($B1$)	$a = 4.4707 \pm 0.0003$[a]	Kempter *et al.* (1960)

[a] Corrected for refraction.

TABLE 21
COPPER RADIATION, POWDER PATTERN FOR Nb[a]

2θ	$\sin^2 \theta$	d spacing	Intensity	$h\ k\ l$
38.55	0.1090	2.3335	45	1 1 0
55.66	0.2179	1.6500	10	2 0 0
69.74	0.3269	1.3472	25	2 1 1
82.63	0.4358	1.1667	10	2 2 0
95.14	0.5448	1.0436	15	3 1 0
107.91	0.6538	0.9526	5	2 2 2
121.70	0.7627	0.8820	35	3 2 1
138.02	0.8717	0.8250	5	4 0 0
164.01	0.9806	0.7778	100	4 1 1, 3 3 0

[a] $a_0 = 3.3000$ Å; $\mu r = 4.0$; structure type $A2$, space group No. 229; $\lambda(K\alpha_1) = 1.54051$ Å.

are also plotted to show the effect of nitrogen impurity. Much work, it would appear, has been influenced by impurity levels which were higher than the investigator suspected.

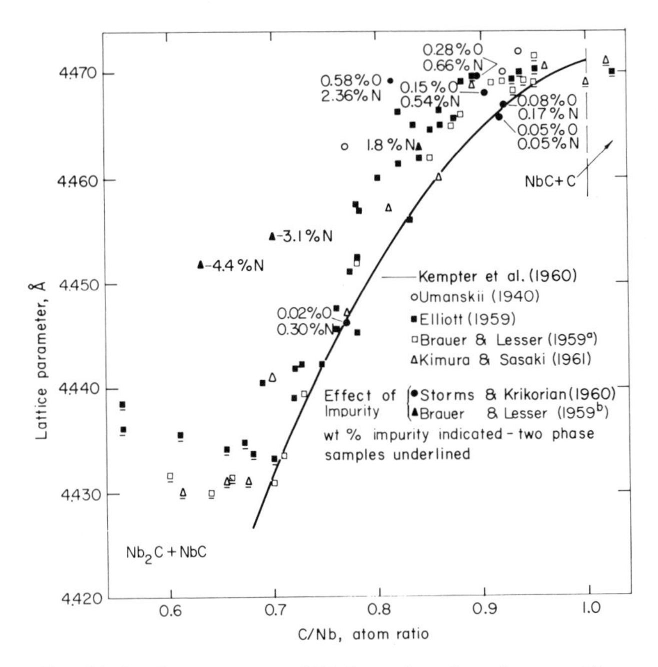

FIG. 26. Lattice parameter of NbC as a function of composition.

TABLE 22
COPPER RADIATION, POWDER PATTERN FOR α-Nb_2C[a]

2θ	$\sin^2 \theta$	d spacing	Intensity	$h\ k\ l$
32.82	0.0798	2.7265	5	4 0 0
33.25	0.0818	2.6923	20	2 1 0
36.12	0.0961	2.4844	35	0 0 2
37.60	0.1038	2.3903	60	4 0 1
37.98	0.1059	2.3672	100	2 1 1
49.60	0.1759	1.8364	10	4 0 2
49.91	0.1780	1.8258	25	2 1 2
58.86	0.2415	1.5675	30	6 1 0
59.68	0.2476	1.5480	15	0 2 0
62.03	0.2655	1.4949	1	6 1 1
65.93	0.2961	1.4156	15	4 0 3
66.19	0.2981	1.4107	30	2 1 3
68.81	0.3192	1.3632	5	8 0 0
69.81	0.3274	1.3462	5	4 2 0
71.05	0.3376	1.3257	30	6 1 2
71.73	0.3433	1.3147	10	8 0 1
71.79	0.3437	1.3138	15	0 2 2
72.71	0.3514	1.2993	30	4 2 1
76.64	0.3845	1.2422	10	0 0 4
80.25	0.4154	1.1951	5	8 0 2
81.20	0.4235	1.1836	5	4 2 2
85.91	0.4643	1.1304	1	4 0 4
86.14	0.4663	1.1279	5	2 1 4
94.07	0.5355	1.0526	5	8 0 3
95.01	0.5437	1.0446	20	4 2 3
97.68	0.5668	1.0231	5	8 2 0
98.86	0.5770	1.0140	5	2 3 0
99.76	0.5847	1.0073	20	10 1 1
100.47	0.5909	1.0021	15	8 2 1
101.66	0.6011	0.9935	15	2 3 1
104.59	0.6260	0.9736	25	6 1 4, 3 3 1
105.32	0.6321	0.9688	10	0 2 4
108.28	0.6568	0.9504	1	10 1 2
109.02	0.6629	0.9460	10	8 2 2
110.26	0.6731	0.9388	5	2 3 2
111.17	0.6806	0.9337	10	4 0 5
111.42	0.6826	0.9323	15	2 1 5
114.05	0.7037	0.9182	5	8 0 4

TABLE 22 (continued)

2θ	$\sin^2 \theta$	d spacing	Intensity	$h\ k\ l$
115.07	0.7119	0.9129	5	4 2 4
115.89	0.7183	0.9088	5	12 0 0
118.25	0.7366	0.8974	15	6 3 0
118.99	0.7423	0.8940	1	12 0 1
123.64	0.7770	0.8738	25	10 1 3
124.49	0.7831	0.8704	15	8 2 3
125.92	0.7933	0.8648	20	2 3 3
128.96	0.8144	0.8535	10	12 0 2
131.72	0.8328	0.8441	30	6 3 2
136.90	0.8651	0.8281	10	0 0 6
147.14	0.9200	0.8030	15	8 0 5
148.91	0.9282	0.7995	40	4 2 5
150.36	0.9346	0.7968	1	12 0 3
152.85	0.9449	0.7924	5	4 0 6
152.92	0.9452	0.7923	5	10 1 4
153.37	0.9470	0.7915	20	2 1 6
154.51	0.9513	0.7897	20	8 2 4
154.94	0.9529	0.7891	1	6 3 3
157.37	0.9615	0.7855	15	2 3 4
158.71	0.9659	0.7837	35	12 2 0
160.70	0.9719	0.7813	1	3 1 6
161.11	0.9731	0.7808	1	5 2 5
167.45	0.9881	0.7749	1	11 0 4
168.47	0.9899	0.7742	10	12 2 1
168.72	0.9903	0.7740	40	0 4 0

[a] $a_0 = 10.9060$ Å; $b_0 = 3.0960$ Å; $c_0 = 4.9688$ Å; $\mu r = 4.0$; Space group type *Pnma* No. 62; $\lambda(K\alpha_1) = 1.54051$ Å.

An additional factor which influences how data will fall with respect to the curve is the uniformity of composition throughout the material. Calculations of lattice parameters from powder patterns of single-phase material generally produce values for the most abundant composition, whereas chemical analysis gives the average composition. Consequently, when this information is plotted, the points will fall to the right or left of the curve depending on whether the sample has been gaining or losing carbon during its previous treatment. In addition, the composition gradients can introduce strains in the lattice which affect the lattice parameter.

TABLE 23

COPPER RADIATION, POWDER PATTERN FOR β-Nb_2C[a]

2θ	$\sin^2\theta$	d spacing	Intensity	$h\ k\ l$
33.06	0.0810	2.7072	15	1 0 0
36.10	0.0960	2.4860	20	0 0 2
37.81	0.1050	2.3776	100	1 0 1
49.75	0.1770	1.8311	25	1 0 2
59.05	0.2429	1.5630	25	1 1 0
66.04	0.2970	1.4135	25	1 0 3
69.37	0.3238	1.3536	5	2 0 0
71.20	0.3389	1.3232	25	1 1 2
72.28	0.3478	1.3060	20	2 0 1
76.58	0.3840	1.2430	5	0 0 4
80.77	0.4198	1.1888	5	2 0 2
85.98	0.4650	1.1296	5	1 0 4
94.57	0.5398	1.0484	15	2 0 3
97.66	0.5667	1.0232	5	2 1 0
100.45	0.5907	1.0022	25	2 1 1
104.70	0.6269	0.9729	20	1 1 4
108.99	0.6627	0.9462	10	2 1 2
111.22	0.6809	0.9334	10	1 0 5
114.56	0.7078	0.9155	5	2 0 4
117.21	0.7286	0.9024	10	3 0 0
124.43	0.7827	0.8706	30	2 1 3
130.48	0.8246	0.8482	20	3 0 2
136.72	0.8640	0.8287	5	0 0 6
147.95	0.9238	0.8014	25	2 0 5
152.86	0.9449	0.7924	15	1 0 6
154.34	0.9507	0.7900	15	2 1 4
160.55	0.9715	0.7815	30	2 2 0

[a] $a_0 = 3.126$ Å; $c_0 = 4.972$ Å; $\mu r = 3.0$; structure type $L'3$, space group No. 194; $\lambda(K\alpha_1) = 1.54051$ Å.

The density, based on the above equation, drops from 7.788 g/cm^3 at $NbC_{0.99}$ to a minimum of 7.716 g/cm^3 at $NbC_{0.785}$ and rises to 7.730 g/cm^3 at the NbC–Nb_2C phase boundary. The x-ray density of Nb_2C in equilibrium with NbC is 7.80 g/cm^3.

D. APPEARANCE

Between the metal and about $NbC_{0.9}$, the powder has a gray metallic color. However, as more carbon is adsorbed, a subtle color change begins which develops into a lavender tint at $NbC_{0.99}$.

TABLE 24
COPPER RADIATION, POWDER PATTERN FOR $NbC_{0.98}$[a]

2θ	$\sin^2\theta$	d spacing	Intensity	$h\ k\ l$
34.72	0.0891	2.5812	100	1 1 1
40.31	0.1187	2.2353	75	2 0 0
58.33	0.2375	1.5806	45	2 2 0
69.70	0.3265	1.3480	40	3 1 1
73.29	0.3562	1.2906	15	2 2 2
87.13	0.4749	1.1177	10	4 0 0
97.35	0.5640	1.0256	20	3 3 1
100.80	0.5937	0.9997	25	4 2 0
115.14	0.7124	0.9126	25	4 2 2
127.08	0.8015	0.8604	30	3 3 3, 5 1 1
154.13	0.9499	0.7903	25	4 4 0

[a] $a_0 = 4.4707$ Å; $\mu r = 2.0$; structure type $B1$, space group No. 225; $\lambda(K\alpha_1) = 1.54051$ Å.

E. CHEMICAL REACTIVITY

NbC is exceedingly unreactive; even boiling aqua regia will not attack the powder. A mixture of HNO_3 and HF is needed to cause dissolution (Kopyleva, 1961).

When heated in oxygen, NbC will burn, and in air corrosion becomes severe above 1100°. By heating in nitrogen + H_2 or ammonia the carbide can be converted to the nitride.

There is apparently no reaction with H_2 (May and Hoekstra, 1961), but this, of course, will depend on the stoichiometry and whether the gas is flowing or static (see Chapter XIII, Section F).

F. HARDNESS

The hardness of NbC depends on the composition. Unfortunately, no study of hardness as a function of composition has appeared. Jones (1956) reported 1950 DPH for NbC + C, Foster *et al.* (1950) obtained 2470 kg/mm^2 for composition near to $NbC_{1.0}$, but which probably contained some tungsten. Meerson and Umanskii (1953) quote Soviet investigators as obtaining 2055 kg/mm^2, and Kieffer and Kölbl (1949) report 2400 kg/mm^2 for $NbC_{0.99}$. The hardness of Nb_2C has not been reported.

G. THERMOCHEMICAL PROPERTIES

1. Heat of Formation

The various heat of formation measurements are compared in Fig. 27. In order to provide a common basis, the results from combustion measurements were all calculated using -455.2 kcal/mole and -94.05 kcal/mole for the heat of formation of Nb_2O_5 and CO_2, respectively.

It was not indicated in the work by Kusenko and Gel'd (1960) whether corrections were made to a constant pressure process and to unit fugacity for oxygen, nor for the effect of impurities. If these corrections were not made, the values in the figure would be too high.

Huber *et al.* (1961) fit their data by the equation ΔH_f^0 (298.15°, kcal/mole niobium) $= 6.60 - 70.95(\text{C/Nb}) + 30.75(\text{C/Nb})^2$ which is shown as the solid curve in the figure. The additional data produce no important change in this curve. These workers also obtained -23.3 ± 0.6 kcal/mole for $NbC_{0.5}$ and -21.55 ± 0.85 kcal/mole at $NbC_{0.489}$.

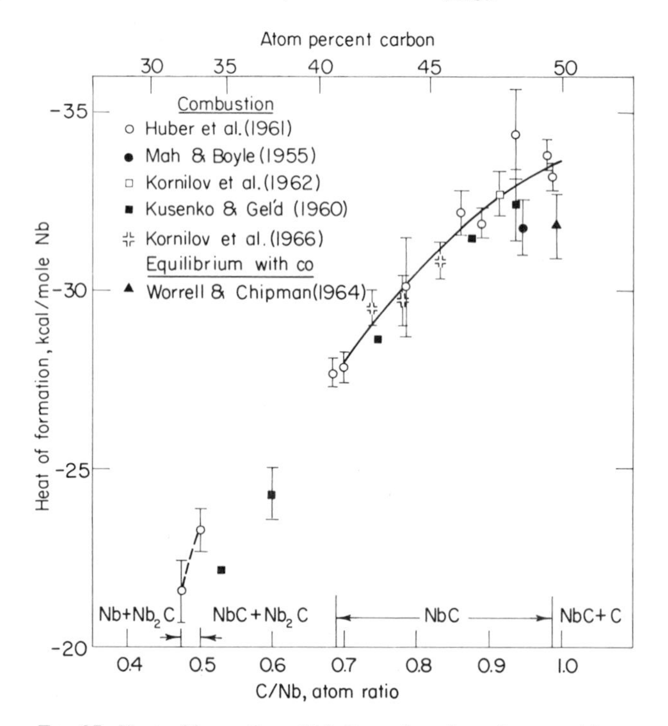

Fig. 27. Heat of formation of NbC as a function of composition.

Worrell and Chipman (1964) measured the CO pressure over a mixture of NbO_2, C and NbC between 1170° and 1260°. The resulting heat of formation, shown in Fig. 27, is raised by 0.3 kcal if the thermal properties in Table 29 are used. Since oxygen was present, this measurement applies to the oxycarbide although, in this system, the difference between the carbide and the oxycarbide would appear to be slight.

2. Low Temperature Heat Capacity

Sandenaw and Storms (1965) have measured the heat capacity of various compositions in the Nb–C system between 7.5° and 320° with the following results at 298.15°:

	C_p° (cal/mole-deg)	$S_{298.15}^\circ - S_0^\circ$ (cal/mole-deg)[a]	$H_{298.15}^\circ - H_0^\circ$ (cal/mole)
$NbC_{0.980}$	8.79	8.29	1390
$NbC_{0.825}$	8.41	7.87	1335
$NbC_{0.702}$	7.97	7.63	1280
β-$NbC_{0.500}(Nb_2C)$	7.59	7.66	1270

[a] Uncorrected for the entropy of mixing between the vacancies and the carbon atoms. See Chapter XIII, Section G.

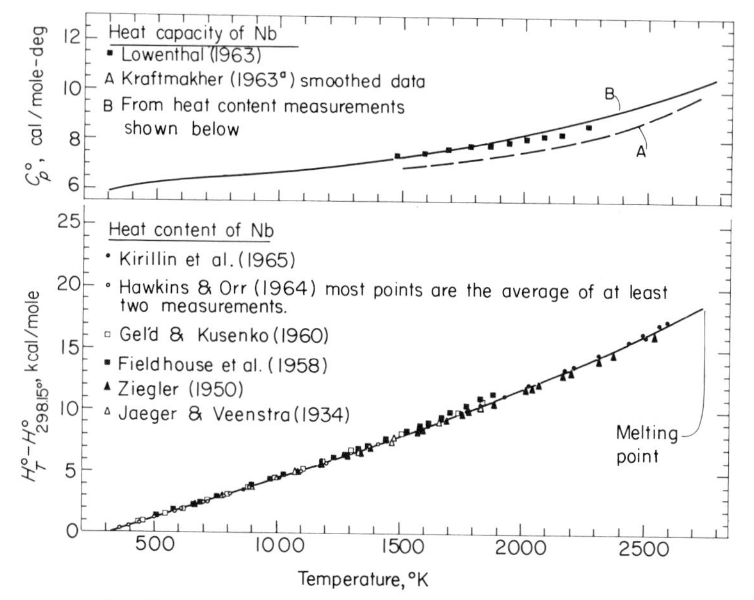

Fig. 28. High temperature heat capacity and enthalpy of Nb.

Using a sample of $NbC_{0.996}$, Pankratz *et al.* (1964) obtained 8.81 cal/mole-deg and 8.46 cal/mole-deg at 298.15° for C_p° and S°, respectively. These two studies agree very well when the comparison is made at a comparable composition.

3. High Temperature Heat Content

Recent heat content and heat capacity measurements of niobium metal make a reexamination of these properties necessary. The various heat content studies, shown in Fig. 28, were fit by an equation (Table 25) while using the two constraints, $C_p = 5.85$ cal/mole and $H_T^\circ - H_{298.15}^\circ = 0$

TABLE 25
Thermal Functions of $Nb_{(s)}$[a]

T (°K)	$H_T^\circ - H_{298}^\circ$ (cal/mole)	C_p° (cal/mole-deg)	S_T° (cal/mole-deg)	$-(F_T^\circ - H_{298}^\circ)/T$ (cal/mole-deg)
298.15	0	5.850	8.730	8.730
300	10.83	5.858	8.766	8.730
400	613.3	6.149	10.50	8.964
500	1236	6.287	11.89	9.414
600	1869	6.374	13.04	9.925
700	2510	6.446	14.03	10.44
800	3158	6.516	14.89	10.95
900	3814	6.591	15.67	11.43
1000	4477	6.676	16.36	11.89
1100	5749	6.773	17.01	12.32
1200	5831	6.882	17.60	12.74
1300	6526	7.005	18.15	13.13
1400	7233	7.141	18.68	13.51
1500	7955	7.292	19.18	13.87
1600	8692	7.458	19.65	14.22
1700	9447	7.638	20.11	14.55
1800	10220	7.834	20.55	14.87
1900	11010	8.044	20.98	15.18
2000	11830	8.269	21.40	15.48
2100	12670	8.509	21.81	15.78
2200	13530	8.765	22.21	16.06
2300	14420	9.036	22.61	16.34
2400	15340	9.322	23.00	16.60
2500	16290	9.623	23.38	16.87
2600	17260	9.940	23.77	17.13
2700	18280	10.27	24.15	17.38
2740	18690	10.41	24.30	17.48

[a] $H_T^\circ - H_{298.15}^\circ = -2.1963 \times 10^3 + 6.7326T - 3.7989 \times 10^{-4}T^2 + 2.5601 \times 10^{-7}T^3 + 6.4391 \times 10^4/T$ (298°–2740°K, cal/mole, ±1.0%); M.W. = 92.906.

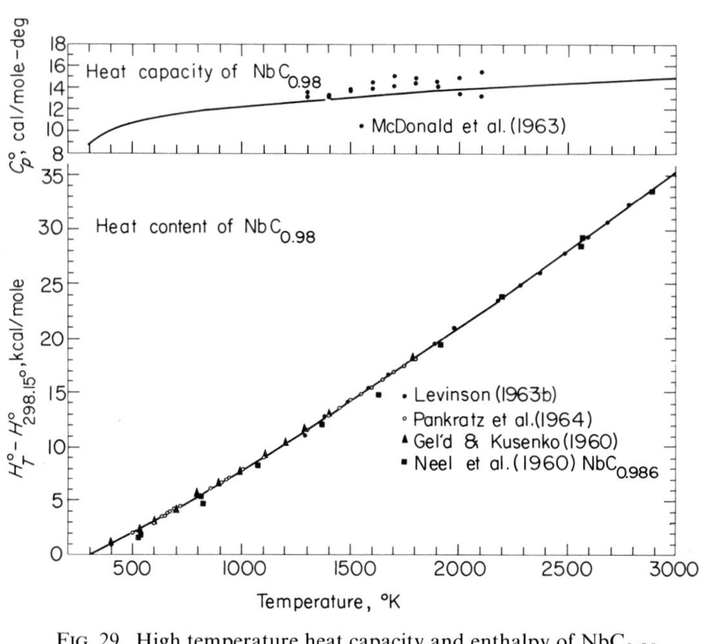

FIG. 29. High temperature heat capacity and enthalpy of $NbC_{0.98}$.

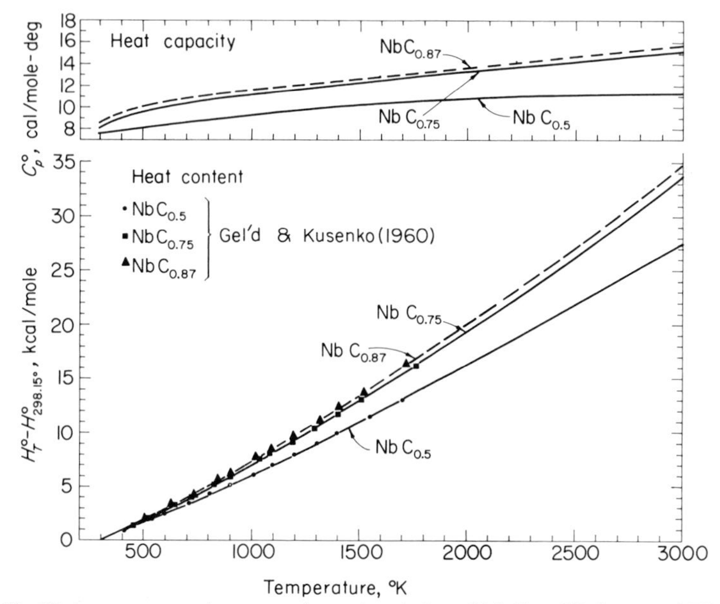

FIG. 30. High temperature heat capacity and enthalpy of $NbC_{0.5}$, $NbC_{0.75}$, and $NbC_{0.87}$.

TABLE 26
THERMAL FUNCTIONS OF $NbC_{0.5}(\beta\text{-}Nb_2C)$[a]

T (°K)	$H_T^\circ - H_{298}^\circ$ (cal/mole)	C_p° (cal/mole-deg)	S_T° (cal/mole-deg)	$-(F_T^\circ - H_{298}^\circ)/T$ (cal/mole-deg)
298.15	0	7.590	7.660	7.660
300	14.05	7.596	7.707	7.660
400	788.2	7.884	9.932	7.962
500	1590	8.158	11.72	8.540
600	2419	8.419	13.23	9.199
700	3274	8.669	14.55	9.871
800	4153	8.907	15.72	10.53
900	5055	9.134	16.78	11.17
1000	5979	9.350	17.76	11.78
1100	6925	9.556	18.66	12.36
1200	7890	9.750	19.50	12.92
1300	8874	9.933	20.29	13.46
1400	9876	10.11	21.03	13.97
1500	10890	10.27	21.73	14.47
1600	11930	10.42	22.40	14.94
1700	12980	10.56	23.04	15.40
1800	14041	10.69	23.64	15.84
1900	15120	10.81	24.22	16.27
2000	16200	10.91	24.78	16.68
2100	17300	11.01	25.32	17.08
2200	18400	11.10	25.83	17.46
2300	19520	11.17	26.32	17.84
2400	20640	11.23	26.80	18.20
2500	21760	11.29	27.26	18.56
2600	22890	11.33	27.70	18.90
2700	24030	11.36	28.13	19.23
2800	25170	11.38	28.55	19.56
2900	26300	11.39	28.95	19.88
3000	27440	11.39	29.33	20.18

[a] $H_T^\circ - H_{298.15}^\circ = -2.1417 \times 10^3 + 6.7057T + 1.5942 \times 10^{-3}T^2 - 1.8076 \times 10^{-7}T^3 + 1.6148 \times 10^3/T$ (298°–1800°K, cal/mole, ±0.4%); M.W. = 98.911; $H_{298.15}^\circ - H_0^\circ = 1270$ cal/mole. A randomization entropy of 1.37 eu is not included.

both at 298.15°. The resulting heat capacity compares well with several direct measurements of this property, also shown in the figure.

A number of enthalpy measurements near $NbC_{1.0}$, compared in Fig. 29, have given excellent agreement. In addition, other compositions including

TABLE 27
THERMAL FUNCTIONS OF $NbC_{0.75}$[a]

T (°K)	$H_T^\circ - H_{298}^\circ$ (cal/mole)	C_p° (cal/mole-deg)	S_T° (cal/mole-deg)	$-(F_T^\circ - H_{298}^\circ)/T$ (cal/mole-deg)
298.15	0.0	8.100	7.720	7.720
300	15.01	8.123	7.770	7.720
400	876.7	9.018	10.24	8.051
500	1807	9.558	12.32	8.703
600	2784	9.958	14.10	9.457
700	3797	10.29	15.66	10.23
800	4841	10.59	17.05	11.00
900	5913	10.86	18.31	11.74
1000	7012	11.12	19.47	12.46
1100	8136	11.36	20.54	13.15
1200	9284	11.60	21.54	13.80
1300	10460	11.84	22.48	14.44
1400	11650	12.07	23.37	15.04
1500	12870	12.29	24.21	15.63
1600	14110	12.51	25.01	16.19
1700	15370	12.72	25.77	16.73
1800	16650	12.94	26.50	17.25
1900	17960	13.15	27.21	17.76
2000	19280	13.35	27.89	18.25
2100	20630	13.56	28.55	18.72
2200	21990	13.76	29.18	19.18
2300	23380	13.96	29.80	19.63
2400	24790	14.15	30.39	20.07
2500	26210	14.35	30.98	20.49
2600	27660	14.54	31.54	20.91
2700	29120	14.73	32.10	21.31
2800	30600	14.91	32.63	21.71
2900	32100	15.10	33.16	22.09
3000	33620	15.28	33.68	22.47

[a] $H_T^\circ - H_{298.15}^\circ = -3.2096 \times 10^3 + 8.8844T + 1.2409 \times 10^{-3}T^2 - 3.8370 \times 10^{-8}T^3 + 1.3460 \times 10^5/T$(298°–1800°K, cal/mole, $\pm 0.2\%$); M.W. = 101.914; $H_{298.15}^\circ - H_0^\circ =$ 1305 cal/mole. A randomization entropy of 1.12 eu is not included.

Nb_2C have also been studied (Fig. 30). The data from each study have been fitted by an equation with the form

$$\Delta H = A + BT + CT^2 + DT^3 + E/T$$

TABLE 28

THERMAL FUNCTIONS OF $NbC_{0.87}$ [a]

T (°K)	$H_T^\circ - H_{298}^\circ$ (cal/mole)	C_p° (cal/mole-deg)	S_T° (cal/mole-deg)	$-(F_T^\circ - H_{298}^\circ)/T$ (cal/mole-deg)
298.15	0.0	8.510	7.980	7.980
300	15.77	8.537	8.033	7.980
400	925.2	9.536	10.64	8.329
500	1909	10.10	12.84	9.017
600	2940	10.50	14.71	9.814
700	4006	10.81	16.36	10.63
800	5101	11.08	17.82	11.44
900	6222	11.33	19.14	12.23
1000	7366	11.57	20.34	12.98
1100	8534	11.79	21.46	13.70
1200	9724	12.01	22.49	14.39
1300	10940	12.22	23.46	15.05
1400	12170	12.44	24.38	15.68
1500	13420	12.65	25.24	16.29
1600	14700	12.86	26.06	16.88
1700	15990	13.06	26.85	17.44
1800	17310	13.27	27.60	17.98
1900	18650	13.48	28.32	18.51
2000	20010	13.69	29.02	19.02
2100	21390	13.90	29.69	19.51
2200	22790	14.11	30.35	19.99
2300	24210	14.32	30.98	20.45
2400	25650	14.53	31.59	20.90
2500	27110	14.74	32.19	21.34
2600	28600	14.96	32.77	21.77
2700	30110	15.17	33.34	22.19
2800	31630	15.38	33.90	22.60
2900	33180	15.60	34.44	23.00
3000	34750	15.82	34.97	23.39

[a] $H_T^\circ - H_{298.15}^\circ = -3.5738 \times 10^3 + 9.8318T + 9.2474 \times 10^{-4}T^2 + 1.6788 \times 10^{-8}T^3 + 1.6691 \times 10^5/T$ (298°–1800°K, cal/mole, ± 0.2%); M.W. = 103.355; $H_{298.15}^\circ - H_0^\circ = 1350$ cal/mole. A randomization entropy of 0.77 eu is not included.

while C_p at 298.15° was fixed at the value obtained from low temperature measurements and $H_T^\circ - H_{298.15}^\circ$ was made equal to zero at 298.15°. The resulting C_p of $NbC_{0.98}$ is compared to direct measurements using

TABLE 29
THERMAL FUNCTIONS OF $NbC_{0.98}$[a]

T (°K)	$H_T^\circ - H_{298}^\circ$ (cal/mole)	C_p° (cal/mole-deg)	S_T° (cal/mole-deg)	$-(F_T^\circ - H_{298}^\circ)/T$ (cal/mole-deg)
298.15	0	8.790	8.290	8.290
300	16.29	8.825	8.344	8.290
400	971.6	10.12	11.08	8.655
500	2021	10.81	13.42	9.381
600	3126	11.26	15.44	10.23
700	4269	11.59	17.20	11.10
800	5442	11.86	18.76	11.96
900	6640	12.10	20.18	12.80
1000	7861	12.30	21.46	13.60
1100	9101	12.49	22.64	14.37
1200	10360	12.67	23.74	15.11
1300	11630	12.84	24.76	15.81
1400	12930	13.00	25.72	16.48
1500	14230	13.15	26.62	17.13
1600	15560	13.30	27.47	17.75
1700	16890	13.44	28.28	18.34
1800	18250	13.58	29.05	18.92
1900	19610	13.71	29.79	19.47
2000	20990	13.84	30.50	20.00
2100	22380	13.97	31.18	20.52
2200	23780	14.09	31.83	21.02
2300	25200	14.21	32.46	21.50
2400	26620	14.32	33.07	21.97
2500	28061	14.43	33.65	22.43
2600	29510	14.54	34.22	22.87
2700	20968	14.64	34.77	23.30
2800	32437	14.74	35.31	23.72
2900	33916	14.84	35.82	24.13
3000	35404	14.93	36.33	24.53

[a] $H_T^\circ - H_{298.15}^\circ = -4.0918 \times 10^3 + 10.8561T + 9.1724 \times 10^{-4}T^2 - 5.2003 \times 10^{-8}T^3 + 2.3105 \times 10^5/T$ (298°–3000°K, cal/mole, ± 0.3%); M.W. = 104.676; $H_{298.15}^\circ - H_0^\circ$ = 1390 cal/mole.

pulsed heating techniques. Not shown are the rather scattered values of Barriault *et al.* (1961) which are much above the curve, and are claimed to show a transition near 2437°. No other evidence has been reported for such a transition. The use of rather impure material (0.22 wt % O_2, 0.47 wt % N_2) may provide an explanation.

The thermal functions for Nb, $NbC_{0.5}$, $NbC_{0.75}$, $NbC_{0.87}$, and $NbC_{0.98}$ are listed in Tables 25, 26, 27, 28, and 29, respectively.

4. Vaporization

Niobium carbide vaporizes congruently into a vacuum at $NbC_{0.748}$ and 2910° (Fries, 1962; Storms, 1962). At higher temperatures the composition drops, reaching $NbC_{0.735}$ at 3130° (Storms, 1962).

Because of obvious difficulties, the metal pressure over NbC + C has not yet been measured by effusion techniques. However, the known thermochemical properties allow a pressure to be calculated. This was based on the following values: $\Delta H_f^\circ(298.15°) = -33.4$ kcal/mole (Huber *et al.*, 1961); heat of vaporization from the metal, 172.1 ± 0.6 kcal/mole [calculated from the data of Speiser *et al.* (1959) using the free energy functions in Table 25]; free energy functions found in Tables 25 and 29; the JANAF tables (1963) for $C_{(s)}$; and Schick (1966) for $Nb_{(g)}$.

The resulting pressure of Nb over $NbC_{0.98}$ + C is given by the equation

$$\log P(\text{atm}) = -4.542 \times 10^4/T + 8.154$$

This is compared in Fig. 31 to several Langmuir measurements of NbC and the pressure over pure Nb.

Fries (1962) measured the weight lost by a freely evaporating sample, initially $NbC_{\sim 0.95}$, and attributed it solely to the evaporation of carbon. On this basis the results agree very well with a similar study by Hoch *et al.* (1955) and Coffman *et al.* (1960) using TaC, for which the same assumption was made. However, if the evaporating surface is assumed to have been nearly congruent, the calculated metal pressures, shown in Fig. 31, are consistent with the study by Fesenko and Bolgar (1963). It is surprising indeed that Fries' (1962) work should show such good agreement with each of these measurements when two mutually exclusive assumptions are made. It is probable that both agreements are coincidental. As Fries demonstrated, the evaporation rate not only depended on the overall composition, but a concentration gradient existed within the samples. Thus, the evaporating surface was neither at the congruent composition nor did it have the total analyzed composition. Even though the pressure was obtained from a small weight loss, the effect of the resulting composition change would have been magnified by the rapidly changing activities in this region. Consequently, the measured evaporation rates cannot be

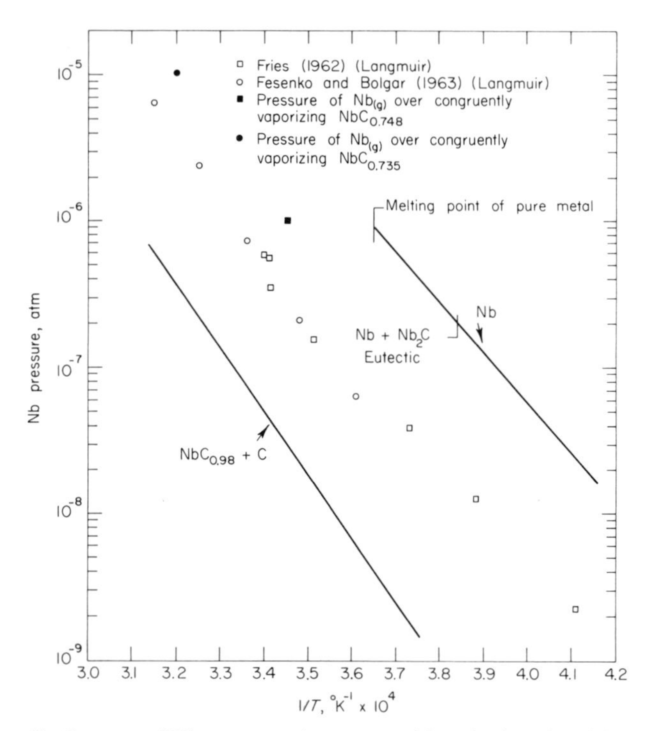

FIG. 31. Pressure of $Nb_{(g)}$ over various compositions in the Nb–NbC system.

related to the thermodynamic properties without considerable uncertainty. Both measurements are well below the pressures which can be calculated from known thermochemical data at the congruent composition.

VI

THE TANTALUM–TANTALUM CARBIDE SYSTEM

A. PREPARATION

Tantalum carbide was first prepared by Joly in 1876 when the pentoxide or tantalites and Na_2CO_3 were heated with carbon at about 1500°. The pentoxide has been a common starting material for modern investigations.

This system is relatively easy to free of oxygen and nitrogen impurities. However, because of the very low diffusion rate for carbon, composition uniformity is difficult to obtain. A procedure adopted by Lesser and Brauer (1958) gives satisfactory results. They heated the outgassed powdered elements in a graphite crucible in vacuum until, at about 1000°; the materials began to react, producing an evolution of gas and heat. After the reaction had subsided, the temperature was raised to above 2000° and held there for about 15 minutes. Heatings were continued, with intermittent grindings, until a homogeneous and pure product was obtained. Reducing the compact to a powder between heatings helps overcome the slow rate with which carbon diffuses into the carbide. Naturally, the higher the temperature the more quickly equilibrium will be obtained. However, above $\sim$2400° the evaporation of carbon can reestablish a concentration gradient. The use of a hydrogen atmosphere is also helpful in promoting the reaction. Such a treatment should be followed by a vacuum anneal to remove the dissolved hydrogen. This procedure should also be followed when methane is used.

Although TaC cannot be deposited directly onto a W wire from a hydrocarbon + $TaCl_5$ + H_2 vapor—because of the immediate formation of Ta metal—subsequent heating in a hydrocarbon atmosphere will lead to the carbide (Moers, 1931; Becker and Ewest, 1930). Eliminating the first step, Robins (1959) produced TaC by heating Ta wires in methane. He also prepared TaC by melting iron or aluminum containing tantalum and carbon in a graphite crucible. The TaC crystals were separated by dissolving the menstruum in HCl. Carbon will acquire a layer of TaC + Ta_2C when heated in $TaCl_5$ vapor (Burgers and Basart, 1934).

Arc-melting techniques have also been employed. This, unfortunately, tends to produce a carbon-deficient and inhomogeneous carbide.

B. PHASE RELATIONSHIP

The Ta–C system contains two compounds: one has the formula Ta_2C with an α–β transition near 2000°, and the other is a fcc compound designated TaC. A probable phase diagram based mainly on the work of Rudy and Harmon (1965) is shown in Fig. 32.

Numerous measurements of the melting point of tantalum (Table 30) show unusually good agreement with the early and often quoted value of 2996° (Malter and Langmuir, 1939). Most of this unanimity results because this element self-purifies easily near its melting point (Klopp *et al.*, 1960). This demonstrates, once again, that the high temperatures involved are not the sole cause of poor agreement between melting point measurements in other systems. Recently Rudy and Harmon (1965) have shown that, when the impurity content is reduced to below a total of 150 ppm (O + N + Si + Fe), the melting temperature is raised to 3014°. This value is in agreement with a study by Pemsler (1961) using similarly pure material.

Dissolved carbon lowers the melting point to a eutectic with Ta_2C, reported to be at 2902° ± 30° (Nadler and Kampter, 1960); 2825° (Sara and Lowell, 1964); 2843° ± 7° (Rudy and Harmon, 1965); and 2800° (Ellinger, 1943). At the eutectic temperature, tantalum dissolves 7.5 ± 0.5 at. % C ($TaC_{0.081}$), and the solubility drops rapidly as the temperature

TABLE 30

Determinations of Melting Point for Tantalum Metal

Investigator	Melting point (°C)
Malter and Langmuir (1939)	2996
Knapton *et al.* (1960)	3030, 3010
Schmidt *et al.* (1959)	2996 ± 25
Pemsler (1961)	3017
Sara *et al.* (1963)	3000
Riley (1964)	3006 ± 15
Rudy and Harmon (1965)	3014 ± 10[a]

[a] Error based on reproducibility.

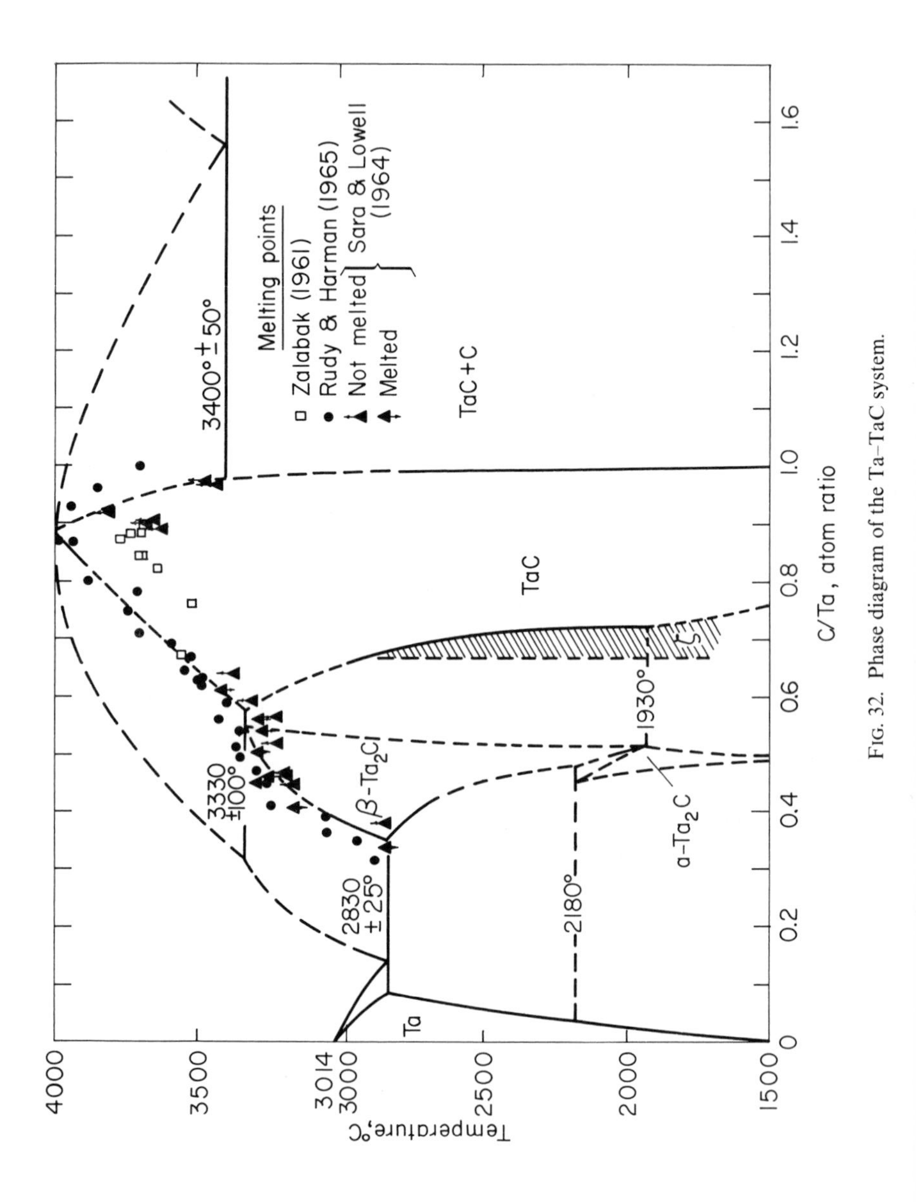

FIG. 32. Phase diagram of the Ta–TaC system.

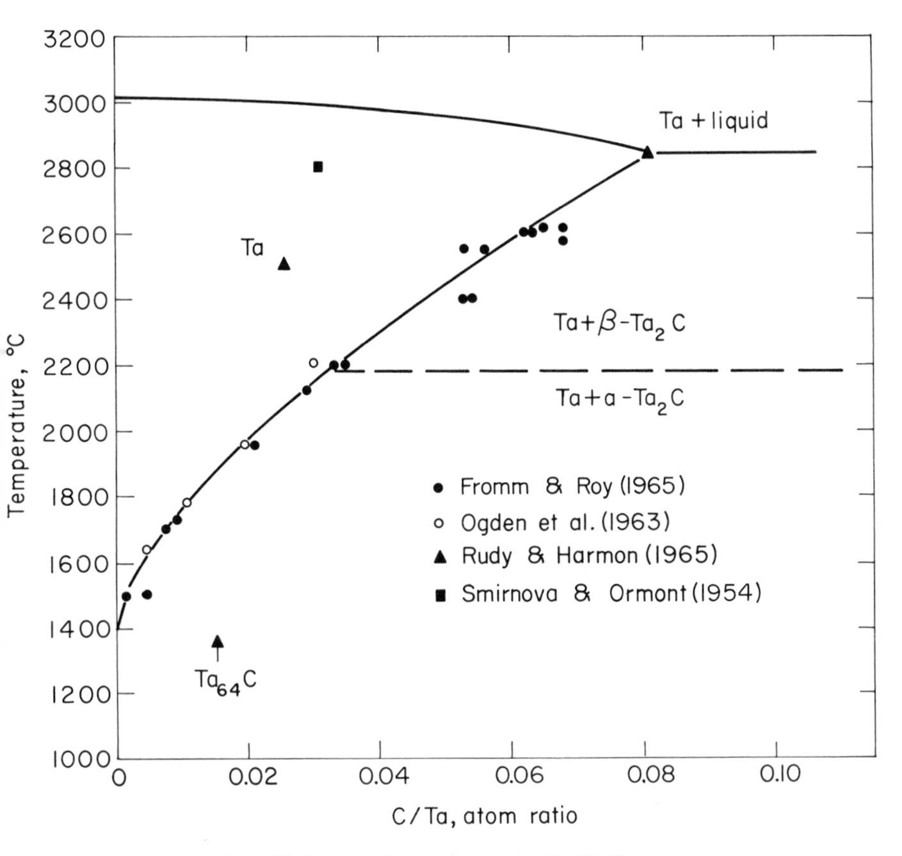

FIG. 33. Low carbon region of the Ta–TaC system.

is lowered. The resulting precipitation of Ta_2C not only produces considerable heat, but it cannot be suppressed even by a very rapid quench (Rudy and Harmon, 1965). There is no indication in the measurements, shown in Fig. 33, of an effect owing to the α–β transition in Ta_2C.

On the basis of metallographic examination, the eutectic composition has been found at $TaC_{0.143}$ (Sara and Lowell, 1964); $TaC_{0.14}$ (Rudy and Harmon, 1965); $TaC_{0.12}$ (Pochon *et al.*, 1959); and $TaC_{0.06}$ (Ellinger, 1943).

Until recently, the Ta_2C phase was thought to be hexagonal (*L'*3) at all temperatures. A. L. Bowman *et al.* (1965) found, from neutron diffraction patterns, that the normally observed low temperature form has the *C*6 cadmium iodide antitype structure due to ordering of the carbon atoms. The inability to see this in x-ray patterns accounts for the past oversight. This will be discussed further in the next section. Using thermal analysis and metallographic techniques, Rudy and Harmon (1965) observed a structure change near 2000°, which, no doubt, is due to a *C6–L'3* conversion. Since previous workers were unaware of this complication, their observations of the phase limits in this region are open to some misinterpretation. Lesser and Brauer (1958) give $TaC_{0.41}$ as the lower boundary between 1800° and 2100°. However, any value up to $TaC_{0.47}$ is equally consistent with their data. Ellinger (1943) reports $TaC_{0.47}$–$TaC_{0.5}$ as the range at the eutectic temperature. On the other hand, Sara and Lowell (1964) and Rudy and Harmon (1965) are in agreement with a range of $TaC_{0.36}$ to $TaC_{0.5}$ at the same temperature. At 2200°, Dubrovskaya *et al.* (1964) found only Ta_2C between $TaC_{0.43}$ and $TaC_{0.50}$. McMullin and Norton (1953) place the upper boundary of α-Ta_2C below $TaC_{0.47}$ for material cooled from 1820°. This boundary, apparently, moves to lower carbon contents as the temperature is dropped below 1800° (Santoro and Probst, 1965). Values for the Ta_2C melting point have included 3400° (Ellinger, 1943); 3240° (Sara and Lowell, 1964); 3500° $\pm$ 50° (Nadler and Kempter, 1960); and 3330 $\pm$ 8° (Rudy and Harmon, 1965).

TaC, like the other monocarbides, has a wide range of composition. Values for the lower-phase limit range from $TaC_{0.58}$ claimed by Smirnova and Ormont* (1954, 1955, 1956) and Robins (1959) to $TaC_{0.74}$ determined by Lesser and Brauer (1958) from an extrapolation of the lattice parameter. The latter value agrees well with the observations of Rudy and Harmon (1965) for material quenched from 1700° and with the findings of A. L. Bowman (1961) after quenching from 1850°. As the temperature is raised, the quenched composition decreases. Dubrovskaya *et al.* (1964) obtained $TaC_{0.73}$ after quenching from 2200°, Sara and Lowell (1964) give $TaC_{0.715}$ for 2250°, and A. L. Bowman (1961) reports $TaC_{0.71}$ after quenching from 2400°. Rudy and Harmon (1965) were unable to retain compositions below $TaC_{0.72}$ after a quench of 100°/second from above 3500°. In order to retain equilibrium compositions of TaC above ~2500°, the need for a very rapid quench rate is indicated. The upper-phase limit extends at least to $TaC_{0.99}$ at 2400° (A. L. Bowman, 1961) with a trend to higher carbon contents as the temperature is lowered. Because of the limitations in analytical techniques, this composition shift was determined by noting an increase in the superconducting transition temperature after a lengthy anneal at 1200° (A. L. Bowman, 1965;

* This value is not only inconsistent with the data presented, but the rest of their work is at odds with most accepted measurements.

Giorgi *et al.*, 1962). Rudy and Harmon (1965) place the boundary at $TaC_{0.98}$ at the eutectic temperature, based on lattice parameter measurements. The failure of some workers to reach such high compositions owes, in part, to the very low diffusion rate for carbon in this phase, especially at the high carbon boundary. Many hours of heating are needed to reach saturation even at 2400°.

The melting point of TaC goes through a maximum near 4000°. Because of the very rapid preferential evaporation of carbon at this extreme temperature, it is difficult to assign the resulting melting point to the correct composition. Even when the final composition is determined, composition gradients create an additional uncertainty. Various techniques have been used to minimize this problem with mixed success. Zalabak (1961) tried melting in a hydrocarbon atmosphere but was unable to prevent a composition shift from $TaC_{\sim 1.0}$. Both Sara and Lowell (1964) and Rudy and Harmon (1965) used direct resistance heating (the Pirani technique), the former in an atmosphere of $CH_4 + H_2 + Ar$, while the latter workers used only He at 2.5 atm with some effect. As can be seen in Fig. 32, the difficulties in making a reproducible measurement are considerable. Unlike the other carbides, TaC appears to have a rather sharp maximum in the solidus at $TaC_{\sim 0.89}$. Dissociation in the liquid would appear to be incomplete. This composition, it is interesting to note, is the highest melting substance known. At higher carbon contents, the melting point drops to a eutectic with carbon. Measurement of this temperature is especially difficult because the very high loss rate of carbon quickly shifts the composition into the single-phase region. Thus, when evaluating data, the lower values should be given the greater weight. To lessen this problem, Sara and Lowell (1964) used the unusual technique of encapsulating the eutectic within a crucible of single-phase TaC. While this prevented the loss of carbon, the temperature had to be measured at the lid of the crucible. If an error exists, the reported value of 3375° is probably too low. Other measurements of the eutectic temperature include 3710° ± 50° (Nadler and Kempter, 1960); 3445° ± 5° (Rudy and Harmon, 1965); 3310° ± 50° (Portnoĭ *et al.*, 1961); and 3300° (Ellinger, 1943). A value of 3400° ± 50° is recommended. Eutectic compositions of $TaC_{1.56}$ (Rudy and Harmon, 1965); $TaC_{1.58}$ (Sara and Lowell, 1964); $TaC_{1.67}$ (Ellinger, 1943); and $TaC_{4.0}$ (Portnoĭ *et al.*, 1961) have been reported.

Evidence for additional phases has been presented. The dissolution of small amounts of carbon in Ta has been found to give a tetragonal distortion to the lattice (Villagrana and Thomas, 1965). This phase, designated $Ta_{64}C$, may be similar to the delta phase found in the NbC system by Pochon *et al.* (1959). In the latter case the phase was found to contain most of the dissolved carbon. Read and Altman (1965) also found a similar phase in thin films of Ta containing 1.1 at. % C. As can be seen in Fig. 33, there is no break in the solubility curve which would support such a claim.

Lesser and Brauer (1958) observed additional diffraction pattern lines when samples between Ta_2C and $TaC_{0.7}$ were examined. These they attributed to a zeta phase. Heating $TaC_{0.64}$ at 1800° for up to 26 hours produced an increasing amount until only a little TaC and Ta_2C remained. By examining diffusion couples, a number of workers have demonstrated that the zeta phase precipitates only within carbon-deficient TaC with no sharp boundary between this and the remaining TaC layer (Santoro and Probst, 1965; Rudy and Harmon, 1965; Zaplatynsky, 1966). An x-ray examination of sections through the couple, by Rudy and Harmon (1965), showed a mixture of Ta_2C, ζ, and TaC_{1-x} in the precipitation layer next to single-phase Ta_2C, but only TaC_{1-x} and ζ were found in the area next to the single-phase TaC zone. From this behavior, they concluded that at high temperatures the reaction speed is sufficient to allow the precipitation of Ta_2C, but at lower temperatures the nonequilibrium ζ phase grows epitaxially on TaC_{1-x} instead. By heating for 400 hours at 1700°, they were able to decompose part of the ζ phase. This conflicts with the experience of Lesser and Brauer (1958), as noted above. Zaplatynsky (1966) was able to decompose the ζ phase by grinding at room temperature. He suggested that the ζ phase was formed from TaC_{1-x} during cooling because of stresses induced by the adjacent Ta_2C layer. Their release, upon comminution to a -200 mesh powder, allowed the TaC_{1-x} to reform. This interpretation does not account for the formation of ζ in the complete absence of Ta_2C, as was observed by Rudy and Harmon (1965). Unfortunately, the nature of this phase is still a matter of speculation.

The observation of a sharp change in the spectral emissivity of TaC near 2000° has led Shaffer (1963) to suggest the existence of a high temperature phase transition. A similar claim was made for ZrC. Thermal analysis and metallographic studies (Rudy and Harmon, 1965) as well as heat content measurements (Levinson, 1963b) have failed to give support for this observation. Also Kempter and Nadler (1965) were unable to find evidence for this transition between 25° and 3000° from a study of the thermal expansion of $TaC_{1.0}$. In addition, the emissivity study by Coffman *et al.* (1960), which Shaffer cites as support for his data, does not show any evidence for such a transition either. In fact, they mentioned that when a noticeable change in emissivity occurred near 1927°, the surface was later found to contain Ta and Ta_2O_5 as well as TaC. Clean specimens showed only a slight drop in emissivity in going between 1560° and 2610°, and the value was essentially equal to that reported by Shaffer for temperatures above the "transition." There is no doubt Shaffer's observations were due to a reaction with the atmosphere below 2000° to form a carbon-depleted and oxide-contaminated surface.

C. LATTICE PARAMETER AND STRUCTURE

Phase boundary lattice parameter values are given in Table 31 for the phases Ta, Ta_2C, and TaC. In addition, the calculated powder patterns for Ta, α-Ta_2C, β-Ta_2C, and $TaC_{0.99}$ are listed in Tables 32 through 35.

Tantalum is bcc with no reported phase transitions. The absorption of a small amount of carbon is said to result in a phase with a tetragonal lattice and the formula, $Ta_{64}C$ (Villagrana and Thomas, 1965). These workers propose a long range ordering of carbon atoms to account for this. If this phenomenon is similar to that observed in Nb (Pochon *et al.*, 1959) it could also be due to a local increase in the carbon concentration with the formation of a metastable phase.

TABLE 31
STRUCTURE AND LATTICE PARAMETER OF Ta, α-Ta_2C, AND TaC

Phases in equilibrium	Composition of first phase	Structure	Lattice parameter (Å)	Investigator
Ta	Pure	*A2*	$a = 3.3025$	Goldschmidt *et al.* (1963)
Ta + Ta_2C	Carbon saturated quenched from 2500°C	*A2*	$a = 3.3095$	Goldschmidt *et al.* (1963)
α-Ta_2C + Ta	$TaC_{0.41}$	*C6*, $P\bar{3}ml(D^3_{3d})$	$a = 3.101^a$ $c = 4.933$	Lesser and Brauer (1958)
α-Ta_2C + TaC	$TaC_{0.50}$	*C6*, $P\bar{3}ml(D^3_{3d})$	$a = 3.106^a$ $c = 4.945$	Lesser and Brauer (1958)
TaC + Ta_2C	$TaC_{0.70}$	*B1*	$a = 4.4100 \pm 0.0005$	A. L. Bowman (1961)
TaC + C	$TaC_{0.99}$	*B1*	$a = 4.4555 \pm 0.0003$	A. L. Bowman (1961)

[a] Based on *L'3* indexing.

TABLE 32

COPPER RADIATION, POWDER PATTERN FOR Ta[a]

2θ	$\sin^2\theta$	d spacing	Intensity	$h\ k\ l$
38.52	0.1088	2.3352	35	1 1 0
55.61	0.2176	1.6513	10	2 0 0
69.68	0.3264	1.3482	25	2 1 1
82.55	0.4352	1.1676	10	2 2 0
95.05	0.5440	1.0443	15	3 1 0
107.79	0.6528	0.9533	5	2 2 2
121.54	0.7616	0.8826	35	3 2 1
137.79	0.8704	0.8256	5	4 0 0
163.40	0.9792	0.7784	100	4 1 1, 3 3 0

[a] $a_0 = 3.3025$ Å; $\mu r = 6.0$; Space group type $A2$, No. 229; $\lambda(K\alpha_1) = 1.54051$ Å.

Ta_2C has two crystal structures. The low temperature form shows an ordering of the carbon atoms such that the hexagonal metal layers are separated by alternately completely filled and completely empty carbon layers. This is the cadmium iodide antitype structure found by A. L. Bowman *et al.* (1965). However, the difference between the x-ray pattern of this phase and an $L'3$ structure is very slight. Near 2000° (Rudy and Harmon, 1965) the carbon lattice presumably disorders to give the $L'3$ structure.

By quenching Ta_2C + Ta in tin, Rudy and Harmon (1965) were able to reduce the c parameter to 4.923 with little change in the a parameter. A similar treatment of Ta_2C + TaC resulted in a c parameter as high as 4.947.

TaC shows a linear relationship between lattice parameter and composition, in contrast to the other carbides. A. L. Bowman (1961) fitted his data by a linear equation which has been used by a number of workers to convert from lattice parameter to composition. In view of the additional information, it is advisable to reexamine this property. Hence, the open points in Fig. 34, which are based on well-characterized material, were used to obtain the equation C/Ta(± 0.01) $= -25.641 + 5.9757\,a_0$ by the method of least squares. This amounts to a minor change when compared to the equation given by A. L. Bowman (1961). As can be seen from the figure, the excellent agreement between numerous independent measurements gives overwhelming confirmation to this relationship. In fact, if a measurement is found to deviate from this line, the explanation is best sought in the experimental technique. For example, if a sample has

TABLE 33

COPPER RADIATION, POWDER PATTERN FOR α-Ta_2C[a]

2θ	$\sin^2 \theta$	d spacing	Intensity	$h\ k\ l$
33.28	0.0820	2.6898	20	1 0 0
36.30	0.0971	2.4725	20	0 0 2
38.05	0.1063	2.3629	100	1 0 1
50.07	0.1791	1.8203	25	1 0 2
55.72	0.2184	1.6482	1	0 0 3
59.47	0.2460	1.5530	30	1 1 0
62.65	0.2703	1.4816	1	1 1 1
66.47	0.3004	1.4054	35	1 0 3
69.88	0.3280	1.3449	5	2 0 0
71.71	0.3431	1.3151	40	1 1 2
72.81	0.3523	1.2978	30	2 0 1
77.08	0.3882	1.2362	5	0 0 4
81.38	0.4251	1.1814	10	2 0 2
85.91	0.4644	1.1303	5	1 1 3
86.58	0.4702	1.1233	10	1 0 4
95.32	0.5464	1.0421	20	2 0 3
98.51	0.5740	1.0167	5	2 1 0
101.33	0.5983	0.9958	45	2 1 1
102.31	0.6066	0.9890	1	0 0 5
105.57	0.6342	0.9672	25	1 1 4
110.01	0.6711	0.9403	20	2 1 2
112.16	0.6886	0.9282	20	1 0 5
115.62	0.7162	0.9102	10	2 0 4
118.42	0.7380	0.8966	15	3 0 0
125.78	0.7924	0.8653	50	2 1 3
132.08	0.8351	0.8429	40	3 0 2
134.84	0.8526	0.8342	10	1 1 5
138.32	0.8735	0.8242	5	0 0 6
150.36	0.9346	0.7968	45	2 0 5
155.63	0.9555	0.7880	40	1 0 6
155.89	0.9564	0.7876	10	3 0 3
157.58	0.9622	0.7852	60	2 1 4
165.47	0.9840	0.7765	80	2 2 0

[a] $a_0 = 3.1060$ Å; $c_0 = 4.9450$ Å; $\mu r = 6.0$; structure type C6, space group No. 164; $\lambda(K\alpha_1) = 1.54051$ Å.

been losing or gaining carbon during its previous treatment, the resulting concentration gradient will cause a displacement from the curve. Since the diffusion rate for carbon is very small in this system, such gradients

TABLE 34

COPPER RADIATION, POWDER PATTERN FOR β-Ta_2C[a]

2θ	$\sin^2\theta$	d spacing	Intensity	$h\ k\ l$
33.28	0.0820	2.6898	15	1 0 0
36.30	0.0971	2.4725	20	0 0 2
38.05	0.1063	2.3629	100	1 0 1
50.07	0.1791	1.8203	25	1 0 2
59.47	0.2460	1.5530	35	1 1 0
66.47	0.3004	1.4054	35	1 0 3
69.88	0.3280	1.3449	5	2 0 0
71.71	0.3431	1.3151	40	1 1 2
72.81	0.3523	1.2978	30	2 0 1
77.08	0.3882	1.2362	5	0 0 4
81.38	0.4251	1.1814	10	2 0 2
86.58	0.4702	1.1233	5	1 0 4
95.32	0.5464	1.0421	20	2 0 3
98.51	0.5740	1.0167	5	2 1 0
101.33	0.5983	0.9958	45	2 1 1
105.57	0.6342	0.9672	30	1 1 4
110.01	0.6711	0.9403	20	2 1 2
112.16	0.6886	0.9282	25	1 0 5
115.62	0.7162	0.9102	5	2 0 4
118.42	0.7380	0.8966	20	3 0 0
125.78	0.7924	0.8653	55	2 1 3
132.08	0.8351	0.8429	40	3 0 2
138.32	0.8735	0.8242	10	0 0 6
150.36	0.9346	0.7968	55	2 0 5
155.63	0.9555	0.7880	25	1 0 6
157.58	0.9622	0.7852	40	2 1 4
165.47	0.9840	0.7765	80	2 2 0

[a] $a_0 = 3.1060$ Å; $c_0 = 4.9450$ Å; $\mu r = 6.0$; structure type $L'3$, space group No. 194; $\lambda(K\alpha_1) = 1.54051$ Å.

are easy to acquire and difficult to eliminate. Indeed, by evaporating plugs in He, Kempter and Nadler (1960) obtained data (Fig. 34) which clearly show such an effect. Recently, Santoro (1965) reported lattice parameters which fall above the line by heating Ta filaments in methane as well as by reacting the powdered elements. In view of the rather low sintering temperatures used, this work is not sufficient to change the above interpretation.

The density is 14.48 g/cm³ at $TaC_{0.99}$, and it increases as carbon is removed.

TABLE 35
COPPER RADIATION, POWDER PATTERN FOR $TaC_{0.99}$[a]

2θ	$\sin^2\theta$	d spacing	Intensity	$h\ k\ l$
34.85	0.0897	2.5724	100	1 1 1
40.46	0.1195	2.2277	75	2 0 0
58.55	0.2391	1.5753	70	2 2 0
69.97	0.3288	1.3434	85	3 1 1
73.58	0.3586	1.2862	30	2 2 2
87.50	0.4782	1.1139	20	4 0 0
97.80	0.5678	1.0222	55	3 3 1
101.27	0.5977	0.9963	65	4 2 0
115.76	0.7173	0.9095	70	4 2 2
127.87	0.8069	0.8575	95	5 1 1, 3 3 3
155.89	0.9564	0.7876	95	4 4 0

[a] $a_0 = 4.4555$ Å; $\mu r = 5.0$; structure type $B1$, space group No. 225. $\lambda(K\alpha_1) = 1.54051$ Å.

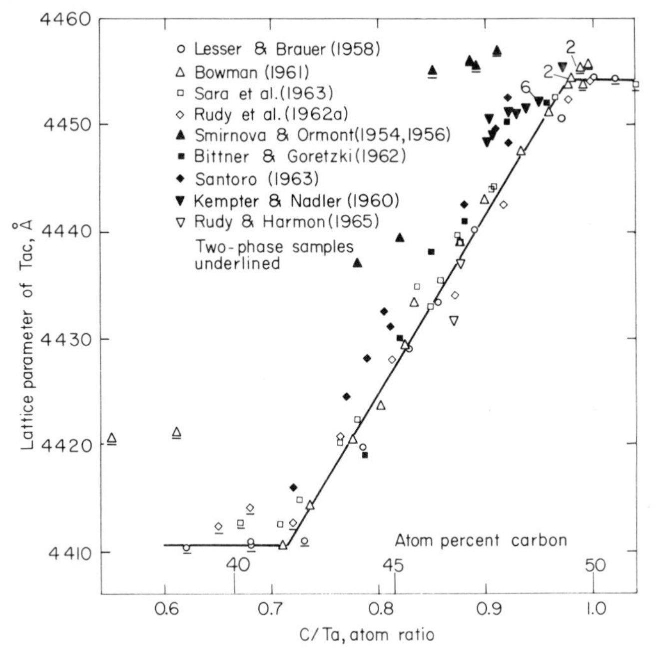

FIG. 34. Lattice parameter of TaC as a function of composition.

A crystal structure has not been determined for the zeta phase. Rudy and Harmon (1965) report that the x-ray pattern contains features which are common to the patterns of both Ta_2C and TaC. Powder patterns have been published by Lesser and Brauer (1958) and Zaplatynsky (1966).

D. APPEARANCE

From the metal to about $TaC_{0.85}$, the powder has a gray metallic color. At higher carbon contents, the material gradually assumes a brown cast which develops into the characteristic golden color at $TaC_{0.99}$.

E. CHEMICAL REACTIVITY

Of the refractory carbides, tantalum carbide is the most stable toward acids, but it will dissolve in a mixture of HNO_3 and HF (Kopyleva, 1961). It is stable in N_2 up to 3315° provided no H_2 is present. In pure O_2, burning will result above 800°; small amounts of oxygen in the atmosphere will cause decarbonization. The oxide film is nonprotecting (Berkowitz-Mattuck, 1963).

F. HARDNESS

A number of measurements have been made using material of uncertain composition. Jones (1956) gives 1400 DPH for TaC in equilibrium with carbon; Meerson and Umanskii (1953) cite 1547 kg/mm^2; Kieffer and Kölbl (1949), using a 50-g load, obtained 1800 kg/mm^2; and Foster *et al.* (1950) measured a Knoop hardness of 1952 kg/mm^2 on a high-carbon sample which probably contained some tungsten. This property has been measured as a function of composition, first by Samsonov and Rukina (1957), who describe a linear variation which extrapolated to 1600 kg/mm^2 at $TaC_{1.0}$, and recently by Santoro (1963) who found a maximum hardness near $TaC_{0.83}$ at 2400 kg/mm^2 (100-g load) and 3000 kg/mm^2 (25-g load). The two works agree at the phase boundaries. However, the apparent maximum is sufficiently novel to warrant confirmation before it is accepted.

Ellinger (1943) placed the Knoop hardness value of Ta_2C at about 1000 kg/mm^2. Samsonov and Rukina (1957) give a value of 947 kg/mm^2 for carbon-saturated and 810 kg/mm^2 for carbon-deficient α-Ta_2C.

G. THERMOCHEMICAL PROPERTIES

1. Heat of Formation

A number of combustion measurements have been reported which appear to show very poor agreement. However, if these are recalculated

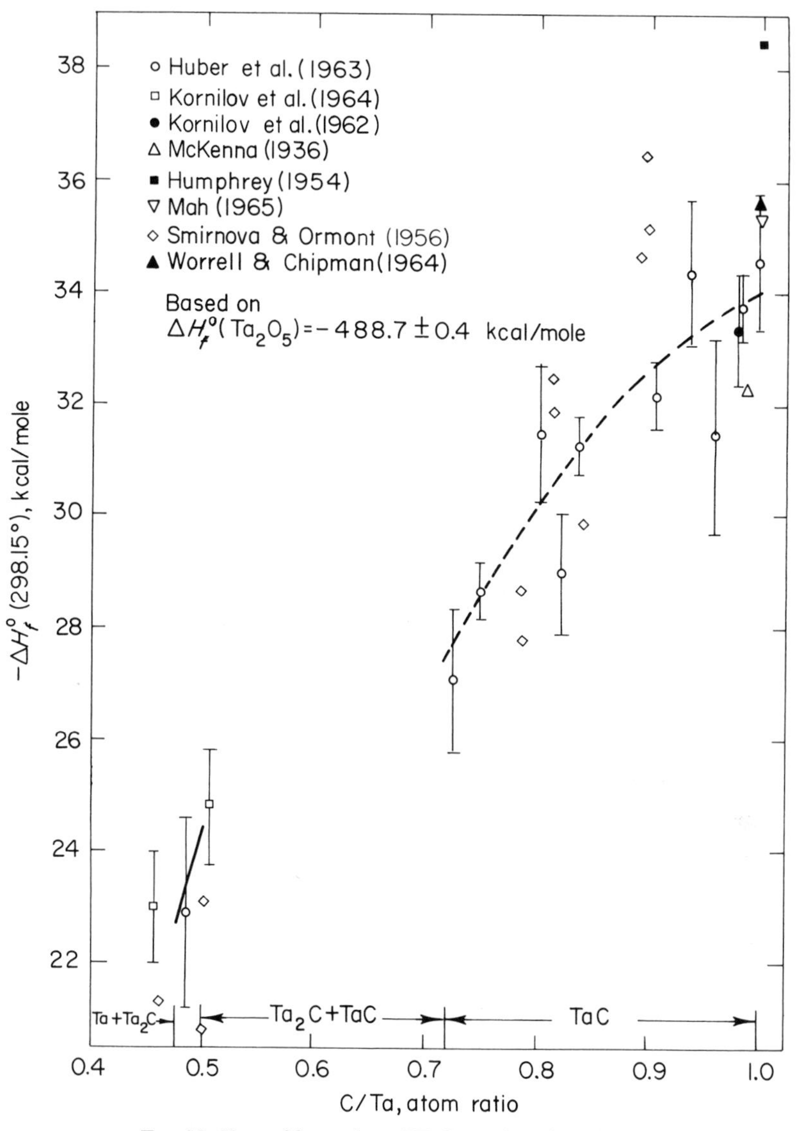

FIG. 35. Heat of formation of TaC as a function of composition.

using the same constants, the agreement improves considerably, as can be seen in Fig. 35. McKenna (1936) reported 38 ± 5 kcal/mole for a sample composition which was probably no higher than $TaC_{0.99}$. If the calculation is based on this composition, with 180.95 as the molecular weight of Ta, and −488.7 kcal/mole (Huber *et al.*, 1963) as the heat of formation of Ta_2O_5 instead of −498.3 kcal/mole, the resulting heat of formation becomes −32.3 kcal/mole for $TaC_{0.99}$. The very high value of Humphrey (1954) can be made to agree with the other work if his sample is assumed to have been $TaC_{0.95}$ + 0.05C instead of $TaC_{1.0}$. Unfortunately, in the absence of an analysis for free carbon, the magnitude of this correction can only be inferred. The work of Smirnova and Ormont (1956) is difficult to evaluate because of the uncertain composition of their samples. Not only do most of the compositions show poor agreement with the lattice parameter curve (Fig. 34), but the sample at $TaC_{0.89}$ contained free carbon which, for this composition, indicates a nonequilibrium condition. Nevertheless, a correction to the same heat of formation of Ta_2O_5 brings their work, except for the latter sample, into good agreement. The measurement of Kornilov *et al.* (1964) was also changed in this way to give −33.4 kcal/mole of $TaC_{0.982}$. Thus, the various studies can be brought into good agreement and are described adequately by the equation $\Delta H_f^\circ(298.15^\circ) = 22.81 - 103.78(\mathrm{C/Ta}) + 46.88(\mathrm{C/Ta})^2$ (kcal/mole), which was used by Huber *et al.* (1963) to fit their data. This same work gave -22.9 ± 1.7 kcal/mole for $TaC_{0.485}$ (Ta_2C). A comparison can be made to -23.1 ± 1.0 kcal/mole for $TaC_{0.455}$ and -24.9 ± 1.0 kcal/mole for $TaC_{0.507}$ (Kornilov *et al.*, 1964) which have been recalculated on the same basis.

By measuring the CO pressure over TaC + C + Ta_2O_5, Worrell and Chipman (1964) were able to calculate a value of -35.6 ± 0.7 kcal/mole for $TaC_{0.99}$ containing a small but unknown amount of dissolved oxygen.

2. Low Temperature Heat Capacity

The only measurement at low temperature was made by Kelley (1940b) using TaC containing 6.26%* total carbon. Values of 10.1 ± 0.1 eu for $S^\circ_{298.15^\circ}$ and 8.764 cal/mole-deg for C_p (extrapolated to 298.15°) were obtained. In view of the uncertain free carbon content, this measurement should be repeated, preferably as a function of composition.

3. High Temperature Heat Content

A reexamination of the high temperature thermal properties of Ta metal was made using the same techniques as were applied to the carbides. The equation for the heat content, shown in Table 36, was based on the enthalpy data in Fig. 36 and the constraints, C_p = 6.045 cal/mole-deg

* The value of 4.26% carbon given in the paper is clearly a typographical error.

TABLE 36

THERMAL FUNCTIONS OF $Ta_{(s)}$[a]

T (°K)	$H_T^\circ - H_{298}^\circ$ (cal/mole)	C_p° (cal/mole-deg)	S_T° (cal/mole-deg)	$-(F_T^\circ - H_{298}^\circ)/T$ (cal/mole-deg)
298.15	0.0	6.04	9.00	9.00
300	11.18	6.05	9.37	9.00
400	627.9	6.26	11.71	10.14
500	1260	6.37	13.12	10.60
600	1901	6.44	14.29	11.12
700	2547	6.49	15.29	11.65
800	3199	6.54	16.16	12.16
900	3855	6.58	16.93	12.64
1000	4515	6.62	17.62	13.11
1100	5179	6.66	18.26	13.55
1200	5847	6.70	18.84	13.96
1300	6520	6.75	19.38	14.36
1400	7197	6.79	19.88	14.74
1500	7878	6.84	20.35	15.10
1600	8564	6.89	20.79	15.44
1700	9256	6.94	21.21	15.77
1800	9952	6.99	21.61	16.08
1900	10654	7.05	21.99	16.38
2000	11362	7.11	22.35	16.67
2100	12080	7.17	22.70	16.95
2200	12800	7.23	23.03	17.22
2300	13520	7.30	23.36	17.48
2400	14260	7.37	23.67	17.73
2500	15000	7.44	23.97	17.97
2600	15740	7.51	24.26	18.21
2700	16500	7.59	24.55	18.44
2800	17260	7.67	24.83	18.66
2900	18030	7.75	25.10	18.88
3000	18810	7.84	25.36	19.09
3100	19600	7.92	25.62	19.30
3200	20400	8.01	25.87	19.50
3287	21100	8.09	26.09	19.67

[a] $H_T^\circ - H_{298.15^\circ}^\circ = -2.0713 \times 10^3 + 6.4733T + 2.7518 \times 10^{-5}T^2 + 4.4493 \times 10^{-8}T^3 + 4.1031 \times 10^4/T$ (298°–m.p., cal/mole, ±0.05%); M.W. = 180.948; $H_{298.15^\circ}^\circ - H_0^\circ = 1358$ cal/mole.

(Kelley, 1940a) and $H_T^\circ - H_{298.15^\circ}^\circ = 0.0$ both at 298.15°. The resulting C_p agrees at the lower temperatures with the direct measurements but

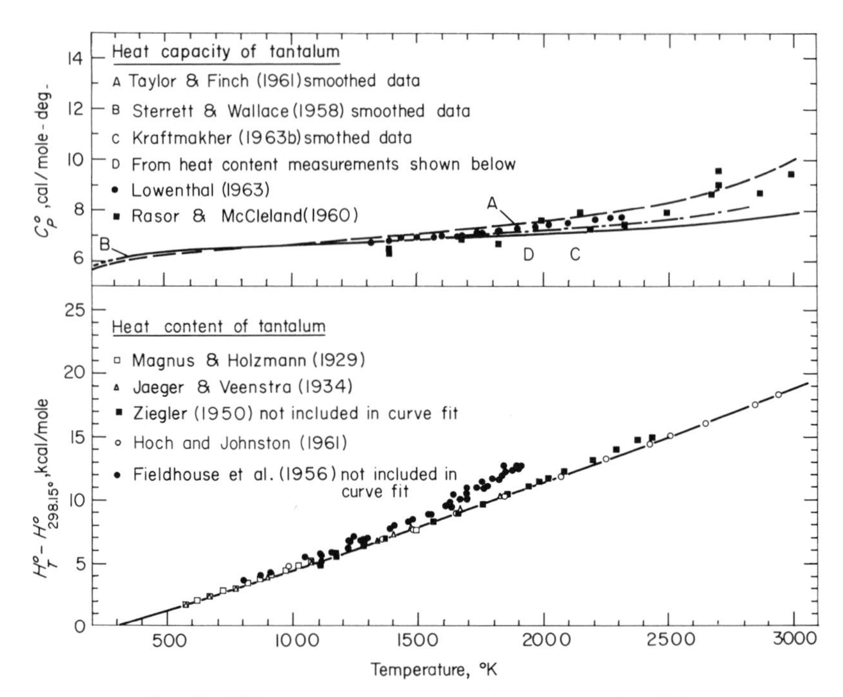

FIG. 36. High temperature heat capacity and enthalpy of Ta.

does not show as much increase as the melting point is approached. The data of Fieldhouse *et al.* (1956) and of Ziegler (1950) were not used to determine the curve, the former for obvious reasons. Inclusion of the latter work causes poorer agreement with the measured heat capacity at the higher temperatures. Thermal values from 298.15° to the melting point are listed in Table 36. C_p and $S°$ at 298.15° were taken from the measurements of Sterrett and Wallace (1958).

A comparison between the various studies of $TaC_{0.99}$ is shown in Fig. 37. The results of Levinson (1963b) and those reported by Mezaki *et al.* (1965) are in fair agreement. However, there is a trend in the slope which, if it continued, would result in considerable difference. Nevertheless, these two studies have been combined and fitted by the equation shown in Table 37. The data of Neel *et al.* (1960) shows too much scatter to be considered. The resulting heat capacity compares well with several direct measurements using pulsed heating techniques.

Based on the above measurements, the thermal functions for $TaC_{0.99}$ were calculated and are listed in Table 37.

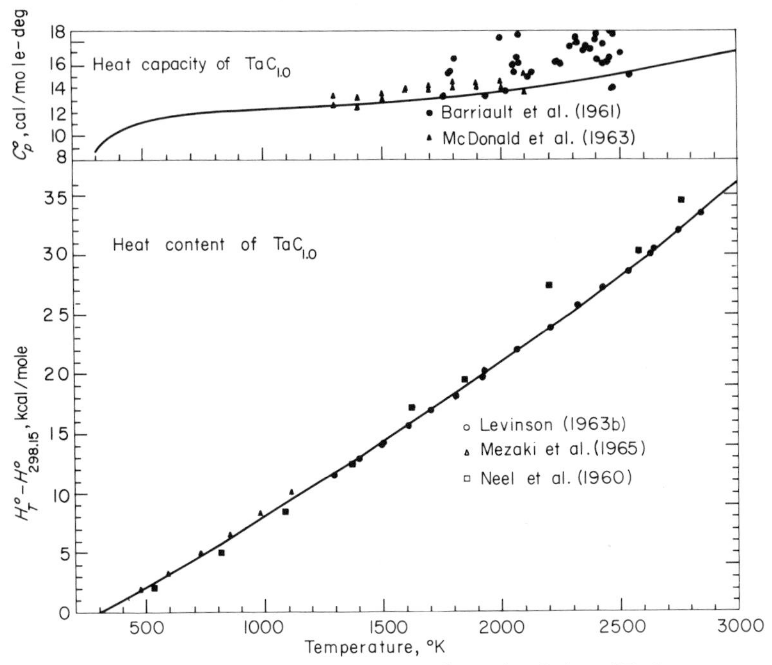

FIG. 37. High temperature heat capacity and enthalpy of $TaC_{0.99}$.

4. VAPORIZATION

The exact congruent composition has not been measured, but Lyon (1962) has shown that it does lie somewhat below $TaC_{0.5}$.

Because of the very high temperatures and the low pressures involved, no Knudsen studies have been undertaken. Even the Langmuir technique should only be used at the congruent composition. In view of this, the metal pressure over TaC + C is best calculated from thermochemical data. This was done using the following information: $\Delta H_f^\circ(298.15^\circ) = -34.0$ kcal/mole (Huber *et al.*, 1963); a heat of vaporization for the metal of 186.5 kcal/mole (Edwards *et al.*, 1951b); the thermal values in Table 37, the JANAF (1963) tables for $C_{(s)}$, and Stull and Sinke (1956) for $Ta_{(g)}$. The resulting equation

$$\log P(\text{atm}) = -4.777 \times 10^4/T + 7.168$$

is compared to the pressure over the metal in Fig. 38. It is worth noting that the pressure of C_3 is nearly a factor of 10^5 higher than the Ta pressure over TaC + C at 2800°.

TABLE 37

THERMAL FUNCTIONS OF $TaC_{0.99}$[a]

T (°K)	$H_T^\circ - H_{298}^\circ$ (cal/mole)	C_p° (cal/mole-deg)	S_T° (cal/mole-deg)	$-(F_T^\circ - H_{298}^\circ)/T$ (cal/mole-deg)
298.15	0.0	8.764	10.10	10.10
300	16.26	8.816	10.15	10.10
400	1001	10.61	12.98	10.47
500	2105	11.38	15.44	11.23
600	3264	11.77	17.55	12.11
700	4453	11.98	19.38	13.02
800	5658	12.12	20.99	13.92
900	6876	12.22	22.42	14.78
1000	8102	12.30	23.72	15.61
1100	9336	12.39	24.89	16.40
1200	10580	12.47	25.97	17.16
1300	11830	12.57	26.98	17.87
1400	13090	12.68	27.91	18.56
1500	14370	12.81	28.79	19.21
1600	15660	12.96	29.62	19.84
1700	16960	13.12	30.41	20.44
1800	18280	13.30	31.17	21.01
1900	19620	13.50	31.89	21.56
2000	20980	13.73	32.59	22.10
2100	22370	13.97	33.26	22.61
2200	23780	14.24	33.92	23.11
2300	25210	14.52	34.56	23.60
2400	26680	14.83	35.18	24.07
2500	28180	15.16	35.80	24.52
2600	29710	15.51	36.40	24.97
2700	31280	15.88	36.99	25.40
2800	32890	16.27	37.57	25.83
2900	34540	16.69	38.15	26.24
3000	36230	17.12	38.72	26.65

[a] $H_T^\circ - H_{298.15^\circ}^\circ = -5.3565 \times 10^3 + 13.7909T - 1.0992 \times 10^{-3}T^2 + 3.6930 \times 10^{-7}T^3 + 3.9735 \times 10^5/T$ (298°–3000°K, cal/mole, ±1.2%); M.W. = 192.84.

Hoch *et al.* (1955), Coffman *et al.* (1960), and Deadmore (1965) have studied the evaporation rate of carbon from a composition near $TaC_{1.0}$, with consistent results. In the latter work it was shown that for the amount of carbon lost during the measurement, the composition of the TaC could change significantly. The resulting composition gradient could not

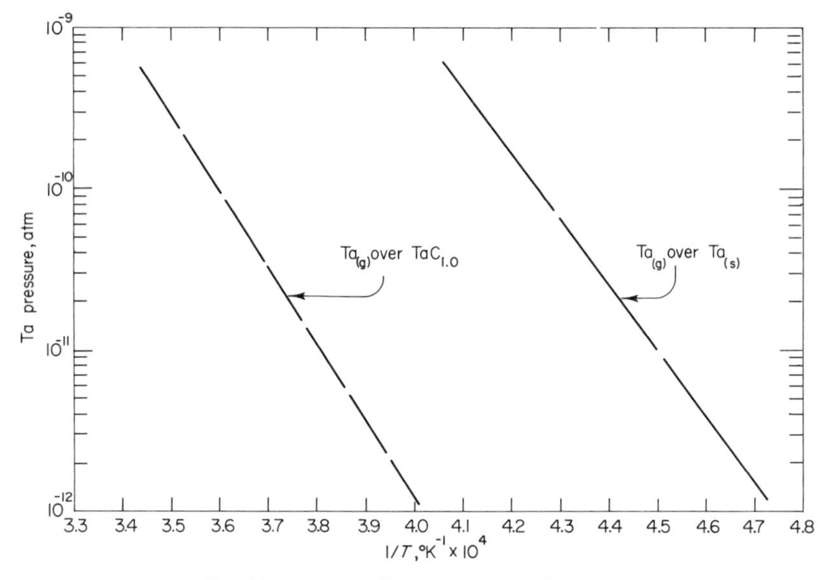

FIG. 38. Pressure of $Ta_{(g)}$ over Ta and TaC + C.

be accurately evaluated, but it was found to become worse as the temperature was increased. Since the evaporation rate of carbon drops rapidly as the composition moves from the phase boundary, the measured rates would have become increasingly low as the temperature was raised. As a result, the reported second law heat of 148 kcal/mole would be too low. In fact, the partial heat of vaporization of carbon from substoichiometric TaC has to be greater than that from graphite. The reasons for this are discussed in Chapter XIII, Section G. If the surface composition could be related to the carbon evaporation rate, the activity of carbon could be obtained as a function of composition. The present data show that the composition used by these workers already was sufficiently low to reduce the carbon activity to 0.1.

VII

THE CHROMIUM–CHROMIUM CARBIDE SYSTEM

A. PREPARATION

The carbides of Cr have been observed since 1893 when Moissan (1893c) prepared Cr_3C_2 and "Cr_4C" in the electric arc and blast furnace.

Because of the useful properties chromium imparts to steels, much knowledge about this system has been obtained by isolating the carbides from such alloys. Even chromium metal is apt to have iron as a major impurity. Thus, many of the data to follow should be viewed with the reservation that they might better apply to the Cr–Fe–C system.

The carbides can be produced by heating a mixture of Cr_2O_3 and carbon in hydrogen. Below 1300°, Cr_7C_3 is the major product, while above 1600°, Cr_3C_2 forms (Kosolapova and Samsonov, 1959; Grigor'eva and Klimenko, 1959). The Cr_3C_2 can be freed of the lower carbides by boiling HCl or H_2SO_4. Since chromium metal can result from the reaction between Cr_2O_3 and Cr_3C_2 (Samsonov and Kosolapova, 1961; Kelley *et al.*, 1944), some care is needed if the presence of the metal is to be avoided. The thermodynamics of the carbon reduction of the oxide can be found in a comprehensive paper by Kelley *et al.* (1944). They found the reaction occurring in the following distinct steps:

1. $3Cr_2O_3 + 13C = 2Cr_3C_2 + 9CO$
2. $5Cr_2O_3 + 27Cr_3C_2 = 13Cr_7C_3 + 15CO$
3. $5Cr_2O_3 + 14Cr_7C_3 = 27Cr_4C + 15CO$
4. $Cr_2O_3 + 3Cr_4C = 14Cr + 3CO$

The first two reactions are slow while the last two are rapid.

Layers containing Cr and Cr_3C_2 have been produced by the thermal decomposition of chromium carbonyl (Owen and Webber, 1948; Lander and Germer, 1948). The metal will react with methane at 600°–800° (Campbell *et al.*, 1949).

These carbides can be prepared by reacting the powdered elements or by arc melting. Liquid chromium held in graphite will quickly give Cr_3C_2.

B. PHASE RELATIONSHIP

The literature at the present time contains evidence for the three phases $Cr_{23}C_6$, Cr_7C_3, and Cr_3C_2. Early workers gave Cr_4C as the formula of the first phase.

Melting of chromium metal has been found over a rather wide range of temperature (Table 38). This is due largely to the effect of oxygen, nitrogen and, to a greater extent, carbon impurities. Since each causes a marked lowering of the melting point, the higher values should be favored.

Below the melting point, various anomalies have been observed, near 40°, 1360°, 1375°, 1400°, 1650°, and 1840°. The effects at 40° and near 1400° appear to be magnetic in origin with no structural change and little energy involved (McGuire and Kriessman, 1952; Krauss, 1958; Beaumont *et al.*, 1960). Two investigations (Grigor'ev *et al.*, 1960; Bloom *et al.*, 1952) have observed a thermal arrest in the cooling curve at 1840°, but a third study (McCaldin and Duwez, 1954) gave no indication. A similar lack of agreement is found in studies of the Cr–Ni system. Stein and Grant (1955) found a eutectoid reaction which is consistent with a transition in pure Cr. Abrahamson and Grant (1956), by quenching a Cr–Ni alloy from 1360°, obtained a fcc lattice which they attributed to the β-Cr–Ni alloy. Using a high-temperature x-ray camera, Hoch (1961) failed to find a structural change in a 70% Cr–30% Ni alloy below 1300°. According to Stein and Grant (1955), as mentioned above, a change to a fcc lattice should have occurred at 1215°. R. O. Williams (1958) was also unable to find a eutectoid reaction at this temperature. At the present time the data are too conflicting to allow any conclusion regarding such a transition.

According to W. H. Smith (1957), the solubility of carbon in Cr is very slight, amounting to $CrC_{0.014}$(0.32 wt %) even at the eutectic. Thus, carbon lowers the melting point of Cr by about 0.13°/ppm C. This behavior is shared with the other members of Group 6.

Bloom and Grant (1950) found peritectic melting of $Cr_{23}C_6$, Cr_7C_3, and Cr_3C_2 at 1520°, 1780°, and 1895°, respectively, and a Cr–$Cr_{23}C_6$ eutectic which melts at 1498°. Friemann and Sauerwald (1931) give this latter temperature as 1515°, which was lowered to 1475° when the formation of $Cr_{23}C_6$ was suppressed by rapid cooling. The various reported melting points are listed in Table 38.

TABLE 38
MELTING POINT DETERMINATIONS IN THE Cr–C SYSTEM

Investigator	Melting point (°C)				
	Cr	$(Cr + Cr_{23}C_6)$	$(Cr_{23}C_6 + Cr_7C_3)$	$(Cr_7C_3 + Cr_3C_2)$	$(Cr_3C_2 + C)$
Smithells and Williams (1929)	1920	—	—	—	—
L. Müller (1930)	1805	—	—	—	—
Hatsuta (1931)	1760	1485	1530	1670	1830
Friemann and Sauerwald (1931)	—	1515	1550	1665	—
Tofaute *et al.* (1935)	—	—	1550	—	—
Grube and Knabe (1936)	1890 ± 10	—	—	—	—
Parke and Bens (1946)	1950 ± 50	—	—	—	—
Carlile *et al.* (1949)	1860	—	—	—	—
Bloom and Grant (1950)	1933	1498	1520	1780	1895
Greenaway *et al.* (1951)	1845 ± 10 (under H_2)	—	—	—	—
Bloom *et al.* (1952)	1903 ± 10	—	—	—	—
Markovskii *et al.* (1957)	—	—	—	—	1850 ± 20
Grigor'ev *et al.* (1960)	1915	—	—	—	—
Pan (1964)	1890	—	—	—	—

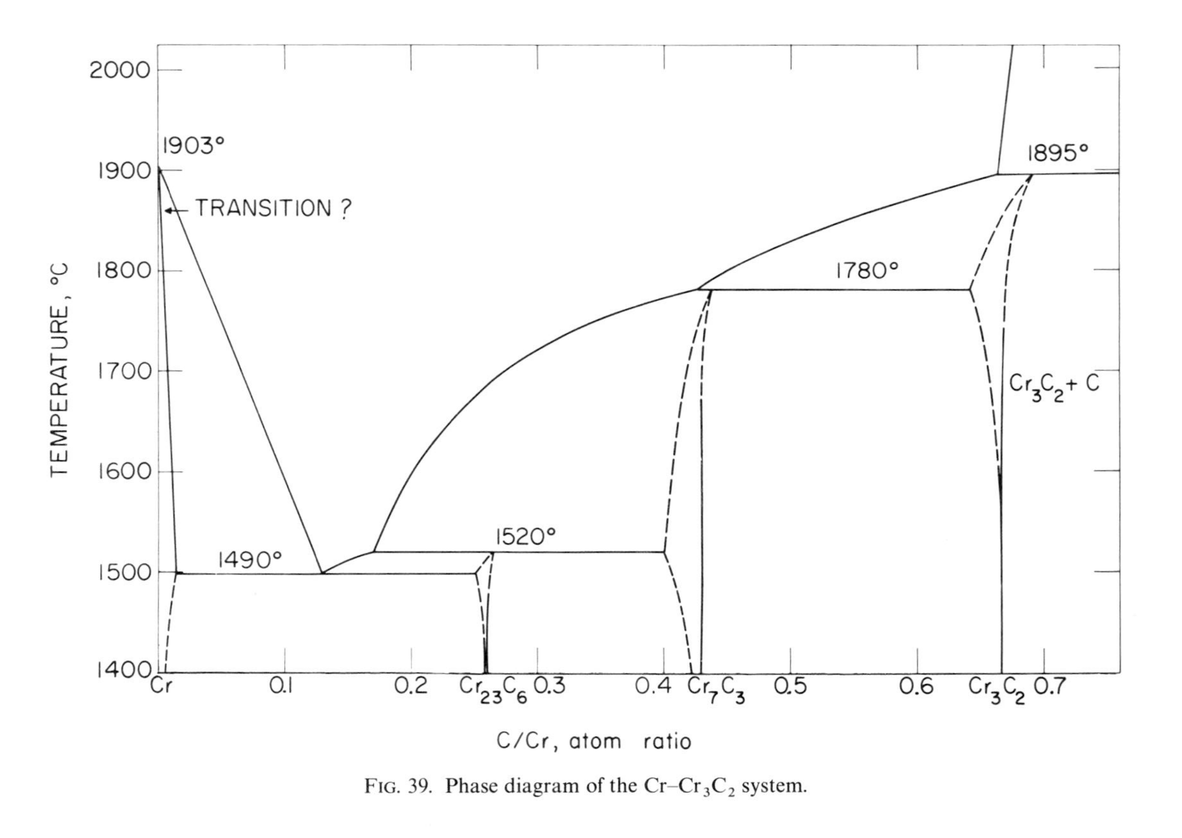

FIG. 39. Phase diagram of the $Cr–Cr_3C_2$ system.

At the present time, much of the phase relationship should be considered as tentative, in view of the recent discoveries of additional high temperature forms in the other carbide systems. For example, Stecher *et al.* (1964) were able to stabilize a Cr_2C phase by adding 10 mole % W. A very pictorial phase diagram has been constructed as Fig. 39. Since some widening of the phases should occur as the temperature is raised, dashed lines have been used to suggest this behavior. There are absolutely no measurements in the literature to indicate the position of these lines.

C. LATTICE PARAMETER AND STRUCTURE

Chromium metal is bcc (*A*2) with $a_0 = 2.8829$ Å (S. Müller and Dünner, 1965). A calculated powder pattern is given in Table 39.

TABLE 39

COPPER RADIATION, POWDER PATTERN FOR Cr[a]

2θ	$\sin^2\theta$	*d* spacing	Intensity	*h k l*
44.40	0.1428	2.0385	100	1 1 0
64.60	0.2855	1.4414	20	2 0 0
81.76	0.4283	1.1769	50	2 1 1
98.17	0.5711	1.0193	20	2 2 0
115.32	0.7139	0.9117	40	3 1 0
135.50	0.8566	0.8322	15	2 2 2

[a] $a_0 = 2.8829$ Å; $\mu r = 5.0$; type *A*2, space group No. 229; $\lambda(K\alpha_1) = 1.54051$ Å.

$Cr_{23}C_6$ is reported to be complex face-centered-cubic crystal ($D8_4$ type) with 116 atoms per unit cell and $a_0 = 10.66$ Å (Westgren, 1933). A calculated powder pattern based on these data is given in Table 40. The structure designation is supported by electron diffraction work of J. F. Brown and Clark (1951). When this phase was formed in steel, Allten *et al.* (1954) referred to it as $(Cr, Fe)_{23}C_6$ and gave $a_0 = 10.60$ Å. Stecher *et al.* (1964) report $a_0 = 10.655$ Å.

The Cr_7C_3 phase has also been found in steels (Crafts and Lamont, 1949). A hexagonal structure with $a_0 = 14.01$, $c_0 = 4.532$ Å was reported by Westgren (1933). Kelley *et al.* (1944) gave parameters of $a_0 = 13.98$, $c_0 = 4.5$ Å* to this phase and Stecher *et al.* (1964) report $a_0 = 14.01$, $c_0 = 4.525$ Å.

Cr_3C_2 was first designated as orthorhombic by Hellström and Westgren (1933), and parameters of $a_0 = 2.82$, $b_0 = 5.52$, $c_0 = 11.46$ Å* were

* It is uncertain whether this is in kx or Angstrom units.

TABLE 40

COPPER RADIATION, POWDER PATTERN FOR $Cr_{23}C_6$[a]

2θ	$\sin^2\theta$	d spacing	Intensity	$h\ k\ l$
33.60	0.0835	2.6650	5	4 0 0
37.71	0.1044	2.3836	25	4 2 0
41.46	0.1253	2.1760	25	4 2 2
44.11	0.1410	2.0515	100	3 3 3, 5 1 1
48.25	0.1671	1.8844	20	4 4 0
50.61	0.1827	1.8019	25	5 3 1
51.38	0.1880	1.7767	15	6 0 0, 4 4 2
54.39	0.2088	1.6855	5	6 2 0
56.56	0.2245	1.6256	5	5 3 3
57.28	0.2297	1.6071	10	6 2 2
62.13	0.2663	1.4927	5	7 1 1, 5 5 1
62.81	0.2715	1.4783	1	6 4 0
70.63	0.3341	1.3325	5	8 0 0
73.15	0.3550	1.2927	10	6 4 4, 8 2 0
75.63	0.3759	1.2563	30	6 6 0, 8 2 2
77.48	0.3916	1.2309	15	5 5 5, 7 5 1
80.52	0.4177	1.1918	5	8 4 0
82.34	0.4333	1.1701	10	7 5 3, 9 1 1
87.15	0.4751	1.1175	5	9 3 1
90.14	0.5012	1.0880	20	8 4 4
91.93	0.5169	1.0714	15	7 7 1, 7 5 5, 9 3 3
92.53	0.5221	1.0660	1	10 0 0, 8 6 0
96.74	0.5586	1.0305	1	7 7 3, 9 5 1
97.34	0.5639	1.0258	5	6 6 6, 10 2 2
101.59	0.6004	0.9941	1	9 5 3
102.20	0.6056	0.9898	5	10 4 0, 8 6 4
104.66	0.6265	0.9731	5	10 4 2
106.52	0.6422	0.9612	5	11 1 1, 7 7 5
109.67	0.6683	0.9422	1	8 8 0
111.59	0.6840	0.9314	10	11 3 1, 9 5 5, 9 7 1
112.23	0.6892	0.9278	5	10 4 4, 8 8 2
114.84	0.7101	0.9141	1	8 6 6, 10 6 0
116.84	0.7257	0.9042	1	11 3 3, 9 7 3
117.51	0.7309	0.9009	5	10 6 2
120.24	0.7518	0.8883	5	12 0 0, 8 8 4
122.34	0.7675	0.8792	5	11 5 1, 7 7 7
132.12	0.8354	0.8427	10	12 4 0
134.59	0.8510	0.8350	5	9 9 1
135.44	0.8562	0.8324	10	12 4 2, 8 8 6, 10 8 0
138.96	0.8771	0.8224	10	10 8 2

TABLE 40 (continued)

2θ	$\sin^2 \theta$	*d* spacing	Intensity	*h k l*
141.77	0.8928	0.8152	65	11 7 1, 11 5 5, 13 1 1, 9 9 3
146.91	0.9189	0.8035	5	12 4 4
150.36	0.9346	0.7968	15	11 7 3, 9 7 7, 13 3 1
151.59	0.9398	0.7945	35	12 6 0, 10 8 4
157.12	0.9607	0.7859	5	12 6 2
162.30	0.9763	0.7795	20	13 3 3, 9 9 5

[a] $a_0 = 10.660$ Å; $\mu r = 3.0$; space group type No. 225; $\lambda(K\alpha_1) = 1.54051$ Å.

calculated by Kelley *et al.* (1944). This can be compared to $a_0 = 11.47$, $b_0 = 5.545$, $c_0 = 2.830$ Å found by Stecher *et al.* (1964). The basic structure was later confirmed by Meinhardt and Krisement (1960), using thermal neutrons, but slightly different carbon positions resulted. A space group D_{2h}^{16}-*Pbnm*(*Pnma*) was assigned. This results in the calculated powder pattern given in Table 41.

D. CHEMICAL REACTIVITY

In powdered form, all of the carbides begin to oxidize at 700°. However, massive samples of Cr_3C_2 and $Cr_{23}C_6$ remain practically unaffected up to 1000°. Cr_7C_3 is attacked at 800° (Kosolapova and Samsonov, 1961). These carbides are even more reactive in steam. Kelley *et al.* (1944) observed that Cr_3C_2 burned in O_2 below 1050° and was insoluble in hot H_2SO_4, but would dissolve in boiling perchloric acid; Cr_7C_3 required 1100°–1150° to burn and would dissolve in hot dilute H_2SO_4; and Cr_4C gave incomplete combustion even at 1200° and was easily soluble in warm dilute H_2SO_4. Boiling 1:1 HCl will also dissolve $Cr_{23}C_6$ and Cr_7C_3 (Grigor'eva and Klimenko, 1959). In the presence of oxidizing agents (such as HNO_3 or H_2O_2) Cr_3C_2, Cr_7C_3, and $Cr_{23}C_6$ are decreasingly reactive in that order, but the reverse is true in HCl or H_2SO_4 (Kosolapova and Samsonov, 1962).

E. HARDNESS

Kieffer and Kölbl (1949) reported a hardness of 1300 kg/mm^2 for Cr_3C_2. Other workers have obtained values between 1000 and 1400 kg/mm^2. Westbrook (1957), from a study of the effect of temperature up to 800°,

TABLE 41

COPPER RADIATION, POWDER PATTERN FOR Cr_3C_2[a]

2θ	$\sin^2\theta$	*d* spacing	Intensity	*h k l*
17.75	0.0238	4.9922	5	1 0 1
22.28	0.0373	3.9864	5	1 0 2
32.56	0.0786	2.7476	25	0 1 1
35.20	0.0915	2.5471	20	1 0 4
35.95	0.0952	2.4961	10	2 0 2
36.46	0.0979	2.4619	20	1 1 1
39.00	0.1114	2.3076	100	1 1 2
39.59	0.1147	2.2747	10	0 1 3
40.14	0.1178	2.2445	80	2 0 3
46.21	0.1320	2.1198	20	1 0 5
42.94	0.1340	2.1045	10	1 1 3
45.47	0.1493	1.9932	20	2 0 4
45.78	0.1513	1.9805	5	2 1 0
46.49	0.1558	1.9516	50	2 1 1
47.52	0.1623	1.9117	40	0 0 6
48.01	0.1655	1.8932	35	1 1 4
48.59	0.1693	1.8720	40	2 1 2
49.94	0.1782	1.8248	30	3 0 1
51.22	0.1868	1.7821	20	0 1 5
51.95	0.1918	1.7585	10	2 1 3
54.00	0.2061	1.6966	25	1 1 5
56.42	0.2234	1.6296	10	2 1 4
58.70	0.2403	1.5714	1	1 0 7
60.30	0.2523	1.5336	10	3 1 1
61.84	0.2640	1.4991	10	2 1 5
64.71	0.2864	1.4393	5	3 0 5
64.99	0.2886	1.4338	1	0 0 8
65.96	0.2963	1.4150	25	0 2 0
67.41	0.3079	1.3881	1	1 0 8
68.07	0.3132	1.3762	5	4 0 1
70.85	0.3360	1.3288	1	3 0 6
72.46	0.3493	1.3032	1	4 0 3
73.80	0.3605	1.2829	5	3 1 5
75.20	0.3722	1.2625	5	2 1 7
76.22	0.3809	1.2481	1	4 0 4
76.35	0.3820	1.2463	10	1 1 8
76.98	0.3873	1.2376	5	4 1 1
77.03	0.3878	1.2369	5	1 2 4
77.47	0.3915	1.2310	1	2 2 2
77.83	0.3946	1.2261	10	3 0 7

TABLE 41 (continued)

2θ	$\sin^2\theta$	*d* spacing	Intensity	*h k l*
78.56	0.4009	1.2166	10	4 1 2
79.64	0.4101	1.2028	10	3 1 6
80.11	0.4141	1.1970	20	2 2 3
81.19	0.4234	1.1837	5	4 1 3
81.76	0.4284	1.1769	5	1 2 5
83.03	0.4394	1.1620	1	0 1 9
83.09	0.4399	1.1614	5	2 1 8
83.39	0.4425	1.1580	5	2 0 9
83.76	0.4457	1.1538	5	2 2 4
84.83	0.4550	1.1419	10	4 1 4
85.26	0.4587	1.1373	20	1 1 9, 0 2 6
86.41	0.4687	1.1251	1	3 1 7
86.59	0.4703	1.1232	5	1 0 10
87.08	0.4745	1.1182	10	3 2 1
89.49	0.4956	1.0942	5	4 1 5
90.05	0.5004	1.0888	5	5 0 2
91.90	0.5165	1.0717	1	2 1 9
93.23	0.5281	1.0599	5	2 0 10
93.41	0.5297	1.0583	1	4 0 7
94.20	0.5366	1.0515	1	1 2 7
94.47	0.5389	1.0492	1	3 0 9
95.09	0.5443	1.0440	1	1 1 10
96.26	0.5546	1.0343	5	5 0 4
97.47	0.5650	1.0248	5	1 0 11
98.57	0.5745	1.0162	1	5 1 2
99.52	0.5827	1.0090	1	3 2 5
100.97	0.5951	0.9984	1	5 0 5
101.19	0.5971	0.9968	1	5 1 3
101.80	0.6022	0.9926	1	2 1 10
101.98	0.6038	0.9913	5	4 1 7
102.03	0.6042	0.9909	1	1 2 8
102.66	0.6096	0.9866	5	4 2 1
103.86	0.6197	0.9784	5	0 1 11
105.35	0.6323	0.9686	1	3 2 6
106.15	0.6390	0.9635	5	1 1 11
106.93	0.6456	0.9586	1	4 2 3
110.05	0.6714	0.9400	5	4 1 8
110.76	0.6772	0.9360	1	4 2 4
112.40	0.6905	0.9269	1	1 3 1
112.45	0.6910	0.9266	10	3 2 7

TABLE 41 (continued)

2θ	$\sin^2 \theta$	d spacing	Intensity	h k l
112.91	0.6947	0.9242	5	6 0 0
114.09	0.7040	0.9180	5	1 3 2
115.82	0.7178	0.9091	1	4 2 5
115.95	0.7188	0.9085	1	5 1 6
116.95	0.7266	0.9036	1	2 0 12, 1 3 3
118.53	0.7388	0.8961	5	2 2 9
119.75	0.7481	0.8905	5	4 1 9
119.79	0.7484	0.8904	5	2 3 1
121.09	0.7582	0.8846	5	1 3 4
121.29	0.7597	0.8837	1	4 0 10
121.59	0.7619	0.8824	5	2 3 2
122.22	0.7666	0.8797	5	1 2 10
122.51	0.7687	0.8785	5	6 1 0
123.13	0.7732	0.8759	5	6 1 1
123.98	0.7795	0.8724	5	0 3 5
124.68	0.7845	0.8696	1	2 3 3
125.00	0.7868	0.8684	1	6 1 2
126.41	0.7968	0.8629	5	5 2 2
126.69	0.7987	0.8618	5	1 3 5
127.94	0.8074	0.8572	1	6 0 5
128.22	0.8093	0.8562	1	6 1 3
129.21	0.8161	0.8527	1	2 3 4
130.25	0.8231	0.8490	1	3 0 12
130.46	0.8245	0.8483	5	2 2 10
130.70	0.8260	0.8475	5	4 2 7
131.88	0.8338	0.8435	5	4 1 10
132.11	0.8353	0.8428	1	3 2 9
132.25	0.8362	0.8423	5	0 1 13
133.61	0.8449	0.8380	1	3 3 1
133.65	0.8451	0.8379	5	5 1 8
134.57	0.8509	0.8350	15	5 2 4
135.50	0.8566	0.8322	5	2 3 5
135.56	0.8570	0.8320	5	6 0 6
136.27	0.8613	0.8300	5	1 2 11
139.72	0.8815	0.8204	5	6 1 5
141.53	0.8915	0.8158	5	5 2 5
141.94	0.8937	0.8148	1	4 2 8
142.59	0.8971	0.8132	20	3 1 12
143.74	0.9032	0.8105	1	1 0 14
145.77	0.9134	0.8059	1	2 1 13

TABLE 41 (continued)

2θ	$\sin^2\theta$	d spacing	Intensity	$h\ k\ l$
146.23	0.9156	0.8050	1	6 0 7
146.96	0.9192	0.8034	1	2 2 11
147.51	0.9218	0.8023	15	5 1 9
148.98	0.9285	0.7994	5	4 1 11
149.56	0.9311	0.7983	10	6 1 6
150.08	0.9334	0.7973	10	5 0 10
150.64	0.9358	0.7962	5	3 0 13
153.05	0.9457	0.7921	1	0 2 12
154.99	0.9531	0.7890	5	3 3 5
157.24	0.9611	0.7857	1	2 0 14
157.98	0.9635	0.7847	1	7 0 2
158.39	0.9649	0.7842	5	2 3 7
161.67	0.9746	0.7802	15	1 3 8
162.66	0.9773	0.7792	15	1 1 14
163.72	0.9800	0.7781	5	4 3 1
169.09	0.9910	0.7738	20	6 2 0

[a] $a_0 = 5.545$ Å; $b_0 = 2.830$ Å; $c_0 = 11.470$ Å; $\mu r = 2.0$; space group type No. 62; $\lambda(K\alpha_1) = 1.54051$ Å.

found room temperature values for Cr_7C_3 and $Cr_{23}C_6$ of 1600 kg/mm^2 and 1000 kg/mm^2, respectively.

F. THERMOCHEMICAL PROPERTIES

1. Heat of Formation

As yet no heats of combustion have been reported for any of the chromium carbides. Nevertheless, measurements have been made using gas-phase equilibria which can be used, with some reservation, to obtain heats of formation. To provide a common basis, all of the following values were recalculated by the third law method using the data listed at the bottom of Table 42.

Kelley *et al.* (1944), as part of a complete thermodynamic study of these compounds, measured the CO pressure over a mixture of the oxide, Cr_3C_2, and C. This equilibrium was also investigated earlier by Heusler (1926) and recently by Gleiser (1965). The resulting free energy values are compared in Fig. 40, while ΔH_R° (298.15°) and $\Delta H_f^\circ(CrC_{2/3})$ are listed in Table 42. Although the differences could be due to errors in the technique,

TABLE 42

THIRD LAW TREATMENT OF REACTIONS IN THE Cr–C SYSTEM[a]

Reaction	ΔH°_R(298.15°) (kcal/mole)	H°_f(298.15°) (kcal/mole CrC_x)	Investigator
$CrC_{2/3}$			
$\frac{1}{3}Cr_2O_3 + \frac{13}{9}C = \frac{2}{9}Cr_3C_2 + CO$	57.95 ± 0.24	−9.79	Heusler (1926)
	59.09 ± 0.08	−8.09	Kelley *et al.* (1944)
	58.39 ± 0.06	−9.12	Gleiser (1965)
$Cr_3C_2 = 3Cr_{(g)} + 2C_{(s)}$	298.29 ± 0.42	−4.54	Vintaikin (1963)
	309.3 ± 1.7	−8.2	Fujishiro and Gokcen (1961a)
$CrC_{3/7}$			
$\frac{1}{3}Cr_2O_3 + Cr_7C_3 = \frac{1}{3}Cr_{23}C_6 + CO$	72.61 ± 0.12	—	Kelley *et al.* (1944)
$\frac{1}{3}Cr_2O_3 + \frac{9}{5}Cr_3C_2 = \frac{13}{15}Cr_7C_3 + CO$	65.09 ± 0.08	—	Kelley *et al.* (1944)
$CrC_{6/23}$			
$\frac{1}{6}Cr_{23}C_6 + 2H_{2(g)} = \frac{23}{6}Cr + CH_{4(g)}$	−6.4 ± 0.9	−3.0	Alekseev and Shvartzman (1961)
$\frac{1}{6}Cr_{23}C_6 + \frac{1}{3}Cr_2O_3 = \frac{27}{6}Cr + CO_{(g)}$	78.14 ± 0.10	−3.56	Kelley *et al.* (1944)
Cr			
$Cr_{(s)} = Cr_{(g)}$	94.86 ± 0.26	—	McCabe *et al.* (1958)
	94.70 ± 0.21	—	Speiser *et al.* (1950)
	95.24 ± 0.21	—	Gulbransen and Andrew (1952)
	94.89 ± 0.31	—	Composite value

[a] Based on the following data: Thermal functions for $CrC_{6/23}$, $CrC_{3/7}$, and $CrC_{2/3}$ from Tables 43, 44, and 45, respectively. Thermal functions for Cr_2O_3, Kelley *et al.* (1944). Thermal functions for $Cr_{(s)}$ and $Cr_{(g)}$ Stull and Sinke (1956). Thermal functions for CO, CH_4, and H_2, JANAF Tables (1963). $\Delta H^\circ_f(CH_4) = -17.895 + 0.08$ kcal/mole (JANAF Tables). $\Delta H^\circ_f(Cr_2O_3) = -272.7 \pm 0.4$ kcal/mole (Mah, 1954). $\Delta H^\circ_f(CO) = -26.42 \pm 0.62$ kcal/mole (JANAF Tables). $R \ln = 4.576 \log$.

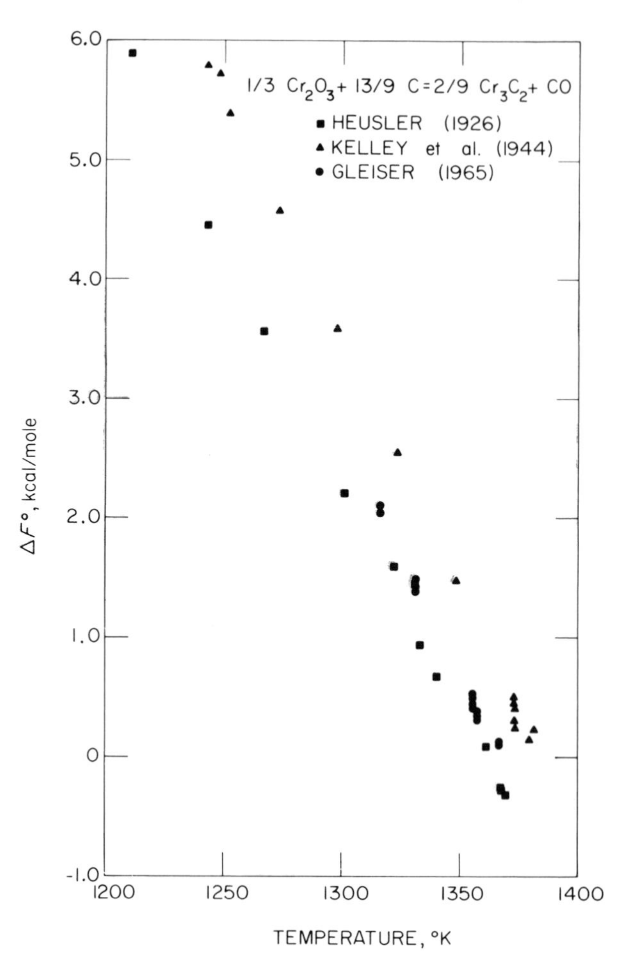

FIG. 40. Free energy for the reaction involving Cr_3C_2, C, Cr_2O_3, and CO.

it is more probable that an oxycarbide of different oxygen content was actually being studied in each case. Such behavior is common in the other carbide systems. Further evidence for this view is given in the following sections.

A heat of formation of $CrC_{6/23}$ can be calculated both from the oxide system (Kelley *et al.*, 1944) as well as from the equilibrium involving CH_4 and H_2 (Alekseev and Shvartsman, 1961). The two heats, shown in Table 42, are close, but the result from the oxide system is the more negative.

TABLE 43
THERMAL FUNCTIONS OF $CrC_{2/3}$[a]

T (°K)	$H_T^\circ - H_{298}^\circ$ (cal/mole)	C_p° (cal/mole-deg)	S_T° (cal/mole-deg)	$-(F_T^\circ - H_{298}^\circ)/T$ (cal/mole-deg)
298.15	0.0	7.84	6.81	6.81
300	14.53	7.87	6.86	6.81
400	870.7	9.11	9.31	7.14
500	1819	9.81	11.43	7.79
600	2826	10.30	13.26	8.55
700	3876	10.70	14.88	9.34
800	4963	11.04	16.33	10.13
900	6083	11.35	17.65	10.89
1000	7234	11.65	18.86	11.63
1100	8413	11.94	19.99	12.34
1200	9621	12.22	21.04	13.02
1300	10860	12.49	22.02	13.67
1400	12120	12.76	22.96	14.30
1500	13410	13.04	23.85	14.91
1600	14730	13.30	24.70	15.50
1700	16070	13.57	25.51	16.06
1800	17440	13.84	26.30	16.61
1900	18840	14.12	27.05	17.14
2000	20260	14.39	27.78	17.65
2100	21720	14.66	28.49	18.15
2200	23200	14.93	29.18	18.64
2300	24700	15.21	29.85	19.11
2400	26240	15.48	30.50	19.57
2500	27800	15.76	31.14	20.02

[a] $H_T^\circ - H_{298.15}^\circ = -3.6074 \times 10^3 + 9.4443T + 1.1635 \times 10^{-3}T^2 + 2.8241 \times 10^{-8}T^3 + 2.0496 \times 10^5/T$ (cal/mole, 298°–1600°K, ±0.7%); M.W. = 60.00.

No independent heats of formation can be calculated from the available data for $CrC_{3/7}$. However, by combining the two equilibria involving $Cr_2O_3 + Cr_7C_3 + Cr_{23}C_6 + CO$ and $Cr_2O_3 + Cr_3C_2 + Cr_7C_3 + CO$, a comparison can be made between ΔH_f° of $Cr_{23}C_6$ and Cr_3C_2. This, of course, assumes no change in ΔH_f° with composition within a phase. In other words, $Cr_{23}C_6$, for example, would have the same heat of formation whether it is in equilibrium with Cr or with Cr_7C_3. On this basis, −3.56 kcal/mole for oxygen-saturated $CrC_{6/23}$ gives −5.8 kcal/mole for oxygen-saturated $CrC_{2/3}$ containing $CrC_{3/7}$. This can be compared to the direct measurement from the same study which gives −8.09 kcal/mole

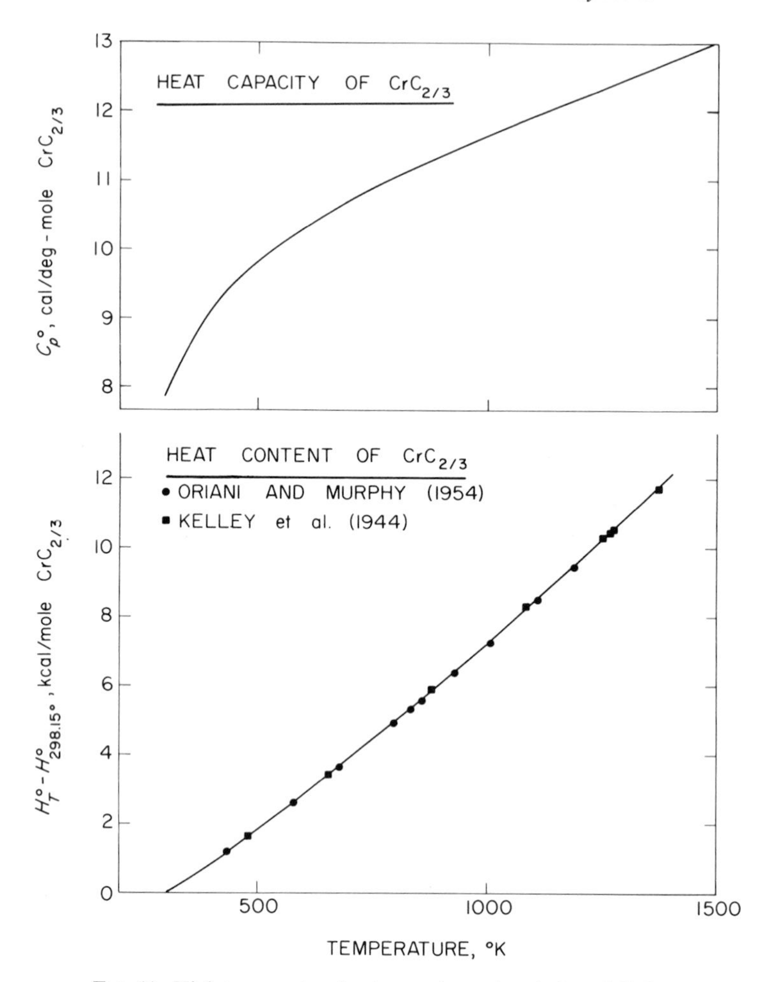

FIG. 41. High temperature heat capacity and enthalpy of $CrC_{2/3}$.

for oxygen-saturated $CrC_{2/3}$ in equilibrium with carbon. The difference could well be overlooked if this comparison had been made between independent measurements of different equilibria. But in this case, errors in experimental technique and in the thermal values tend to cancel. One is left with the conclusions that the above assumption is not valid and/or that the oxygen content of a phase used in one reaction was not the same when that phase was studied in a different reaction. Since these possibilities exist, all of the measurements using oxide equilibria must be used

TABLE 44
THERMAL FUNCTIONS OF $CrC_{6/23}$[a]

T (°K)	$H_T^\circ - H_{298}^\circ$ (cal/mole)	C_p° (cal/mole-deg)	S_T° (cal/mole-deg)	$-(F_T^\circ - H_{298}^\circ)/T$ (cal/mole-deg)
298.15	0.0	6.487	6.325	6.325
300	12.02	6.510	6.365	6.325
400	711.0	7.358	8.370	6.593
500	1471	7.797	10.06	7.122
600	2266	8.091	11.51	7.736
700	3087	8.327	12.78	8.368
800	3931	8.545	13.90	8.991
900	4796	8.761	14.92	9.594
1000	5683	8.986	15.86	10.17
1100	6593	9.224	16.73	10.73
1200	7529	9.480	17.54	11.27
1300	8490	9.754	18.31	11.78
1400	9480	10.05	19.04	12.27
1500	10500	10.37	19.75	12.75
1600	11550	10.70	20.43	13.20
1700	12640	11.06	21.08	13.65
1800	13770	11.45	21.73	14.08
1900	14930	11.85	22.36	14.50
2000	16140	12.28	22.98	14.91

[a] $H_T^\circ - H_{298.15}^\circ = -3.0412 \times 10^3 + 8.3629T - 2.0104 \times 10^{-4}T^2 + 3.9683 \times 10^{-7}T^3 + 1.6551 \times 10^5/T$ (cal/mole, 298°–1700°K, ±0.3%); M.W. = 55.13.

with considerable uncertainty. Additional comments on this problem are included in the section on vaporization.

2. Low Temperature Heat Capacity

Each of the compounds in this system was examined from ~50° to room temperature by Kelley *et al.* (1944). A redetermination of C_p for $CrC_{2/3}$ between 13° and 300° by DeSorbo (1953) resulted in almost identical results. The $S°(298.15°)$ and $C_p(298.15°)$ used in Table 43 are based on this more recent work, in agreement with the reevaluation of this property by Kelley and King (1961).

3. High Temperature Heat Content

Kelley *et al.* (1944) determined the heat content of the carbides as well as the oxide up to ~1600°. In the case of $CrC_{2/3}$, Oriani and Murphy

TABLE 45
THERMAL FUNCTIONS OF $CrC_{3/7}$[a]

T (°K)	$H_T^\circ - H_{298}^\circ$ (cal/mole)	C_p° (cal/mole-deg)	S_T° (cal/mole-deg)	$-(F_T^\circ - H_{298}^\circ)/T$ (cal/mole-deg)
298.15	0.0	7.131	6.857	6.857
300	13.22	7.160	6.901	6.857
400	786.7	8.169	9.120	7.153
500	1631	8.661	11.00	7.739
600	2513	8.973	12.61	8.420
700	3423	9.222	14.01	9.121
800	4357	9.454	15.26	9.811
900	5314	9.695	16.39	10.48
1000	6297	9.954	17.42	11.12
1100	7306	10.24	18.38	11.74
1200	8346	10.56	19.29	12.33
1300	9419	10.91	20.14	12.90
1400	10530	11.29	20.97	13.45
1500	11680	11.71	21.76	13.97
1600	12870	12.17	22.53	14.49
1700	14110	12.67	23.28	14.98
1800	15410	13.20	24.02	15.46
1900	16750	13.77	24.75	15.93
2000	18160	14.38	25.47	16.39

[a] $H_T^\circ - H_{298.15}^\circ = -3.5948 \times 10^3 + 9.8464T - 8.2590 \times 10^{-4}T^2 + 6.5761 \times 10^{-7}T^3 + 2.1319 \times 10^5/T$ (cal/mole, 298°–1600°K, ±0.3%); M.W. = 57.14.

(1954) find slightly lower values. This might have been due, as they suggested, to the supposed lower oxide content of their sample. Nevertheless, the thermal values shown in Table 43 were obtained by combining the two studies. A comparison between the data and the fitted curve along with the resulting C_p values are shown in Fig. 41.

The thermal values for $CrC_{6/23}$ and $CrC_{3/7}$, given in Tables 44 and 45, respectively, are based solely on the work of Kelley *et al.* (1944). Their data are compared to the fitting curves in Fig. 42.

4. VAPORIZATION

a. Chromium

In order to have internal consistency, the various measurements of the vapor pressure of Cr metal were reevaluated using the same free energy functions as were used for the carbide system. The data of Speiser *et al.*

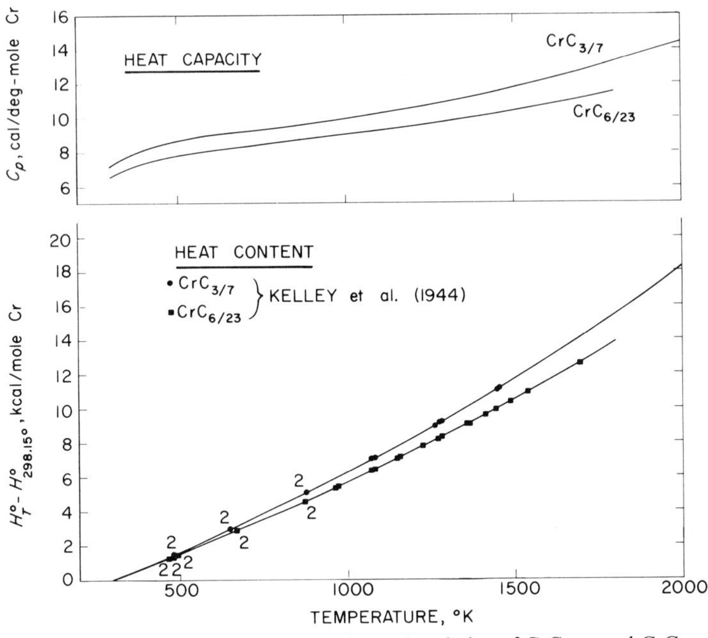

FIG. 42. High temperature heat capacity and enthalpy of $CrC_{6/23}$ and $CrC_{3/7}$

(1950), Gulbransen and Andrew (1952), and McCabe *et al.* (1958) were treated separately by the third law then combined as shown in Table 42. The resulting linear equation,

$$\log P(\text{atm}) = -2.086(\pm 0.011) \times 10^4/T + 7.695 \pm 0.079,$$

is compared to the data in Fig. 43. Although Kubaschevski and Heymer (1960) and Vintaikin (1959) did not tabulate the actual measurements, their least-squares equations are close to the one above. The agreement between the Langmuir study by Speiser *et al.* (1950) and the Knudsen values obtained by the other workers does not support the conclusion (Nesmeyanov and Man, 1960) that the evaporation coefficient is near 0.5. Although the latter work gave Knudsen pressures which are high, so did the Langmuir study of Burlakov (1957). For this reason, neither data were included in the composite treatment.

b. Chromium Carbide

The two vapor pressure measurements of $Cr_3C_2 + C$ are compared in Fig. 43. Fujishiro and Gokcen (1961a) monitored the weight of a graphite

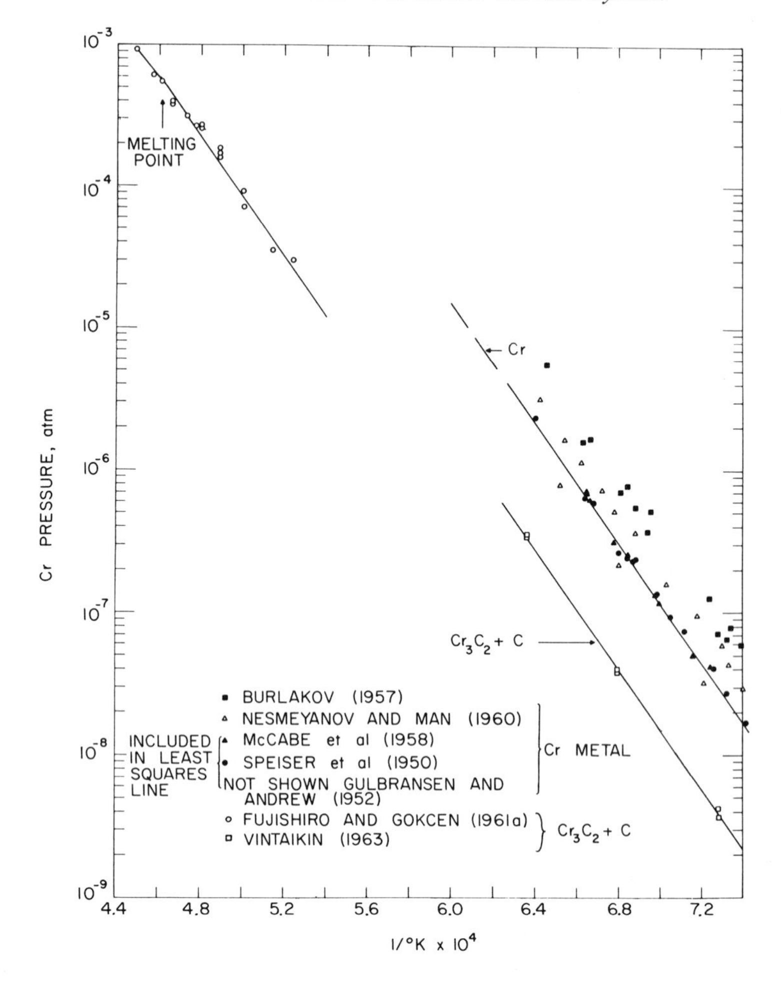

FIG. 43. Pressure of $Cr_{(g)}$ over $Cr_{(s)}$ and over Cr_3C_2 + C.

Knudsen cell. Unfortunately, nearly half of the weight loss was due to diffusion through the crucible walls. Although this was corrected for, it does create some uncertainty. Vintaikin (1963) determined, by radioanalysis, the amount of Cr^{51} collected on a target. He did not measure the pressure directly but obtained the ratio of the pressure over the carbide to that over pure Cr metal with the same apparatus. In order to compare these two studies, the reported ratios were multiplied by the pressure over the metal given by the above equation. A third law treatment of this data shows no significant trend with temperature. As can be seen in Table 42, the resulting heat of formation of $CrC_{2/3}$ is much lower than the one obtained from the oxide system. A similar analysis of Fujishiro and Gokcen's (1961a) work does show a slight trend in the third law values with temperature. In this case, the heat of formation of $CrC_{2/3}$ is closer to that obtained from the oxide studies.

In order to evaluate these discrepancies it is necessary to consider two important factors. Since the oxide studies were probably based on an oxycarbide, there is a good chance the heat of formation obtained therefrom is too high. On the other hand, the difference between the two vapor pressure measurements is not surprising even if there were no errors in the data. As the melting point is approached one would expect the phase to dissolve increasing amounts of carbon accompanied by a reduction in the Cr pressure. The two studies do, indeed, show the expected relationship to each other. Thus, the pressures and slope obtained by Vintaikin (1963) at the lower temperatures probably better represent the behavior of Cr_3C_2 of stoichiometric composition. With these factors in mind, the heat of formation for $CrC_{2/3}$ is placed between -4.5 and -6.5 kcal/mole.

VIII

THE MOLYBDENUM–MOLYBDENUM CARBIDE SYSTEM

A. PREPARATION

Like most of the other carbides, Mo_2C was prepared by Moissan 1893b, 1895b, 1897a) in an electric arc. Later, he and Hoffmann (1904) obtained "MoC" from an aluminum menstruum.

The reduction of MoO_2 by carbon leads to the carbide in two steps: between 420° and 640° MoO_2 is formed by an exothermic reaction, and above 820° the metal begins to form. The carbide Mo_2C results only after the oxide has been eliminated (Hegedüs and Neugebauer, 1960). This, however, does not preclude the possibility of a solid solution between the carbide and oxide. The reaction is promoted by the presence of hydrogen (Hüttig *et al.*, 1950).

Molybdenum metal can be converted to Mo_2C by the action of CO (Browning and Emmett, 1952; Hilpert and Ornstein, 1913); the reaction with CH_4 will produce Mo_2C and MoC_{1-x} (Tutiya, 1932); and the direct reaction with graphite will lead, under the proper conditions, to both carbides. The latter reaction starts at about 1000°C (Arkharov *et al.*, 1960; Hüttig *et al.*, 1950) forming the Mo_2C phase first.

Deposition from the gas phase can be accomplished by heating a wire to 300°–800° in an atmosphere of molybdenum carbonyl and hydrogen (Lander and Germer, 1948; Campbell *et al.*, 1949) or by heating graphite in molybdenum chloride vapors (Pring and Fielding, 1909).

Fused-salt electrolysis of carbonate–borate–fluoride–metal oxide salt baths has produced both carbides, which deposit as silvery crystals on a graphite electrode (Weiss, 1946).

It is not advisable to prepare these carbides from the oxide or any other oxygen-containing compound unless the resulting material is afterwards purified in high vacuum.

Pure carbides are conveniently prepared by arc-melting as well as by powder metallurgical techniques.

B. PHASE RELATIONSHIP

This system consists of two compounds, Mo_2C and MoC_{1-x}, each having two crystal forms. Only Mo_2C is stable at room temperature.

The metal melts at 2620° ± 10° (Worthing, 1925; A. Taylor *et al.*, 1961; Riley, 1964; Rudy *et al.*, 1965b) with no confirmed structure change below this temperature.

At the eutectic temperature (2205°), the solubility of carbon in the metal falls between 0.018 and 0.022 wt % ($MoC_{0.0014}$–$MoC_{0.0018}$) with a marked reduction as the temperature is reduced (Few and Manning, 1952; Speiser *et al.*, 1952). This amounts to about a 3°/ppm C reduction in melting point as carbon is added to molybdenum.

Eutectic melting occurs between Mo and Mo_2C at 2205° (Nowotny *et al.*, 1954b; Rudy *et al.*, 1965b, 1966; Storms, 1966b). This phase change is sufficiently sharp and reproducible to make it useful as a secondary temperature standard with an error of ±3° (based on reproducibility). The eutectic composition has been found at $MoC_{0.15}$ (Sykes *et al.*, 1935) and $MoC_{0.20}$ (Rudy *et al.*, 1965b).

Before discussing the remaining carbide system, it is necessary to make some comments about nomenclature. According to common practice, Rudy *et al.* (1965b) designated the low temperature form of Mo_2C as α and the newly discovered high temperature form as β. The situation at the high-carbon phase is not as simple. Early workers, being unaware of the carbon-deficient nature of the higher carbide, referred to it as MoC. Later, Rudy *et al.* (1962b) realized that the quenched phase extended only to $MoC_{0.667}$ and assigned the formula η-Mo_3C_2 to the low temperature form and α-Mo_3C_2 to the high temperature allotrope. In a recent report, Rudy *et al.* (1965b) changed the designation to η-MoC_{1-x} and α-MoC_{1-x} for the respective structures. Of course any designation is arbitrary, but it is unfortunate that the ones used for this phase should be inconsistent with those used to describe Mo_2C and similar phases in the other carbide systems. It would be better to use α-MoC (or α-MoC_{1-x}) for the low temperature hexagonal structure and β-MoC (or β-MoC_{1-x}) for the high temperature cubic form. This convention will be used in the following discussion.

Until recently, an understanding of the Mo–C system has rested on the composite phase diagram constructed by Nowotny *et al.* (1954b). It showed one Mo_2C phase which as stable between room temperature and the melting point, and a γ'-MoC phase which decomposed below ~1400° into Mo_2C and C. In view of recent developments in this system, this and the other early work is only of historical interest and will not be discussed here. The reader is directed to Hansen and Anderko (1958), Kieffer and Benesovsky (1963), or Schwarzkopf and Kieffer (1953) for such a description.

Rudy *et al.* (1965b, 1966) have made a very complete and extensive study of this system using x-ray, metallographic, and thermal analysis techniques (DTA). They demonstrated for the first time a high temperature phase change in Mo_2C and they confirmed the earlier observation that MoC_{1-x} also has two crystal forms. The available data led them to conclude that Mo_2C in equilibrium with Mo shows long range disordering by a single-phase reaction as the temperature is raised, but that Mo_2C containing carbon converts to a disordered form at 1190° ± 20°, isothermally. Above this temperature, two single-phase regions of partially disordered Mo_2C were thought to be parallel with a narrow two-phase region between them. Long range disorder continues to increase as the temperature is raised until, finally, each phase melts congruently. This, however, is not the only interpretation consistent with their data. By using high temperature neutron diffraction, A. L. Bowman (1966) not only found an order–disorder (D_{2h}^{14}–$L'3$) transition in high carbon Mo_2C, in agreement with Rudy *et al.* (1965b), but demonstrated that a similar transition occurs near 1490° when Mo is the second phase. In addition, he found the transition to be much faster for $Mo_2C + C$ compared to Mo_2C in the presence of Mo.

In view of these differences in interpretation, it is instructive to examine the other evidence presented by Rudy in some detail, starting first with the DTA studies.

Thermograms of $MoC_{0.65}$, $MoC_{0.56}$, and $MoC_{0.53}$ showed a thermal effect near 1200°, but, as the composition was further reduced, the transition rose to ~1420° at $MoC_{0.50}$. Samples of $MoC_{0.47}$ and $MoC_{0.45}$ both gave only a broad, poorly resolved thermal effect. This was attributed to a heat capacity anomaly associated with the single-phase disordering process. It is also consistent with a slow isothermal transition. X-ray evidence for the isothermal reaction at 1190° is based on the coexistence of two apparently hexagonal lattices having different *c* parameters. The relative quantity of these changed as the overall composition was changed in the vicinity of $MoC_{0.5}$. A consistent behavior was seen metallographically.

A similar examination in the Mo-rich region failed to show the coexistence of two Mo_2C phases in quenched material. The material examined by Bowman (1966), both Mo-rich and carbon-rich, always showed x-ray line splitting after heating below the disorder transition. Heating above the transition, on the Mo-rich side, eliminated the splitting. This splitting was attributed to a distortion in the Mo lattice which was produced when the carbon sublattice became ordered. Rudy (1966), on the other hand, argues that the line splitting is not associated with the disorder transition at 1190°, but with a transition at some lower, but unknown temperature. One can also suggest that the observation by Rudy *et al.* (1966), of two hexagonal phases is due to a difference in composition between the α and β phases at the transition. Failure to see a similar effect in the Mo-rich region could be explained if there were very little difference between the composition of the two phases here. This conflict, however, remains to be resolved.

A number of metallographic studies were also presented, the more interesting being the results of a temperature gradient and a diffusion couple. For the first, a sample of $MoC_{0.488}$ was heated with a gradient of 580°/cm and then quenched in tin. A narrow precipitation band was produced which was interpreted as a narrow two-phase region between α- and β-Mo_2C near 2300°. This observation is difficult to reconcile with the neutron diffraction work using the limited description given, especially since x-ray identification of the phases is so difficult.

These limitations are not present to the same degree when the diffusion couple experiment is examined. The couple was made by heating Mo in contact with graphite at 2200° for 22 minutes then cooling at 14°/second. Four distinct layers formed between the elements. Using their designation, these were described as (A) α-Mo_2C, (B) β-Mo_2C, (C) η-MoC_{1-x} and (D) α-MoC_{1-x}. The (B) β-Mo_2C layer showed two bands (B_1, B_2), but this was clearly single phase at temperature. To be consistent with the neutron diffraction study, this would have to be interpreted as (A) Mo_2C, unconverted high temperature form; (B_1) Mo_2C, high temperature form which converted to the low temperature form upon cooling; (B_2) Mo_2C high temperature form which has converted and precipitated η-MoC_{1-x}; (C) η-MoC_{1-x}, and (D) α-MoC_{1-x}. The regions designated A, B_1, and B_2 would have been single-phase Mo_2C at temperature. Upon cooling, the A and B_1 layers form because of the slow conversion between α- and β-Mo_2C when the carbon content is low, but which becomes more rapid as the upper-phase boundary is approached. Thus, the relative widths of the regions A and B_1 should depend on the cooling rate, with the disappearance of A when very slow cooling rates or a low temperature anneal is used. Whether an additional low temperature transition exists is still uncertain, but, in view of the neutron diffraction work, the order–

disorder transition, found by Rudy *et al.* (1966), clearly extends across the homogeneity range of Mo_2C. Types of ordering which cannot be detected by x-ray or neutron diffraction may, indeed, be present, but by the usual criteria for a phase change, Mo_2C is *L′*3 at all compositions above the transition temperature and is ordered below this temperature.

Based on the composite phase diagram (Fig. 44), β-Mo_2C extends from $MoC_{0.36}$ to $MoC_{0.53}$ at the eutectic temperature. Rudy *et al.* (1965b) found that quenching is effective only below 2000°. Slowly cooled material usually gives a lower boundary near $MoC_{0.44}$ (Westgren and Phragmén, 1926; Takei, 1928; Sykes *et al.*, 1935; Wallace *et al.*, 1963; Rudy *et al.*, 1965b).

Melting of β-Mo_2C has been observed at ~2400° (Sykes *et al.*, 1935), 2410° ± 15° (Nadler and Kempter, 1960); 2450° ± 30° (Wallace *et al.*, 1963); and 2486° ± 5° (Rudy *et al.*, 1965b). Rudy *et al.* (1962b, 1965b) have proposed congruent melting.

Both α-MoC_{1-x} and β-MoC_{1-x} are stable only at high temperatures, although the former is easily retained by normal cooling. A very rapid quench will preserve the cubic form (Rudy *et al.*, 1962b; Nowotny and Kieffer, 1952) as well as the addition of a little NbC (Rudy *et al.*, 1961), ThC, UC, VC (Rudy *et al.*, 1962b), ZrC (Wallace *et al.*, 1963), or WC (Dawihl, 1950). High pressures are also said to stabilize cubic MoC_{1-x} (Clougherty *et al.*, 1961). According to Rudy *et al.* (1965b), the transition between the two forms occurs at 1960° ± 20° and α-MoC_{1-x} decomposes into Mo_2C and graphite at 1655° ± 15°. The value of 1450° ± 100° reported by Wallace *et al.* (1963) is apparently too low. The β-MoC_{1-x} phase has also been seen in thin films after quenching from 1200° (Kaye, 1962). However, in this case oxygen stabilization cannot be ruled out.

β-MoC_{1-x} melts peritectically or congruently with a very slight maximum. When excess carbon is present a melting point of 2580° ± 10° is the most probable value, based on recent measurements (Wallace *et al.*, 1963; Rudy *et al.*, 1965b).

Several other phases have been observed when the material contained excessive oxygen. Lander and Germer (1948) observed a cubic lattice for what they thought was Mo_2C. When molybdenum carbonyl–steam mixtures are used, oxycarbides result (Ferguson *et al.*, 1964), which are, in some cases, cubic. This could be viewed as oxygen-stabilized β-MoC_{1-x}. Kuo and Hägg (1952) obtained a hexagonal phase, designated γ', when Mo and CO were allowed to react at low temperatures. Above 800° it converted to another hexagonal structure, designated γ. Both phases were also observed by Clougherty *et al.* (1961) after heating under pressure.

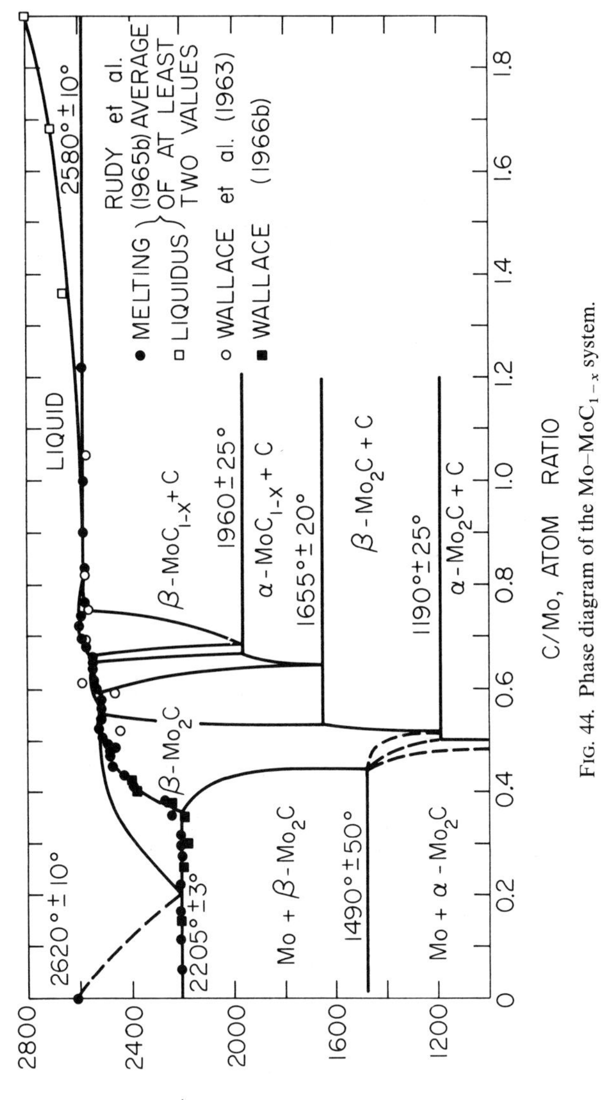

FIG. 44. Phase diagram of the Mo–MoC_{1-x} system.

Nowotny *et al.* (1954b), when they were unable to obtain the γ phase and found higher parameters for the γ' phase, suggested the discrepancy was due to oxygen contamination.

C. LATTICE PARAMETER AND STRUCTURE

A calculated powder pattern for molybdenum is shown in Table 46. Mo_2C has two crystal forms, an orthorhombic low temperature form (α) which converts to a hexagonal structure (β) before melting.

TABLE 46

COPPER RADIATION, POWDER PATTERN FOR Mo[a]

2θ	$\sin^2\theta$	*d* spacing	Intensity	*h k l*
40.51	0.1198	2.2251	100	1 1 0
58.62	0.2397	1.5733	20	2 0 0
73.68	0.3595	1.2846	55	2 1 1
87.63	0.4793	1.1125	20	2 2 0
101.44	0.5992	0.9951	35	3 1 0
115.98	0.7190	0.9084	15	2 2 2
132.66	0.8389	0.8410	100	3 2 1
156.55	0.9587	0.7867	25	4 0 0

[a] $a_0 = 3.1467$ Å; $\mu r = 4.0$; structure type *A*2, space group No. 229; $\lambda(K\alpha_1) = 1.54051$ Å.

Powder patterns of α-Mo_2C usually are sufficiently diffuse to obscure many of the lines. In addition, the hexagonal structure is often quenched in when the composition is below $MoC_{0.50}$. This has led most workers to assume a hexagonal lattice for α-Mo_2C. Using neutron diffraction techniques, Parthé and Sadagopan (1963) showed that the structure is orthorhombic, but they assumed a hexagonal metal lattice. Well-developed x-ray patterns clearly show this is not the case. A redetermination of the structure by A. L. Bowman (1966), using neutron diffraction, demonstrated that the metal positions are indeed slightly perturbed. Nevertheless, the structure is basically the same as the one reported by Parthé and Sadagopan (1963). A calculated powder pattern is listed in Table 47. Naturally, lattice parameters based on a hexagonal indexing for the α phase are not correct. The high temperature (β) form is the disordered *L*′3 hexagonal structure (A. L. Bowman, 1966). Its calculated diffraction pattern is listed in Table 48.

TABLE 47
COPPER RADIATION, POWDER PATTERN FOR α-Mo_2C[a]

2θ	$\sin^2\theta$	d spacing	Intensity	$h\ k\ l$
34.32	0.0871	2.6104	20	0 2 1
34.43	0.0876	2.6028	10	0 0 2
37.90	0.1059	2.3667	35	2 0 0
39.38	0.1135	2.2859	100	1 2 1
39.48	0.1141	2.2807	50	1 0 2
52.12	0.1930	1.7534	20	2 2 1
52.19	0.1935	1.7510	10	2 0 2
61.40	0.2607	1.5086	15	0 4 0
61.60	0.2622	1.5042	25	0 2 3
69.56	0.3254	1.3503	25	3 2 1
69.62	0.3259	1.3493	15	3 0 2
72.33	0.3483	1.3052	5	0 4 2
72.58	0.3503	1.3014	1	0 0 4
74.53	0.3666	1.2721	15	2 4 0
74.71	0.3681	1.2695	25	2 2 3
75.49	0.3747	1.2582	20	1 4 2
75.73	0.3768	1.2548	10	1 0 4
81.22	0.4237	1.1834	5	4 0 0
84.74	0.4542	1.1429	5	2 4 2
84.98	0.4562	1.1404	5	2 0 4
91.23	0.5108	1.0778	5	4 2 1
91.29	0.5113	1.0772	1	4 0 2
99.97	0.5866	1.0057	15	3 4 2
100.21	0.5886	1.0040	10	3 0 4
102.53	0.6084	0.9875	1	0 6 1
102.83	0.6110	0.9854	1	0 4 4
103.01	0.6125	0·9842	1	0 2 5
105.65	0.6349	0.9667	15	1 6 1
105.96	0.6375	0.9647	15	1 4 4
106.14	0.6390	0.9636	15	1 2 5
111.64	0.6844	0.9311	10	4 4 0
111.83	0.6859	0.9300	20	4 2 3
115.39	0.7144	0.9113	5	2 6 1
115.71	0.7169	0.9097	5	2 4 4
115.91	0.7184	0.9087	5	2 2 5
119.88	0.7491	0.8900	20	5 2 1
119.94	0.7496	0.8897	10	5 0 2
122.95	0.7719	0.8767	5	4 4 2
123.23	0.7740	0.8755	5	4 0 4
124.55	0.7836	0.8701	15	0 6 3

TABLE 47 (continued)

2θ	$\sin^2\theta$	d spacing	Intensity	$h\ k\ l$
125.20	0.7882	0.8676	5	0 0 6
133.90	0.8467	0.8371	20	1 7 1, 3 6 1
134.32	0.8493	0.8358	20	3 4 4
134.56	0.8508	0.8350	20	3 2 5
141.17	0.8895	0.8167	35	2 6 3
142.02	0.8941	0.8146	15	2 0 6
155.04	0.9533	0.7889	15	6 0 0

[a] $a_0 = 4.7360$ Å; $b_0 = 6.0354$ Å; $c_0 = 5.2050$ Å; $\mu r = 3.0$; space group D_{2h}^{14}, No. 60; $\lambda(K\alpha_1) = 1.54051$ Å.

TABLE 48

Copper Radiation, Powder Pattern for β-Mo_2C[a]

2θ	$\sin^2\theta$	d spacing	Intensity	$h\ k\ l$
34.35	0.0872	2.6084	15	1 0 0
37.96	0.1058	2.3680	20	0 0 2
39.40	0.1136	2.2848	100	1 0 1
52.12	0.1930	1.7533	20	1 0 2
61.52	0.2616	1.5060	25	1 1 0
69.54	0.3253	1.3506	25	1 0 3
72.40	0.3488	1.3042	5	2 0 0
74.62	0.3674	1.2708	25	1 1 2
75.55	0.3752	1.2574	20	2 0 1
81.17	0.4232	1.1840	5	0 0 4
84.79	0.4546	1.1424	5	2 0 2
91.19	0.5104	1.0781	5	1 0 4
100.00	0.5869	1.0055	15	2 0 3
102.76	0.6104	0.9859	5	2 1 0
105.88	0.6368	0.9652	25	2 1 1
111.69	0.6848	0.9308	20	1 1 4
115.62	0.7162	0.9102	10	2 1 2
119.80	0.7485	0.8903	15	1 0 5
122.96	0.7720	0.8766	5	2 0 4
124.72	0.7848	0.8695	10	3 0 0
134.18	0.8485	0.8362	35	2 1 3
141.37	0.8906	0.8162	25	3 0 2
154.75	0.9522	0.7893	5	0 0 6

[a] $a_0 = 3.012$ Å; $c_0 = 4.736$ Å; $\mu r = 3.0$; structure type $L'3$, space group No. 194; $\lambda(K\alpha_1) = 1.54051$ Å.

MoC also has two crystal modifications: a complex hexagonal structure (α) and a fcc form (β) at high temperatures. Nowotny *et al.* (1954b) assigned the space group D_{6h}^4 to the α form (designated γ' or η by them) from a powder pattern. If only the strongest lines were considered, a cubic indexing resulted with $a = 4.27$ Å. By using a very rapid quenching rate, Rudy *et al.* (1965b) succeeded in obtaining various compositions for which the lattice parameter was measured. They found a nearly linear variation

TABLE 49

COPPER RADIATION, POWDER PATTERN FOR α-MoC_{1-x} [a]

2θ	$\sin^2\theta$	*d* spacing	Intensity	*h k l*
34.93	0.0901	2.5663	20	1 0 1
36.56	0.0984	2.4555	70	1 0 2
36.83	0.0998	2.4383	45	0 0 6
39.15	0.1123	2.2989	100	1 0 3
42.55	0.1317	2.1228	75	1 0 4
46.62	0.1566	1.9464	20	1 0 5
56.38	0.2231	1.6306	15	1 0 7
61.57	0.2619	1.5050	55	1 1 0
61.93	0.2647	1.4971	30	1 0 8
67.89	0.3118	1.3793	25	1 0 9
72.79	0.3520	1.2982	5	2 0 1
73.78	0.3603	1.2831	15	2 0 2
73.95	0.3617	1.2807	55	1 1 6
74.28	0.3645	1.2758	15	1 0 10
75.43	0.3742	1.2592	20	2 0 3
77.71	0.3936	1.2277	15	2 0 4
78.36	0.3992	1.2192	10	0 0 12
80.63	0.4186	1.1906	5	2 0 5
81.11	0.4227	1.1847	5	1 0 11
88.29	0.4851	1.1059	5	2 0 7
93.06	0.5267	1.0614	10	2 0 8
96.40	0.5558	1.0332	5	1 0 13
98.49	0.5738	1.0169	10	2 0 9
103.18	0.6140	0.9830	5	2 1 1
104.16	0.6223	0.9764	15	2 1 2
104.65	0.6264	0.9732	10	2 0 10
105.14	0.6306	0.9700	10	1 0 14
105.80	0.6362	0.9657	25	2 1 3
108.13	0.6556	0.9513	20	2 1 4
108.80	0.6611	0.9473	45	1 1 12

TABLE 49 (continued)

2θ	$\sin^2 \theta$	d spacing	Intensity	$h\ k\ l$
111.16	0.6805	0.9337	10	2 1 5
111.67	0.6847	0.9309	5	2 0 11
114.96	0.7110	0.9135	15	1 0 15
119.61	0.7470	0.8912	10	2 1 7
124.87	0.7858	0.8689	25	3 0 0
125.26	0.7886	0.8674	25	2 1 8
126.43	0.7969	0.8628	15	1 0 16
129.45	0.8177	0.8518	5	2 0 13
132.18	0.8357	0.8426	35	2 1 9
140.46	0.8856	0.8185	55	3 0 6
140.97	0.8884	0.8172	35	2 1 10, 1 0 17
141.73	0.8926	0.8153	15	2 0 14
142.77	0.8981	0.8128	10	0 0 18
153.28	0.9466	0.7917	10	2 1 11
161.06	0.9729	0.7809	45	2 0 15

[a] $a_0 = 3.010$ Å; $c_0 = 14.63$ Å; $\mu r = 3.0$; space group D_{6h}^4, No. 194; $\lambda(K\alpha_1) = 1.54051$ Å.

TABLE 50

COPPER RADIATION, POWDER PATTERN FOR $MoC_{0.75}$(β-MoC_{1-x})[a]

2θ	$\sin^2 \theta$	d spacing	Intensity	$h\ k\ l$
36.32	0.0971	2.4716	100	1 1 1
42.18	0.1295	2.1405	80	2 0 0
61.18	0.2590	1.5136	60	2 2 0
73.27	0.3561	1.2908	55	3 1 1
77.11	0.3885	1.2358	25	2 2 2
92.06	0.5180	1.0702	15	4 0 0
103.31	0.6151	0.9821	35	3 3 1
107.15	0.6475	0.9573	45	4 2 0
123.63	0.7769	0.8739	55	4 2 2
138.43	0.8741	0.8239	70	3 3 3, 5 1 1

[a] $a_0 = 4.2810$ Å; $\mu r = 3.0$; structure type $B1$, space group No. 225; $\lambda(K\alpha_1) = 1.54051$ Å.

between 4.266 Å ($MoC_{0.69}$) and 4.281 Å ($MoC_{0.75}$). Calculated powder patterns for the two forms are given in Tables 49 and 50. A summary of the lattice parameter values and structures is given in Table 51.

A number of other phases have been found in this system, as described in the previous section, but these are due to the oxycarbide.

TABLE 51

STRUCTURE AND LATTICE PARAMETER OF THE MOLYBDENUM CARBIDES

Equilibrium	Composition of first phase	Structure	Lattice parameter (Å)	Investigator
Mo	Pure	bcc ($A2$)	$a = 3.1467$	Speiser *et al.* (1952)
Mo + Mo_2C	$MoC_{0.0016}$	bcc ($A2$)	$a = 3.1478$	
β-Mo_2C + Mo	$MoC_{0.44}$	hcp ($L'3$)	$a = 2.994 \pm 0.005$ $c = 4.722 \pm 0.005$	Wallace *et al.* (1963)
β-Mo_2C	$MoC_{0.48}$	hcp ($L'3$)	$a = 3.0028 \pm 0.0001$ $c = 4.7288 \pm 0.0001$	Fries and Kempter (1960)
α-Mo_2C + C	$MoC_{0.50}$	Orthorhombic	$a = 4.7334 \pm 0.0007$ $b = 6.0344 \pm 0.003$ $c = 5.2056 \pm 0.002$	Wallace and Bowman (1966)
α-MoC_{1-x}	$MoC_{0.67}(\eta)$	Hex, D^4_{6h}	$a = 3.010 \pm 0.002$ $c = 14.63 \pm 0.01$	Wallace *et al.* (1963)
β-MoC_{1-x} + C	$MoC_{>0.67}(\alpha)$ (quenched from 2580°C)	fcc ($B1$)	$a = 4.2810$	Rudy *et al.* (1965b)

D. APPEARANCE

All compositions have a metallic color which becomes darker as the carbon content increases.

E. CHEMICAL REACTIVITY

The molybdenum carbides are rapidly attacked in air at 700°–800° (Powell *et al.*, 1955). According to Schwarzkopf and Kieffer (1953), the higher carbide is dissolved by concentrated HF, by cold HNO_3, and by boiling H_2SO_4, but concentrated HCl has very little effect. Also this carbide is attacked by the halogens to a varying degree. Mo_2C is similar in this behavior (Kopyleva, 1961).

The carbides are stable in static H_2 below 2000° (Ohlinger, 1959b).

F. HARDNESS

The following values have been reported for the hardness of Mo_2C: 1479 kg/mm^2 (Meerson and Umanskii, 1953); 1500 kg/mm^2 (Kieffer and Kölbl, 1949); 1550 DPH (Jones, 1956); 1600 ± 150 kg/mm^2 (KHN100) (Mersol *et al.*, 1966); and 1800 kg/mm^2 (Bückle, 1955). Mersol *et al.* (1966) observed the hardness of a $MoC_{0.485}$ single crystal to decrease regularly from 1650 to 1260 kg/mm^2 after successively higher annealing temperatures were used.

α-MoC_{1-x} is reported to be somewhat harder than Mo_2C, but no values have appeared.

G. THERMOCHEMICAL PROPERTIES

1. Heat of Formation

Mah (1963b) measured the heats of formation of Mo_2C and "MoC" by combustion calorimetry and obtained -11.0 ± 0.7 kcal/mole and -2.4 ± 1.0 kcal/mole, respectively. However, the "MoC" sample, for which analysis gave $MoC_{0.86}$, was assumed to be a mixture of MoC and Mo_2C. Since the high-carbon carbide actually has a stoichiometry of $MoC_{0.67}$, the material was no doubt a mixture of mainly MoC_{1-x} and free carbon. Whatever Mo_2C was present must have resulted from the decomposition of MoC_{1-x} into Mo_2C and C upon cooling. Therefore, the uncertainty for this value is a good deal larger than indicated.

2. Low Temperature Heat Capacity

No measurements have been reported.

3. High Temperature Heat Content

A considerable interest in the high temperature thermal properties of molybdenum metal within recent years makes a reevaluation of these

TABLE 52

Thermal Functions of $Mo_{(s)}$[a]

T (°K)	$H_T^\circ - H_{298}^\circ$ (cal/mole)	C_p° (cal/mole-deg)	S_T° (cal/mole-deg)	$-(F_T^\circ - H_{298}^\circ)/T$ (cal/mole-deg)
298.15	0.0	5.71	6.820	6.820
300	10.57	5.72	6.855	6.820
400	603.3	6.08	8.558	7.050
500	1222	6.27	9.937	7.494
600	1855	6.39	11.09	8.000
700	2498	6.49	12.08	8.514
800	3152	6.58	12.96	9.015
900	3815	6.68	13.74	9.497
1000	4488	6.79	14.45	9.957
1100	5173	6.91	15.10	10.40
1200	5870	7.04	15.70	10.81
1300	6581	7.19	16.27	11.21
1400	7308	7.35	16.81	11.59
1500	8051	7.52	17.33	11.96
1600	8812	7.71	17.82	12.31
1700	9593	7.91	18.29	12.65
1800	10400	8.13	18.75	12.97
1900	11220	8.37	19.19	13.29
2000	12070	8.62	19.63	13.59
2100	12940	8.88	20.06	13.89
2200	13850	9.16	20.48	14.18
2300	14780	9.46	20.89	14.46
2400	15740	9.77	21.30	14.74
2500	16730	10.10	21.70	15.01
2600	17760	10.44	22.11	15.28
2700	18820	10.80	22.51	15.54
2800	19920	11.17	22.91	15.79
2900	21060	11.56	23.31	16.05
2893	20970	11.54	23.28	16.03

[a] $H_T^\circ - H_{298.15}^\circ = -2.2215 \times 10^3 + 6.6650T - 2.9290 \times 10^{-4}T^2 + 2.6181 \times 10^{-7}T^3 + 7.5572 \times 10^4/T$ (cal/mole, 298°–2893°K, ±0.8%); atomic weight = 95.94.

properties necessary. A total of 167 heat content values were used to obtain the equation shown in Table 52, for which C_p and $H_T^\circ - H_{298.15}^\circ$ at 298.15° were forced to equal 5.71 cal/mole-deg and zero, respectively. As can be seen in Fig. 45, there is excellent internal consistency in the data, and the resulting C_p values agree well with the direct measurements of this property. In general, the data of Fieldhouse *et al.* (1956) are outside the expected deviation from the curve and were not included in the least-squares fit. The heat capacity measurements reported by R. E. Taylor and Finch (1961), Rasor and McClelland (1960), and those by Lehman (1960) (not shown) were all done at Atomics International, Canoga Park, California over a period of several years and there is only a slight difference between the reported values.

Osment (1963) has reported heat content values for $MoC_{0.46}$ above 591°. After cooling from 2480°, signs of melting were noted and the highest point was out of line compared to the other measurements. Since material of the reported composition should have melted near 2750°, one must assume either that the sample was actually of a lower composition or that it contained significant amounts of impurity. When attempts were made to fit this data by an equation, as was done with the other carbide systems, C_p at 298.15° had to be made unreasonably low or the values near this temperature would go through a minimum. Until this property is re-measured, thermal values for this compound are better obtained by estimation.

It is not surprising to find no energy change at the transition temperature. Because this phase change is very slow at compositions below $MoC_{0.5}$, the lower four points of the above data describe the behavior of the α form while the upper two points would give the heat content of quenched β-Mo_2C. If one wishes to find the heat of transition, it must be done using hyperstoichiometric material.

4. Equilibria Measurements

The free energy of formation of Mo_2C and MoC_{1-x} have been estimated by numerous authors from equilibria in multicomponent systems. Some of this work is in error because the results are based on incorrect compositions for the equilibrium phases. These have been recalculated in light of later findings.

A number of workers have studied the equilibria between various gases and Mo_2C + Mo. As can be seen in Fig. 46, there is a regular change in the resulting free energy of formation which invites an explanation. One might suggest, in view of the known presence of oxygen in the

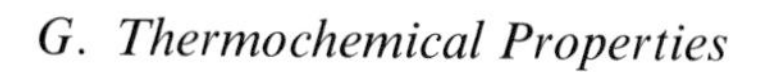

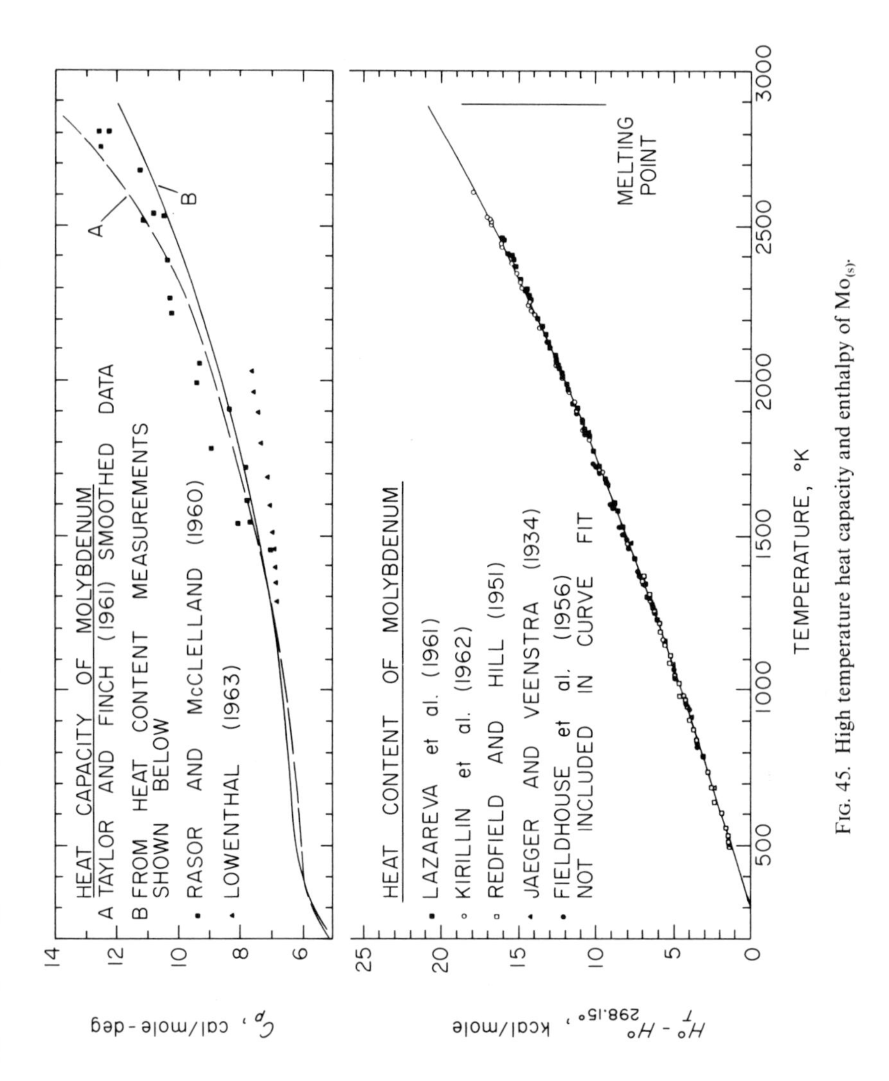

FIG. 45. High temperature heat capacity and enthalpy of $Mo_{(s)}$.

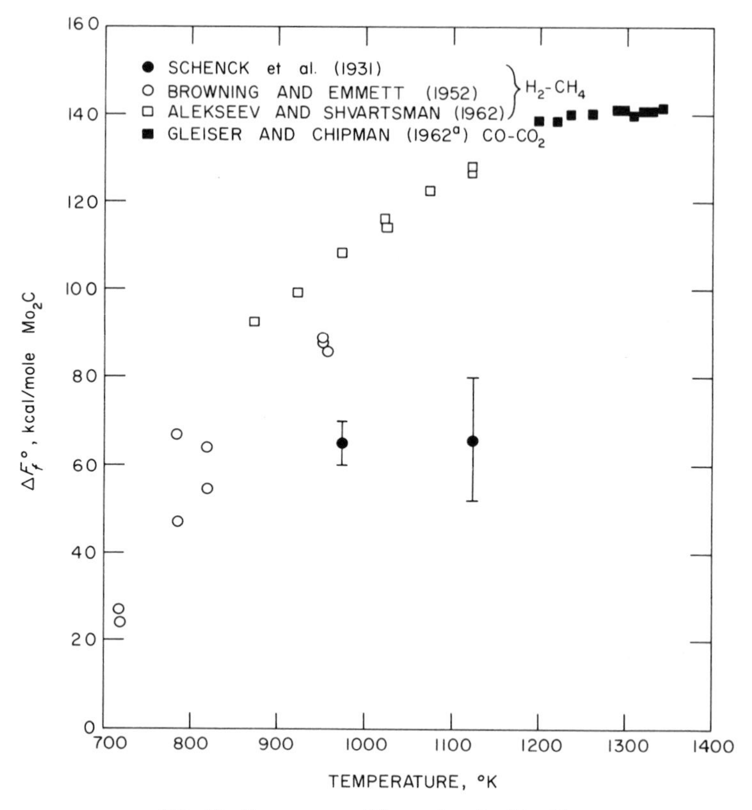

FIG. 46. Free energy of formation for Mo_2C.

materials studied and the proclivity to oxycarbide formation, that at low temperatures an oxycarbide formed which, indeed, was unstable below 600°. As the temperature was raised, it lost oxygen and converted to the carbide. Thus, the data of Gleiser and Chipman (1962a) at the higher temperature would more nearly typify the pure carbide even though CO and CO_2 were present.

Browning and Emmett (1952)* attempted to measure the equilibrium Mo_2C–CH_4–MoC–H_2 between 936° and 1098°. Since MoC is not stable in this temperature range, the reaction can not be truly at equilibrium. The resulting free energy is, however, consistent with the decomposition of MoC into Mo_2C and C, but is not much different from what one would

* Because of the arithmetical error in their paper, as noted by Kempter (1956), the following discussion is based on a recalculation of the data.

expect if graphite were controlling the reaction rather than MoC. Their study as well as a similar one by Schenck *et al.* (1931) are compared to the free energy of formation of CH_4 in Fig. 47. The presence of oxygen should also influence this measurement.

ΔF_f° for MoC_{1-x} has been estimated from equilibrium studies within solid systems. By studying the Nb–Mo–C system, Rudy *et al.* (1961) proposed a free energy for MoC_{1-x} between -6 and -9 kcal/mole at 2120°. Wallace *et al.* (1963) reexamined this value in light of a more reasonable composition for the equilibrium phases and suggested that the free energy of $MoC_{0.61}$ (β-MoC_{1-x}) lies between -1 and -4 kcal/mole. Using a similar analysis of the Zr–Mo–C system, Wallace *et al.*

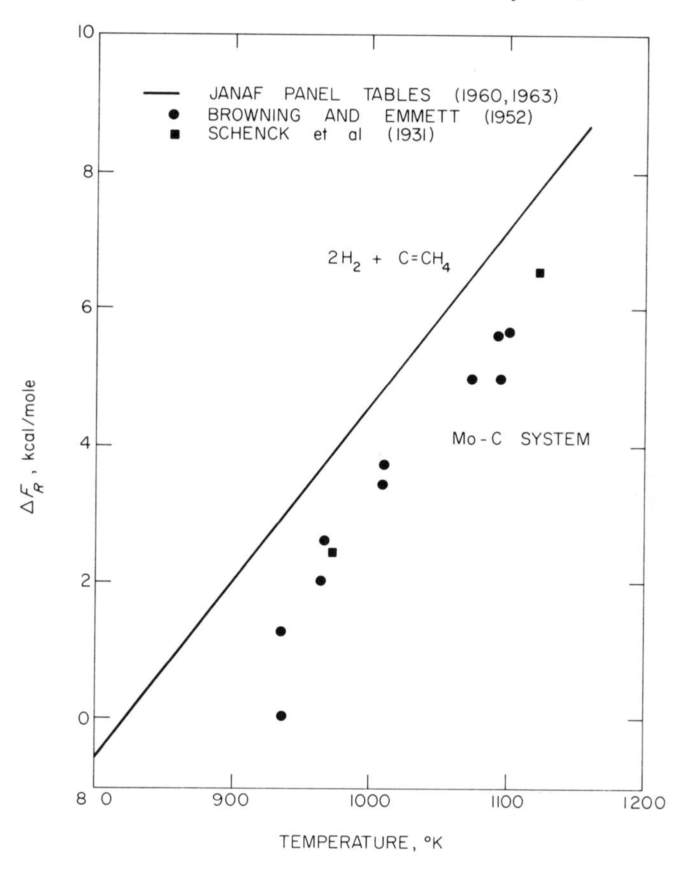

FIG. 47. Free energy of the reaction $MoC + H_2 = \frac{1}{2}Mo_2C + \frac{1}{2}CH_4$ compared to the reaction $\frac{1}{2}CH_4 = H_2 + \frac{1}{2}C$.

(1963) obtained -2.6 ± 1.5 kcal/mole for ΔF_f° over the temperature range 1720°–2370°.

5. Vaporization

Fries (1966b) has reexamined various measurements, including his own, of the vapor pressure of Mo metal. The equation $\log P(\text{atm}) = -3.320 \times 10^4/T + 7.118$ resulted. Based on the thermal functions in Table 52 and those given by Stull and Sinke (1956), a third law treatment gives 157.0 ± 0.5 kcal/mole as the heat of vaporization at 298.15°.

The carbide system vaporizes congruently at $MoC_{0.49}$ between 2525° and 2575° (Fries, 1966a).

Using a vacuum thermobalance, Fries (1966a) has measured the evaporation rate from plugs having the composition $MoC_{0.43}$, $MoC_{0.475}$, and $MoC_{0.490}$. Assuming unity evaporation coefficients for all species (Mo, C_1, C_2, and C_3), the pressure of Mo over $MoC_{0.490}$ was described

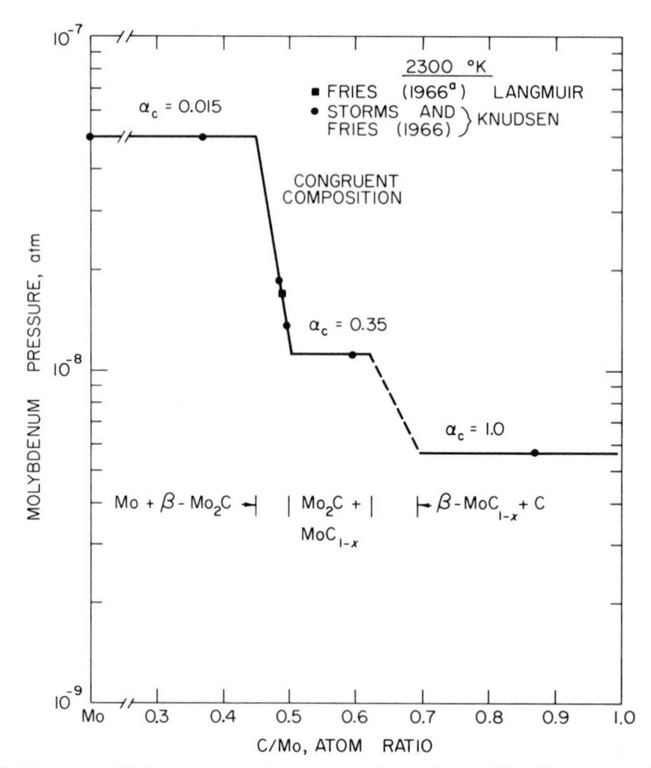

FIG. 48. Pressure of $Mo_{(g)}$ over various compositions in the Mo–C system at 2300°K.

by log $P(\text{atm}) = -3.486 \times 10^4/T + 7.395$ (2125°–2550°). When this was combined with estimated thermal values, good agreement with the calorimetric heat of formation was found. A mass spectrometric study has been undertaken by Storms and Fries (1966) to measure the Mo pressure at a number of compositions under Knudsen conditions. The machine calibration was adjusted to make the measured pressure over $Mo_{(s)}$ equal the values given by Fries (1966b). The results at 2300° are shown in Fig. 48. There is excellent agreement with the Langmuir measurements of Fries (1966a) at the congruent composition. Carbon activities for the two-phase regions were obtained from a Gibbs-Duhem integration of the Mo activity and are also noted in the figure. The partial heats of vaporization for Mo, from the two studies, are compared in Fig. 49. In

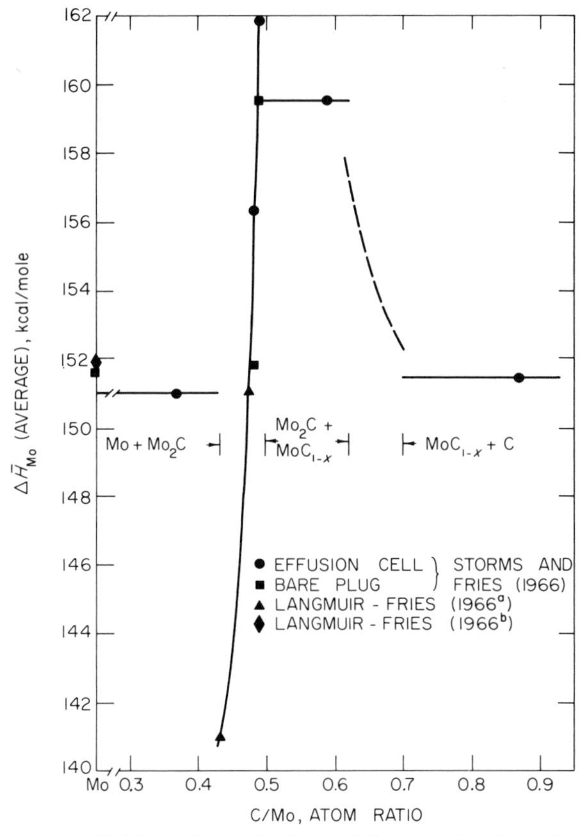

FIG. 49. Average partial heat of vaporization for $Mo_{(g)}$ as a function of composition.

the case of the noncongruent Langmuir work, it was necessary to assume that the surface and bulk compositions were the same and that the vapor composition did not change appreciably with temperature. Even so, the values are consistent with those from the Knudsen study, and reveal a rather striking change in the partial heat as the composition is changed. Apparently, strong Mo—C bonds are being formed in this phase as the carbon content is increased. On the other hand, formation of the cubic MoC_{1-x} causes a weakening of the bonding for Mo as carbon is added to the lattice. Thus, the hexagonal Mo_2C phase is like the cubic MC compounds of the lower periods, while the cubic MoC_{1-x} phase is much different.

IX

THE TUNGSTEN–TUNGSTEN CARBIDE SYSTEM

A. PREPARATION

Starting with Moissan (1893b, 1896, 1897a), the tungsten carbides have been prepared by melting together either W or WO_3, and carbon. Most later work has been based on preparations obtained by heating the powdered metal or tungsten compounds with carbon or CH_4, sometimes in the presence of H_2, but below the melting point.

WC can be prepared by heating tungstic acid (H_2WO_4) or ammonium paratungstate in a mixture of H_2 and CH_4 at 850° to 1000°. With tungstic acid, the reduction to W metal is complete before carbonization takes place (Newkirk and Aliferis, 1957).

The reaction between WO_3 and carbon proceeds in a similar fashion. Intermediate oxides are formed between W and unreacted WO_3, leading to the formation of the carbides only after the oxide has been eliminated (Hegedüs and Gadó, 1960).

Carbide formation from the powdered elements is possible at 1050° (Hüttig *et al.*, 1950). Below 650° this reaction leads mainly to W_2C, but above this temperature WC is formed (Kotö and Suzuki, 1948). The presence of H_2 or a hydrocarbon gas promotes this reaction.

Methods of producing carbide coats from the gas phase have been described by Campbell *et al.* (1949) and Lander and Germer (1948).

A comprehensive description of the various preparation techniques is given in the review by Schwarzkopf and Kieffer (1953). It should be borne in mind that these carbides, like the other systems, are susceptible to oxycarbide formation. For this reason, it is advisable not to use the oxide or oxygen-containing compounds for their preparation unless a final heating above 1500° in vacuum follows. With this precaution, pure carbides are easily obtained.

B. PHASE RELATIONSHIP

Two phases, W_2C and WC, are found in this system, each with a structure change at high temperatures. Apparently, only the α-WC phase is stable at room temperature. Two recent phase diagrams are compared in Fig. 50.

Until recently the knowledge of this system rested on the early work of Sykes (1930) as modified by Norton (see Schwarzkopf and Kieffer, 1953). Although this phase diagram is correct in many respects, several important modifications must be made in light of recent work. For this reason, the older studies will not be discussed in any detail.

While pure tungsten is the highest melting metal, the presence of impurities will, without exception, lower the melting temperature. Therefore, the higher reported values should be given the greater weight. A melting point of 3410° ± 20°C is indicated by the measurements listed in Table 53. According to Goldschmidt and Brand (1963), 0.3 at. % ($WC_{0.003}$) carbon is sufficient to lower this to the eutectic. Unfortunately,

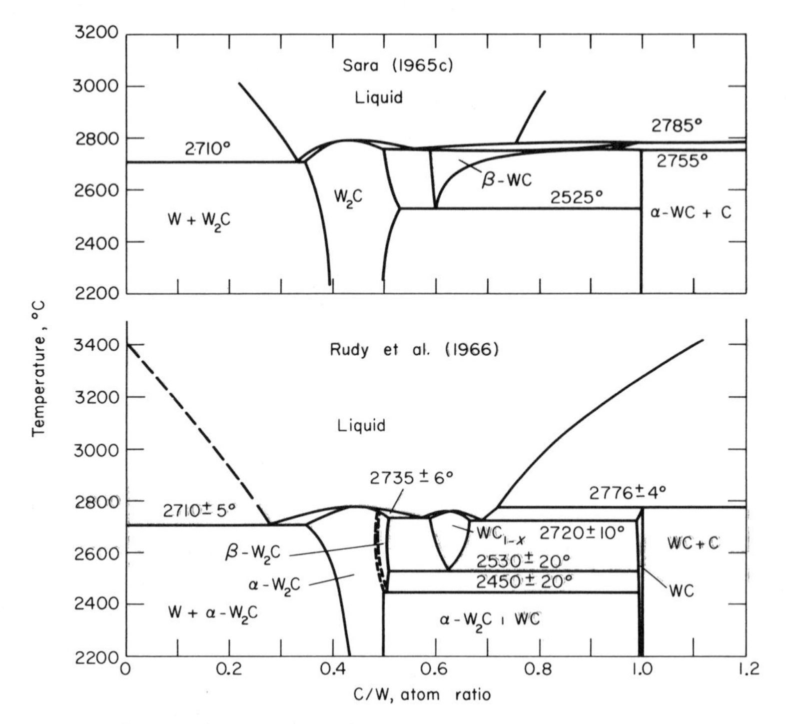

FIG. 50. A comparison of phase studies in the W–WC system.

TABLE 53
MELTING POINT MEASUREMENTS IN THE W–C SYSTEM

Temperature (°C)				
W	W + W_2C	W_2C	WC + C	Investigator
—	2741 (average of 8)	—	2650	Ruff and Wunsch (1914)
3387	—	—	—	Pirani and Alterthum (1923)
3370	—	—	—	Henning and Heuse (1923)
—	—	2880	2780	Andrews (1923)
3377	—	—	—	Worthing (1924)
—	—	—	2880	Friederich and Sittig (1925)
—	—	2730	—	Barnes (1929)
—	—	2860	2870	Agte and Alterthum (1930)
—	2475	2750	2600	Sykes (1930)
—	—	—	2820	Engelke *et al.* (1960)
—	2732 ± 22	—	2720 ± 20	Nadler and Kempter (1960)
3407	—	—	—	Zalabak (1961)
3389	2710	2800	2785	Sara (1965c)
3423	2710 ± 5[a]	2776 ± 5[a]	2776 ± 4[a]	Rudy (1965)

[a] Error is based on reproducibility.

they observed eutectic melting nearly 300° below the accepted value. On the other hand, Allen *et al.* (1961–1962) find $WC_{0.0015-0.0030}$ (100–200 ppm) as the limit at 2000°. Neither of these observations is inconsistent with the work of Rudy *et al.* (1966) and Sara (1965c).

A comparison between the various reported W–W_2C eutectic temperatures is made in Table 53. The two most recent measurements are in perfect agreement with a value of 2710° ± 15°C. The following eutectic compositions have been reported: $WC_{0.22}$ (Ruff and Wunsch, 1914); $WC_{0.23}$ (Sykes, 1930); $WC_{0.33}$ (Sara, 1965c); $WC_{0.28}$ (Rudy *et al.*, 1966).

The W_2C phase begins near $WC_{0.35}$ (Rudy *et al.*, 1966; Sara, 1965c) at the eutectic temperature, but compositions below $WC_{0.41}$ cannot be retained even by a rapid quench (Rudy *et al.*, 1966). According to Rudy *et al.* (1966), a phase change occurs at 2450° in the high-carbon region of W_2C. In view of recent neutron diffraction studies of the Mo–C system, there is the possibility of a phase change extending across the W_2C region, but with a very sluggish transition rate at the lower compositions. Until this phenomenon is better understood, workers using W_2C which has been quenched from above 2400° must be careful when attributing their results to the α form. Although the structure of the β form has not been determined, there is little doubt it results from the randomization of the carbon atoms with the formation of an *L′*3 lattice. Rudy *et al.* (1966), in agreement with Orton (1961) and Gleiser and Chipman (1962b), observed α-W_2C to decompose into W and WC below ~1250°. β-W_2C melts congruently but, according to Rudy *et al.* (1966), the maximum is slightly below the stoichiometric composition.

Recent workers have consistently reported WC as a line compound at the stoichiometric composition. Sara (1965c) suggests an α–β phase change at 2755° before peritectic melting occurs at 2785°. On the other hand, Rudy *et al.* (1966) show peritectic melting of the α form at 2776° in contact with graphite while the β form melts congruently at 2747°. Although this conflict is unresolved, these studies are in agreement with a fcc form of WC above 2525° in the region near $WC_{0.6}$. Like the other cubic carbides, β-WC has a defect structure, but the phase cannot be retained by normal cooling.

Early high temperature x-ray patterns reported by Skaupy (1927) and Becker (1928) revealed an unidentified phase at 2600°C which they attributed to β-W_2C. When allowance is made for thermal expansion and different compositions, the reported powder pattern is very similar to that given by quenched β-WC + W_2C. Following the lead of this work, Goldschmidt and Brand (1963), after sparking electrodes of W against C, argued that the resulting cubic phase was β-W_2C. A similar designation was applied by Lautz and Schneider (1961) to the cubic phase that they produced by sparking WC electrodes together under oil. Clearly, in each case the phase was β-WC, not β-W_2C.

C. LATTICE PARAMETER AND STRUCTURE

Tungsten metal is bcc (*A*2) with no confirmed transitions below the melting point. The various observations of a β form were actually due to the presence of oxygen impurity (Charlton and Davis, 1955; Hägg and Schönberg, 1954).

Powder patterns of α-W_2C can be indexed as *L′*3 although the carbon atoms are apparently ordered. Butorian and Pinsker (1960) proposed a CdI_2 antitype (D_{3d}^3) structure based on an electron diffraction study of W_2C which was prepared by reacting W films with CO. Results from a neutron diffraction study by A. L. Bowman *et al.* (1966) do not agree with this structure, but a better understanding is not yet available. Various reported lattice parameters based on the *L'*3 form are compared in Fig. 51 and Table 54.

TABLE 54

STRUCTURES AND LATTICE PARAMETERS OF THE TUNGSTEN CARBIDES

Phase	Composition	Structure type	Lattice parameters (Å) *a*	*c*	Investigator
W	Pure	bcc (*A*2)	3.16522 ± 0.00009	—	Parrish (1960)
W_2C	$WC_{0.52}$	hcp	2.992	4.722	Westgren and Phragmén (1926)
W_2C	W_2C + WC	hcp	3.025	4.726	Coffman *et al.* (1963)
W_2C	W_2C + WC	hcp	2.99	4.72	Nowotny *et al.* (1954a)
	W_2C + W	hcp	2.99	4.69	Nowotny *et al.* (1954a)
α-WC	$WC_{1.0}$	hcp	2.9063	2.8386	Metcalfe (1946)
α-WC	$WC_{0.986}$	hcp	2.90	2.83	Parthé (1961)
α-WC	$WC_{0.973}$	hcp	2.906	2.825	Coffman *et al.* (1963)
β-WC	$WC_{0.82}$	fcc (*B*1)	4.215	—	Sara (1965c)
β-WC	$WC_{0.61}$	fcc (*B*1)	4.220	—	Rudy *et al.* (1966)

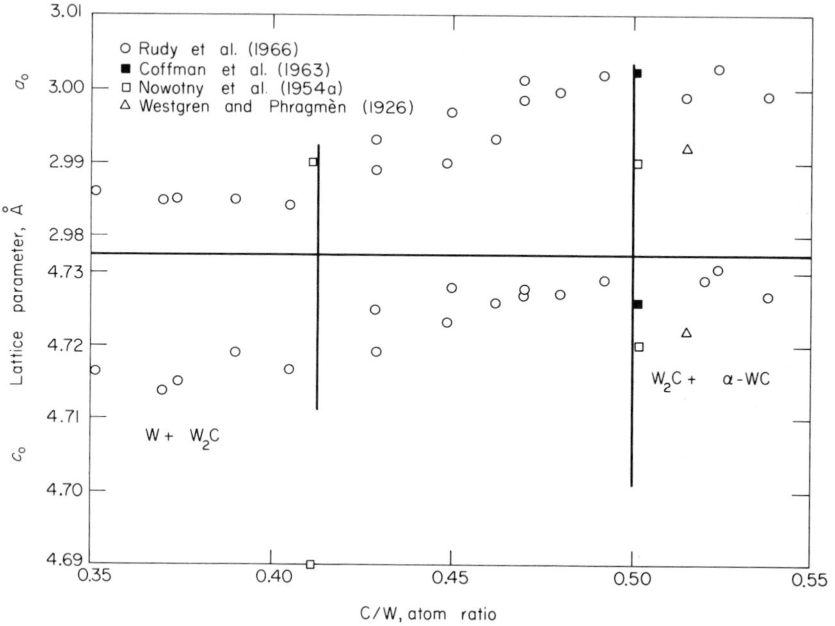

FIG. 51. Lattice parameter of α-W_2C as a function of composition.

TABLE 55
COPPER RADIATION, POWDER PATTERN FOR W[a]

2θ	$\sin^2 \theta$	d spacing	Intensity	$h\ k\ l$
40.26	0.1184	2.2381	65	1 1 0
58.25	0.2369	1.5826	15	2 0 0
73.18	0.3553	1.2922	45	2 1 1
86.99	0.4738	1.1191	20	2 2 0
100.63	0.5922	1.0009	35	3 1 0
114.91	0.7106	0.9137	15	2 2 2
131.16	0.8291	0.8459	100	3 2 1
153.51	0.9475	0.7913	25	4 0 0

[a] $a_0 = 3.16522$ Å; $\mu r = 8.0$; structure type $A2$, space group No. 229; $\lambda(\mathrm{K}\alpha_1) = 1.54051$ Å.

TABLE 56
COPPER RADIATION, POWDER PATTERN FOR β-W_2C[a]

2θ	$\sin^2 \theta$	d spacing	Intensity	$h\ k\ l$
34.61	0.0885	2.5894	15	1 0 0
38.10	0.1065	2.3600	20	0 0 2
39.67	0.1151	2.2702	100	1 0 1
52.41	0.1950	1.7442	25	1 0 2
62.03	0.2655	1.4950	35	1 1 0
69.90	0.3282	1.3446	40	1 0 3
73.02	0.3539	1.2947	5	2 0 0
75.17	0.3720	1.2629	40	1 1 2
76.18	0.3806	1.2486	35	2 0 1
81.50	0.4261	1.1800	5	0 0 4
85.47	0.4605	1.1351	10	2 0 2
91.67	0.5146	1.0738	5	1 0 4
100.79	0.5936	0.9997	25	2 0 3
103.82	0.6194	0.9787	5	2 1 0
106.98	0.6460	0.9583	50	2 1 1
112.53	0.6916	0.9262	40	1 1 4
116.86	0.7259	0.9040	20	2 1 2
120.56	0.7543	0.8869	30	1 0 5
124.06	0.7800	0.8721	10	2 0 4
126.35	0.7964	0.8631	25	3 0 0
135.90	0.8591	0.8310	80	2 1 3
143.69	0.9029	0.8106	60	3 0 2
156.55	0.9587	0.7867	15	0 0 6

[a] $a_0 = 2.990$ Å; $c_0 = 4.720$ Å; $\mu r = 7.0$; structure type $L'3$, space group No. 194; $\lambda(\mathrm{K}\alpha_1) = 1.54051$ Å.

TABLE 57

COPPER RADIATION, POWDER PATTERN FOR $WC_{0.61}$(β-WC_{1-x})[a]

2θ	$\sin^2\theta$	d spacing	Intensity	$h\ k\ l$
36.86	0.0999	2.4364	55	1 1 1
42.82	0.1333	2.1100	40	2 0 0
62.16	0.2665	1.4920	40	2 2 0
74.51	0.3665	1.2724	50	3 1 1
78.44	0.3998	1.2182	20	2 2 2
93.79	0.5330	1.0550	10	4 0 0
105.43	0.6330	0.9681	40	3 3 1
109.43	0.6663	0.9436	45	4 2 0
126.81	0.7996	0.8614	60	4 2 2
143.04	0.8995	0.8121	100	5 1 1, 3 3 3

[a] $a_0 = 4.2200$ Å; $\mu r = 7.0$; structure type $B1$, space group No. 225; $\lambda(K\alpha_1) = 1.54051$ Å.

TABLE 58

COPPER RADIATION, POWDER PATTERN FOR α-$WC_{1.0}$[a]

2θ	$\sin^2\theta$	d spacing	Intensity	$h\ k\ l$
31.51	0.0737	2.8370	15	0 0 1
35.64	0.0937	2.5166	45	1 0 0
48.30	0.1674	1.8827	60	1 0 1
64.03	0.2810	1.4530	20	1 1 0
65.78	0.2949	1.4185	5	0 0 2
73.11	0.3547	1.2932	25	1 1 1
75.49	0.3747	1.2583	10	2 0 0
77.12	0.3885	1.2357	20	1 0 2
84.08	0.4484	1.1503	20	2 0 1
98.73	0.5759	1.0150	20	1 1 2
108.15	0.6557	0.9512	20	2 1 0
109.08	0.6634	0.9457	5	0 0 3
109.82	0.6696	0.9413	20	2 0 2
117.32	0.7295	0.9019	40	2 1 1
120.94	0.7571	0.8852	20	1 0 3
133.33	0.8431	0.8389	15	3 0 0
146.47	0.9168	0.8044	35	3 0 1
152.74	0.9445	0.7926	45	1 1 3
154.31	0.9506	0.7900	100	2 1 2

[a] $a_0 = 2.906$ Å; $c_0 = 2.837$ Å; $\mu r = 6.0$; space group D^1_{3h}, No. 187; $\lambda(K\alpha_1) = 1.54051$ Å.

Until recently the exact crystal structure of α-WC was in doubt. The original proposal of Westgren and Phragmén (1926) was questioned by Hägg (1931) who suggested a NiAs-type structure which also fits the x-ray data. This was finally resolved by the neutron diffraction work of Leciejewicz (1960) and Parthé (1961). They both assigned the space group D^1_{3h}-$P\bar{6}m2$, corresponding to the structure given by Westgren and Phragmén (1926). The electron diffraction studies of Butorina (1960) gave the same result. Since the lattice parameter may change with composition, values are listed in Table 54 only for well-characterized samples.

The cubic form of WC has a parameter which is remarkably close to the value obtained when the lattice parameter of the TiC–WC solid solution is extrapolated to pure WC (Metcalf, 1946). Sara (1965c) quenched a parameter of $a = 4.215$ Å, while Rudy *et al.* (1966) obtained a constant value of $a = 4.220$ Å, regardless of the composition or the quenching temperature. On the other hand, Willens and Buehler (1965) gave $a = 4.266$ Å when the α and β forms were found together, $a = 4.252$ Å for pure β-WC and $a = 4.240$ Å for a mixture of β-WC and W_2C. The superconductivity transition temperature showed the same trend. When the phase was prepared by sparking electrodes of α-WC under oil, a parameter of 4.250 Å was observed (Lautz and Schneider, 1961).

A calculated powder pattern for each phase in this system is shown in Tables 55 through 58.

D. CHEMICAL REACTIVITY

WC is stable in air to 700°, it is decarbonized when heated in hydrogen, and it is not attacked by N_2 even at high temperatures. W_2C is attacked by Cl_2 at 300°–400°, but WC is unaffected.

Dilute 1:4 HNO_3 + HF will dissolve W_2C at room temperature, and WC after the solution has been heated (Kachik *et al.*, 1946).

E. HARDNESS

Most hardness measurements for these carbides were made in the middle 1940's when the technique was less accurate. Consequently, there is rather poor consistency between the values. More recently, Jones (1956) reported 2250 DPH for WC when W_2C was present, while Kieffer and Kölbl (1949) measured 3000 kg/mm² (50-g load) for W_2C when WC was present. On the other hand, Dolloff and Sara (1961) give 1450 and 2085 kg/mm² as being representative of W_2C and WC, respectively.

F. THERMOCHEMICAL PROPERTIES

1. Heat of Formation

Mah (1963b) obtained $\Delta H°(298.15°) = -6.3 \pm 0.6$ kcal/mole for α-W_2C by burning a sample which contained both W and WC. Suitable corrections were applied.

Two combustion studies of α-WC have given -285.94 kcal/mole (Mah, 1963b) and -285.80 kcal/mole (McGraw *et al.*, 1947) as the heat of combustion, with almost perfect agreement. This gives -9.67 ± 0.4 kcal/mole as the heat of formation of α-WC.

2. Low Temperature Heat Capacity

No data have been reported.

3. High Temperature Heat Content

Using pure α-$WC_{0.99}$, Levinson (1964a) measured the heat content between 1275° and 2640°. These data are combined with an estimated $C_p(298.15°)$ of 9.5 cal/mole-deg and fitted by the equation shown in Table 59.

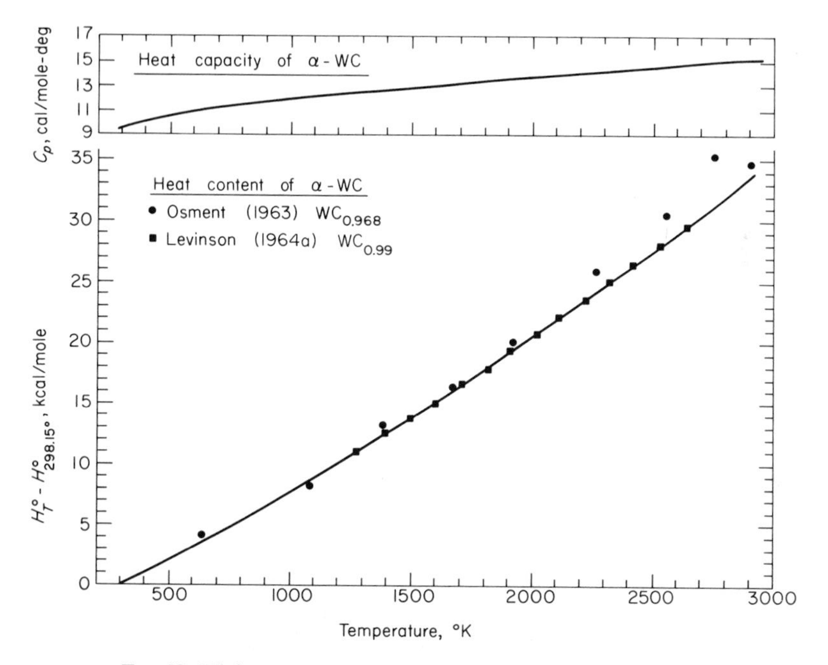

Fig. 52. High temperature heat capacity and enthalpy of α-WC.

TABLE 59
THERMAL FUNCTIONS OF $WC_{0.99}$[a]

T (°K)	$H_T^\circ - H_{298}^\circ$ (cal/mole)	C_p° (cal/mole-deg)	$S_T^\circ - S_{298}^\circ$ (cal/mole-deg)
298.15	0.0	9.50[b]	0.0
300	17.59	9.52	0.0582
400	1005	10.18	2.896
500	2045	10.59	5.21
600	3120	10.90	7.17
700	4224	11.17	8.87
800	5353	11.41	10.38
900	6505	11.63	11.74
1000	7679	11.84	12.98
1100	8874	12.05	14.11
1200	10090	12.24	15.17
1300	11320	12.44	16.16
1400	12580	12.62	17.09
1500	13850	12.81	17.96
1600	15140	12.99	18.80
1700	16440	13.16	19.59
1800	17770	13.33	20.35
1900	19110	13.50	21.07
2000	20470	13.67	21.77
2100	21840	13.83	22.44
2200	23240	13.99	23.09
2300	24640	14.15	23.71
2400	26070	14.31	24.32
2500	27500	14.46	24.90
2600	28960	14.61	25.47
2700	30420	14.75	26.03
2800	31910	14.90	26.57
2900	33400	15.04	27.09
3000	34910	15.18	27.60

[a] $H_T^\circ - H_{298.15}^\circ = -3.3652 \times 10^3 + 9.9213T + 1.0733 \times 10^{-3}T^2 - 4.3507 \times 10^{-8}T^3 + 9.3310 \times 10^4/T$ (cal/mole, 298°–3000°K, ±0.4%); M.W. = 195.
[b] Estimate.

A comparison with the measurements, and the resulting C_p values are shown in Fig. 52. The rather scattered results of Osment (1963) are also shown in the figure but were not used in the data treatment. In the absence of low temperature measurements or a reliable method for estimating $S°(298.15°)$, the free energy function has not been evaluated.

4. Gaseous Equilibria

There have been a number of attempts to measure the thermochemical properties of this system using H_2–CH_4 and CO–CO_2 equilibria. These are compared in Fig. 53 on the basis of the free energy of formation of α-WC. The results of Gleiser and Chipman (1962b) (from the reaction $WC + CO_2 = W + 2CO$) and the known heat of formation can be made to agree only if $S°(298.15°)$ for WC is near 7.6 eu. This would appear to be much too low. The situation is even worse when the data of Orton (1961), using the equilibrium $WC + 2H_2 = W + CH_4$, are considered. Alekseev and Shvartsman (1963) assumed they were studying two different systems; one containing 1% carbon described as $W_2C + 2H_2 = 2W + CH_4$, and the other with 5% carbon as $2WC + 2H_2 = W_2C + CH_4$. Not only is W_2C not stable in the temperature range examined, but the two studies gave almost identical equilibrium constants. Apparently they were measuring the same system in both cases, i.e., $WC + 2H_2 = W + CH_4$, in spite of x-ray evidence to the contrary. The results were recalculated and are shown in Fig. 53 on this basis.

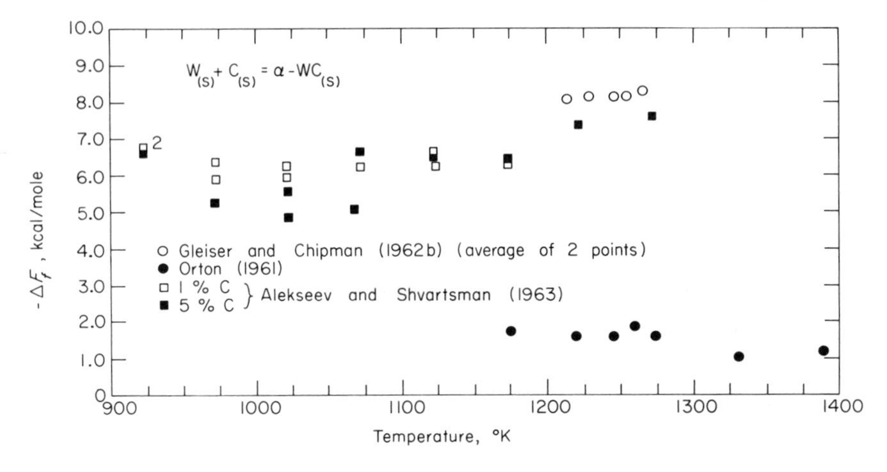

Fig. 53. Free energy of formation of α-WC.

5. Vaporization

The W–C system loses carbon preferentially at all compositions and measured temperatures. For this reason it is not possible to obtain equilibrium pressures of either W or C using the Langmuir technique and very difficult using the Knudsen method. Carbon evaporation is rapid above 2400° (Andrews and Dushman, 1921; Andrews, 1923) and WC heated above 2000° will rapidly form a surface layer of W_2C (Coffman *et al.*, 1963). The evaporation rate of carbon from this composite is consistent with the C_1 pressure over graphite (Coffman *et al.*, 1963; Hoch *et al.*, 1955). This has led to the conclusion that the evaporation coefficient of C_1 is near unity from the carbide. Very little metal evaporates up to 2700°.

X

THE THORIUM–THORIUM DICARBIDE SYSTEM

A. PREPARATION

Recent workers have used material prepared by either arc melting the unpowdered elements together or by heating the powdered elements at a temperature below the melting point. Because of the ease with which Th metal, especially the powder, reacts with oxygen and nitrogen, the arc-melting technique should be used if the highest purity is desired. It is essential to handle the resulting carbide in an inert atmosphere.

ThO_2 will react with C at 1800°–1900° to give ThC or ThC_2 of uncertain purity (Samsonov *et al.*, 1960). According to Scaife and Wylie (1958), 99% of the ThO_2 can be converted to the carbide after 30 minutes at 2130°. This reaction also has been studied by Prescott and Hincke (1927).

B. PHASE RELATIONSHIP

Two compounds comprise this system: a cubic ThC phase, and ThC_2 which is monoclinic at low temperatures but which first converts to a tetragonal then to a cubic form as the temperature is raised.

The early work of Wilhelm and Chiotti (1950), as interpreted by Hansen and Anderko (1958), suggests peritectic melting between Th and ThC, but later work by Chiotti, quoted in the same review, indicated that the melting point of Th is lowered by carbon. Takeuchi *et al.* (1966) support both views with eutectic melting of β-Th and peritectic melting of α-Th between 1800° and 1950°. Their work shows that α-Th and ThC do not form a continuous fcc solid solution. The single-phase conversion of ThC to ThC_2 is due, as was found in the U–C system, to the replacement of carbon atoms by C_2 groups.

There is a basic agreement with 1725° (Chiotti, 1954; Thompson, 1933; McMasters and Larsen, 1961; Korbitz, 1964) as the melting point of

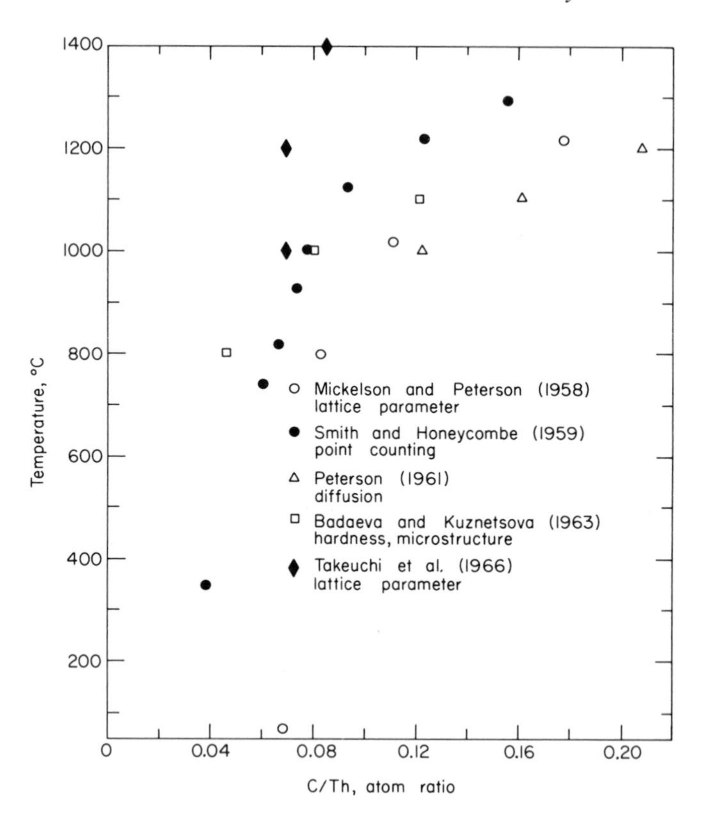

FIG. 54. Solubility of carbon in α-Th.

pure Th. The solubility of carbon in the element has been measured on a number of occasions, but with rather poor agreement. Most of the studies shown in Fig. 54 were based on material containing ThO_2 and, in some cases, a significant amount of nitrogen. Since each should affect the solubility of carbon, little confidence should be placed in any of these measurements. A number of values for the fcc to bcc transition in Th metal have been reported (Chiotti, 1954, 1955; Deem and Winn, 1955; Bannister and Thomson, 1963; McMasters and Larsen, 1961; Korbitz, 1964; Bentle, 1958; Takeuchi *et al.*, 1966), but, in each case, relatively impure metal was used. Reid *et al.* (1963) found the transition at $1325° \pm 10°$ when the total impurity level was reduced to ~ 50 ppm. This is raised by the addition of carbon (Chiotti, 1954, 1955; Korbitz, 1964; Takeuchi *et al.*, 1966).

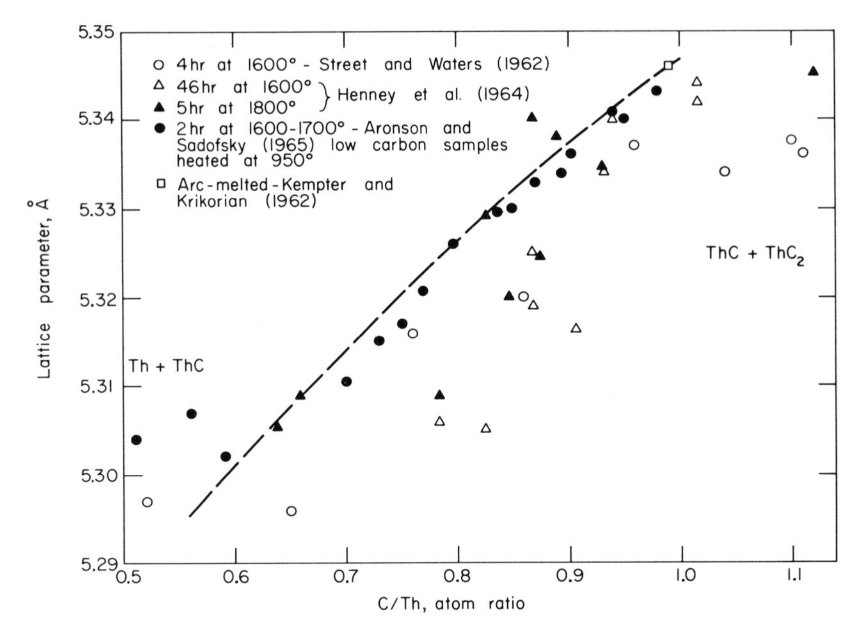

FIG. 55. Lattice parameter of ThC as a function of composition.

Like the other cubic carbides, ThC has a composition range which widens as the temperature is increased. Rudy *et al.* (1962a) found the phase between $ThC_{0.61}$ and $ThC_{1.0}$ at 1500°. This is consistent with the composite lattice parameter curve shown in Fig. 55. Takeuchi *et al.* (1966) found the phase between $ThC_{0.60}$ and $ThC_{0.96}$ below 1350°. At the peritectic temperature, the ThC composition can be between $ThC_{0.47}$ and $ThC_{0.61}$. Based on a boundary measurement of $ThC_{0.69}$ at 1950°, they propose a solidus which changes composition rapidly as the temperature is raised above the peritectic. Such a shape requires that the activity of Th and C in ThC change slowly with composition in this region. This is very unlikely in view of the behavior of the other carbides. Consequently, the boundary in Fig. 56 was drawn to be essentially consistent with the data of Takeuchi *et al.* (1966), but to have a steep rise above the peritectic. Henney *et al.* (1964) noted a change in the lattice parameter which they interpreted as indicating a wider composition range in the presence of oxygen. Since the solubility of oxygen as well as its effect on the lattice parameter will certainly change with the carbon content, their conclusion must be confirmed before it is accepted. At high temperature, ThC forms a complete solid solution with γ-ThC_2, but,

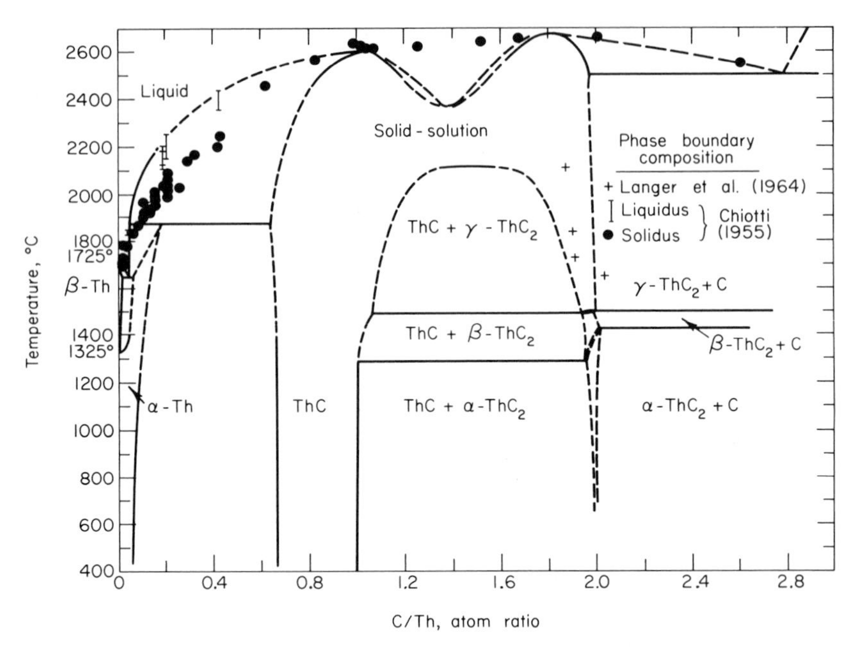

FIG. 56. Phase diagram of the Th–ThC_2 system.

similar to the UC–UC_2 relationship, it breaks into a bell-shaped miscibility gap between ~1500° (Brett *et al.*, 1960; Benesovsky and Rudy, 1961) and 2100° (Henney and Jones, 1965b). Melting of $ThC_{1.0}$ has been observed near 2625° (Wilhelm and Chiotti, 1950) and 2500° (Henney and Jones, 1965b).

The phase relationship in the region of ThC_2 is complicated somewhat by the two phase transitions, monoclinic (α) to tetragonal (β), and tetragonal (β) to cubic (γ). When carbon was present as the second phase, Gantzel *et al.* (1965), using a high temperature x-ray camera and thermal analysis, observed the transitions at 1427° ± 21° and 1481° ± 28°, respectively. With the same techniques, N. A. Hill and Cavin (1964a) found only one transition (α–γ) at 1415° ± 10°, but in a later report (1964b) a weak transition at 1500° was indicated. Henney and Jones (1965b) give 1410° ± 20° and 1500° ± 20° as the respective temperatures in the presence of graphite and found that the α–β transition was lowered to 1290° ± 20° when ThC was present instead. This is in good agreement with 1430° ± 10° and 1500° ± 25° reported by Cook (1965), as well as with 1430° and 1490° in the presence of graphite and 1295° and 1495° in the low-carbon region observed by N. H. Krikorian and Wallace (1966).

These observations also explain the thermal expansion increase upon heating at ~1290° and the contraction upon cooling at ~1240° reported by Marchal and Accary (1963) using electron-beam-melted ThC_2 which probably was carbon-deficient. Also, this is consistent with and helps explain the resistivity measurements of Korbitz (1964). The change in the α–β transition with composition appears to be rather abrupt at $ThC_{2.0}$ and independent of composition from $ThC_{1.97}$ down to $ThC_{1.04}$ (Henney and Jones, 1965b). Although the limits have not been determined, the composition range of α-ThC_2 is probably quite narrow. Melting of ThC_2 has been observed at 2655° ± 25° (Wilhelm and Chiotti, 1950) and 2550° (Henney and Jones, 1965b), while the ThC_2–C eutectic temperature is reported as 2500° ± 35° (Wilhelm and Chiotti, 1950); 2495° ± 40° (Langer *et al.*, 1964); 2400° (Henney and Jones, 1965b); and 2490° (N. H. Krikorian and Wallace, 1964b), with a eutectic composition between $ThC_{2.27}$ and $ThC_{2.34}$ (Langer *et al.*, 1964). The ThC_2–C phase boundary, unlike the UC_2–C behavior, apparently moves to lower carbon contents as the temperature is raised (Langer *et al.*, 1964), although the reported magnitude (see Fig. 56) is inconsistent with the various melting point studies as well as with compositions found when the compound was arc melted with excess carbon. The considerable difficulties attending a free carbon analysis in this system could account for the difference.

It is surprising, in view of the similarity to the U–C and Pu–C systems, that a Th_2C_3 phase has not been seen. N. H. Krikorian (1963) attempted to form it by heating the indicated compositions in vacuum at the following temperatures and times: $ThC_{1.91}$, 1200° for 69 hours; 1000° for 168 hours; 750° for 168 hours; and $ThC_{0.99}$, 700° for 477 hours. This treatment resulted only in a sharpening of the diffraction pattern of the initial carbide. High temperature neutron diffraction studies also failed to reveal this phase at an overall composition of $ThC_{1.5}$ (A. L. Bowman, 1966).

A phase diagram, constructed from the above information, is shown as Fig. 56. Dashed lines have been used where only meager experimental data are available. Even the measured values may be changed significantly when purer materials are studied. Much more effort is needed before even the basic phase diagram can be relied upon.

C. LATTICE PARAMETER AND STRUCTURE

Because the lattice parameter of α-Th increases with dissolved carbon, nitrogen, and oxygen, the value given in Table 60 is the lowest reported. A calculated powder pattern is listed in Table 61, on this basis. β-Th cannot be retained upon quenching.

TABLE 60

STRUCTURE AND LATTICE PARAMETER OF Th, ThC, AND ThC_2

Phases in equilibrium	Composition of first phase	Structure	Cooled from (°C)	Lattice parameter (Å)	Investigator
α-Th	Pure	fcc, *A1*	at 25	$a = 5.0842 \pm 0.0002$	Evans and Raynor (1959)
β-Th	Pure	bcc, *A2*	at 1450	$a = 4.11$	Chiotti (1954)
α-Th + ThC	$ThC_{0.06}$	fcc, *A1*	1500	$a = 5.12$	Benesovsky and Rudy (1961)
ThC + Th	$ThC_{0.62}$	fcc, *B1*	1600	$a = 5.303 \pm 0.002$	See Fig. 55
ThC + ThC_2	$ThC_{0.99}$	fcc, *B1*	Melt	$a = 5.346 \pm 0.002$	Kempter and Krikorian (1962)
α-ThC_2	$ThC_{2.0}$	Monoclinic *C2/c*	2450	$a = 6.53$	Hunt and Rundle (1951)
				$a = 4.24$	
				$c = 6.56$	
				$\beta = 104°$	
α-ThC_2	$ThC_{2.0}$	Pseudo-orthorhombic	Melt	$a = 10.555$	Kempter and Krikorian (1962)
				$b = 8.233$	
				$c = 4.201$	
γ-ThC_2	—	Cubic	at 1500	$a = 5.808 \pm 0.003$	N. A. Hill and Cavin (1964a)

TABLE 61
COPPER RADIATION, POWDER PATTERN FOR α-Th[a]

2θ	$\sin^2\theta$	d spacing	Intensity	$h\ k\ l$
30.43	0.0689	2.9354	25	1 1 1
35.28	0.0918	2.5421	15	2 0 0
50.75	0.1836	1.7975	20	2 2 0
60.33	0.2525	1.5329	30	3 1 1
63.31	0.2754	1.4677	10	2 2 2
74.60	0.3672	1.2711	5	4 0 0
82.66	0.4361	1.1664	15	3 3 1
85.30	0.4590	1.1369	15	4 2 0
95.84	0.5509	1.0378	15	4 2 2
103.85	0.6197	0.9785	20	5 1 1, 3 3 3
117.97	0.7345	0.8988	10	4 4 0
127.35	0.8033	0.8594	45	5 3 1
130.73	0.8263	0.8474	30	4 4 2, 6 0 0
146.74	0.9181	0.8039	35	6 2 0
166.88	0.9869	0.7753	100	5 3 3

[a] $a_0 = 5.0842$ Å; $\mu r = 9.0$; structure type $A1$, space group No. 225; $\lambda(\text{K}\alpha_1) =$ 1.54051 Å

ThC is cubic (NaCl type) with a very wide composition range. As carbon is removed from the lattice, the lattice parameter decreases in an essentially linear manner. Various studies of this property are compared in Fig. 55. Because the presence of oxygen or nitrogen lowers the parameter (Henney *et al.*, 1964), the curve representing the behavior of the pure phase was drawn favoring the highest values. Attempts to measure this property have been frustrated by the extreme reactivity of ThC. Even if a pure carbide should be obtained, subsequent handling invariably results in surface oxidation. Thus, the chemical form of the oxygen impurity is never certain. Surface oxide will naturally not affect the lattice parameter, but it does influence the analyzed C/Th ratio, while dissolved oxygen affects both. Probable values for the parameters at the phase boundary after cooling are listed in Table 60 based on the curve in Fig. 55. There is, of course, no assurance that the indicated compositions represent the phase boundary at temperature. A calculated powder pattern for $ThC_{0.99}$ is listed in Table 62.

ThC_2 has a monoclinic structure at room temperature, converting to a tetragonal, and finally to a cubic lattice before melting. The latter two structures cannot be quenched in. Until the single crystal and neutron

TABLE 62

COPPER RADIATION, POWDER PATTERN FOR $ThC_{0.99}$[a]

2θ	$\sin^2 \theta$	*d* spacing	Intensity	*h k l*
28.90	0.0623	3.0865	65	1 1 1
33.50	0.0830	2.6730	50	2 0 0
48.10	0.1661	1.8901	60	2 2 0
57.09	0.2284	1.6119	75	3 1 1
59.88	0.2491	1.5433	25	2 2 2
70.38	0.3321	1.3365	15	4 0 0
77.81	0.3944	1.2265	45	3 3 1
80.23	0.4152	1.1954	50	4 2 0
89.80	0.4982	1.0912	45	4 2 2
96.95	0.5605	1.0288	50	3 3 3, 5 1 1
109.18	0·6643	0·9450	25	4 4 0
116.95	0.7266	0.9036	90	5 3 1
119.65	0.7473	0.8910	65	6 0 0, 4 4 2
131.36	0.8304	0.8453	65	6 2 0
141.75	0.8926	0.8153	80	5 3 3
145.77	0.9134	0.8059	100	6 2 2

[a] $a_0 = 5.3460$ Å; $\mu r = 8.0$; structure type *B*1, space group No. 225; $\lambda(K\alpha_1) =$ 1.54051 Å.

diffraction work of Hunt and Rundle (1951), the low temperature structure was thought to be tetragonal (von Stackelberg, 1930). However, their work showed a C-centered monoclinic, C_2/c or Cc, lattice. Kempter and Krikorian (1962) found that the lattice could also be described as pseudo-orthorhombic in agreement with the indexing and parameters reported earlier by Baenziger (1950). A powder pattern indexed on the monoclinic cell was also given in their paper. An additional refinement by Gantzel and Baldwin (1964) revealed that the angle in the pseudo-orthorhombic cell, β, is not quite 90° and slightly different parameters were calculated. A calculated powder pattern is listed in Table 63, based on the structure of Hunt and Rundle (1951) and the monoclinic parameters given by Gantzel and Baldwin (1964).

At higher temperatures ThC_2 has a cubic structure which is no doubt identical to β-UC_2 (see Chapter XI, Section D).

D. APPEARANCE

Compositions below ThC_2 are metallic gray, whereas freshly broken surfaces of ThC_2 have a very pale metallic yellow color which darkens with time.

TABLE 63
COPPER RADIATION, POWDER PATTERN FOR α-ThC_2[a]

2θ	$\sin^2\theta$	*d* spacing	Intensity	*h k l*
25.10	0.0472	3.5455	5	1 1 0
26.97	0.0544	3.3035	60	1 1 $\bar{1}$
27.21	0.0553	3.2743	35	0 0 2
27.43	0.0562	3.2485	30	2 0 0
30.16	0.0677	2.9604	70	1 1 1
33.88	0.0849	2.6436	40	2 0 $\bar{2}$
34.76	0.0892	2.5789	5	1 1 $\bar{2}$
39.80	0.1159	2.2628	5	1 1 2
42.70	0.1326	2.1155	15	0 2 0
43.65	0.1382	2.0718	25	2 0 2
44.99	0.1464	2.0131	15	0 2 $\bar{1}$, 0 2 1
45.85	0.1517	1.9775	40	1 1 $\bar{3}$
46.13	0.1535	1.9661	45	3 1 $\bar{1}$
47.10	0.1596	1.9278	5	3 1 0
49.46	0.1750	1.8414	5	3 1 $\bar{2}$
51.38	0.1879	1.7769	25	0 2 2, 0 2 $\bar{2}$
51.51	0.1888	1.7727	25	2 2 0
51.58	0.1893	1.7704	10	2 2 $\bar{1}$
51.93	0.1917	1.7592	35	1 1 3
52.19	0.1935	1.7512	30	3 1 1
55.38	0.2160	1.6575	10	2 2 1
55.59	0.2175	1.6517	25	2 2 $\bar{2}$
56.13	0.2214	1.6371	15	0 0 4
56.52	0.2242	1.6269	45	3 1 $\bar{3}$, 2 0 $\bar{4}$
56.62	0.2249	1.6243	15	4 0 0
56.89	0.2269	1.6171	15	4 0 $\bar{2}$
58.92	0.2419	1.5661	5	1 1 $\bar{4}$
60.93	0.2571	1.5191	5	0 2 $\bar{3}$, 0 2 3
62.72	0.2708	1.4802	20	2 2 2
63.04	0.2733	1.4734	10	2 2 $\bar{3}$
67.96	0.3123	1.3782	15	1 3 0
68.84	0.3195	1.3627	10	1 3 $\bar{1}$
70.23	0.3309	1.3390	15	2 0 4
70.47	0.3328	1.3351	10	1 3 1
70.56	0.3336	1.3337	15	4 0 2
71.29	0.3396	1.3218	15	4 0 $\bar{4}$
71.84	0.3442	1.3130	20	3 1 3
71.90	0.3446	1.3121	5	4 2 $\bar{1}$

TABLE 63 (continued)

2θ	$\sin^2\theta$	d spacing	Intensity	$h\ k\ l$
72.94	0.3533	1.2959	10	2 2 3
73.01	0.3539	1.2947	15	0 2 $\bar{4}$, 0 2 4
73.06	0.3543	1.2940	10	1 3 $\bar{2}$
73.36	0.3568	1.2895	15	2 2 $\bar{4}$
73.44	0.3575	1.2883	15	4 2 0
73.68	0.3595	1.2847	15	4 2 $\bar{2}$
73.71	0.3597	1.2842	20	1 1 $\bar{5}$
74.34	0.3650	1.2749	20	5 1 $\bar{1}$
76.23	0.3810	1.2479	15	1 3 2
78.22	0.3980	1.2210	10	4 2 1
78.69	0.4020	1.2149	5	4 2 $\bar{3}$
79.11	0.4055	1.2096	20	3 1 $\bar{5}$
79.52	0.4090	1.2043	20	5 1 $\bar{3}$
80.43	0.4169	1.1930	5	1 3 $\bar{3}$
80.63	0.4186	1.1905	5	3 3 $\bar{1}$
81.35	0.4248	1.1818	15	3 3 0
81.54	0.4264	1.1796	15	1 1 5
82.15	0.4317	1.1723	15	5 1 1
83.12	0.4401	1.1610	10	3 3 $\bar{2}$
85.05	0.4569	1.1396	5	1 3 3
85.25	0.4586	1.1374	5	3 3 1
85.81	0.4635	1.1314	15	2 2 4
86.12	0.4661	1.1282	10	4 2 2
86.33	0.4680	1.1259	5	2 2 $\bar{5}$
86.81	0.4722	1.1210	10	4 2 $\bar{4}$
87.05	0.4743	1.1184	10	2 0 $\bar{6}$
87.53	0.4784	1.1136	5	0 2 5, 0 2 $\bar{5}$
87.86	0.4813	1.1102	10	6 0 $\bar{2}$
88.77	0.4893	1.1012	10	3 3 $\bar{3}$
89.78	0.4981	1.0914	10	0 0 6
90.69	0.5060	1.0828	10	6 0 0
90.81	0.5070	1.0817	10	1 3 $\bar{4}$
92.31	0.5201	1.0680	10	3 3 2
95.06	0.5441	1.0442	15	0 4 1, 0 4 $\bar{1}$
96.07	0.5529	1.0359	5	4 0 4
96.93	0.5604	1.0290	10	1 3 4
97.12	0.5620	1.0275	5	4 2 3
97.23	0.5630	1.0266	10	4 0 $\bar{6}$
97.32	0.5637	1.0259	15	5 1 $\bar{5}$

TABLE 63 (continued)

2θ	$\sin^2 \theta$	d spacing	Intensity	$h\ k\ l$
97.60	0.5661	1.0237	10	$3\ 3\ \bar{4}$
97.74	0.5674	1.0226	10	$6\ 0\ \bar{4}$
98.05	0.5700	1.0202	5	$4\ 2\ \bar{5}$
99.86	0.5856	1.0065	5	$0\ 4\ \bar{2}$, $0\ 4\ 2$
99.96	0.5865	1.0058	5	$2\ 4\ 0$
100.02	0.5870	1.0053	15	$2\ 4\ \bar{1}$
101.69	0.6013	0.9933	5	$2\ 2\ 5$
102.18	0.6055	0.9899	20	$3\ 1\ 5$
102.34	0.6069	0.9888	15	$2\ 2\ \bar{6}$
102.60	0.6090	0.9870	20	$5\ 1\ 3$
102.63	0.6093	0.9868	5	$3\ 3\ 3$
102.99	0.6124	0.9843	5	$6\ 2\ \bar{1}$
103.14	0.6137	0.9833	15	$2\ 4\ 1$
103.17	0.6139	0.9831	10	$6\ 2\ \bar{2}$
104.46	0.6249	0.9744	5	$1\ 3\ \bar{5}$
105.09	0.6302	0.9703	10	$5\ 3\ \bar{1}$
105.15	0.6306	0.9699	15	$0\ 2\ 6$, $0\ 2\ \bar{6}$
105.58	0.6343	0.9671	10	$2\ 0\ 6$
106.06	0.6383	0.9641	10	$5\ 3\ \bar{2}$
106.09	0.6386	0.9639	10	$6\ 2\ 0$
106.42	0.6413	0.9618	10	$6\ 0\ 2$
106.63	0.6431	0.9605	5	$6\ 2\ \bar{3}$
107.42	0.6497	0.9556	10	$5\ 3\ 0$
108.03	0.6548	0.9519	15	$0\ 4\ \bar{3}$, $0\ 4\ 3$
109.69	0.6685	0.9421	5	$2\ 4\ 2$
109.96	0.6707	0.9406	10	$3\ 3\ \bar{5}$
110.00	0.6710	0.9403	15	$2\ 4\ \bar{3}$
110.39	0.6742	0.9381	5	$5\ 3\ \bar{3}$
110.91	0.6785	0.9351	15	$1\ 1\ \bar{7}$
111.77	0.6855	0.9303	15	$4\ 2\ 4$
112.21	0.6890	0.9279	20	$7\ 1\ \bar{1}$
112.53	0.6915	0.9262	10	$1\ 3\ 5$
112.63	0.6924	0.9257	5	$6\ 2\ 1$
113.02	0.6955	0.9236	15	$4\ 2\ \bar{6}$
113.18	0.6968	0.9227	10	$5\ 3\ 1$
113.27	0.6976	0.9222	20	$3\ 1\ \bar{7}$
113.57	0.6999	0.9207	15	$6\ 2\ \bar{4}$
114.38	0.7064	0.9165	15	$7\ 1\ \bar{3}$
116.34	0.7218	0.9066	5	$7\ 1\ 0$

TABLE 63 (continued)

2θ	$\sin^2\theta$	d spacing	Intensity	$h\ k\ l$
116.89	0.7261	0.9039	15	3 3 4
118.39	0.7377	0.8968	15	5 3 $\bar{4}$
118.99	0.7423	0.8940	20	4 4 $\bar{1}$
120.13	0.7510	0.8888	20	2 4 3
120.22	0.7516	0.8884	5	0 4 4, 0 4 $\bar{4}$
120.60	0.7545	0.8867	5	2 4 $\bar{4}$
120.69	0.7552	0.8864	5	4 4 0
120.95	0.7572	0.8852	5	4 4 $\bar{2}$
121.88	0.7641	0.8812	10	6 0 $\bar{6}$
122.26	0.7669	0.8796	15	2 2 6
122.74	0.7704	0.8776	15	1 3 $\bar{6}$
122.91	0.7717	0.8768	15	5 3 2
122.93	0.7718	0.8768	25	1 1 7
123.15	0.7734	0.8759	10	2 2 $\bar{7}$
123.22	0.7739	0.8756	15	6 2 2
123.74	0.7777	0.8734	5	3 1 6
124.38	0.7823	0.8708	25	7 1 1
124.67	0.7844	0.8697	10	6 2 $\bar{5}$
126.25	0.7957	0.8635	25	4 4 1
126.82	0.7997	0.8613	20	4 4 $\bar{3}$
127.28	0.8028	0.8596	15	3 3 $\bar{6}$
128.39	0.8105	0.8556	10	0 2 7, 0 2 $\bar{7}$
131.13	0.8289	0.8460	10	5 3 $\bar{5}$
131.17	0.8291	0.8459	25	5 1 $\bar{7}$
131.98	0.8344	0.8432	30	7 1 $\bar{5}$
132.07	0.8350	0.8429	15	2 0 $\bar{8}$
132.32	0.8367	0.8421	10	4 2 5
133.25	0.8426	0.8391	30	1 5 0
134.14	0.8482	0.8363	15	8 0 $\bar{2}$
134.22	0.8487	0.8361	10	4 2 $\bar{7}$
134.49	0.8504	0.8353	20	1 3 6
136.25	0.8612	0.8300	5	2 4 4
136.69	0.8638	0.8287	5	4 4 2
137.01	0.8657	0.8278	30	2 4 $\bar{5}$
137.71	0.8699	0.8259	5	4 4 $\bar{4}$
137.82	0.8705	0.8256	5	7 1 2
137.84	0.8707	0.8255	10	3 3 5
138.45	0.8742	0.8238	10	5 3 3
138.79	0.8762	0.8229	30	0 4 $\bar{5}$, 0 4 5

TABLE 63 (continued)

2θ	$\sin^2\theta$	d spacing	Intensity	$h\ k\ l$
139.34	0.8793	0.8214	5	1 1 $\bar{8}$
139.98	0.8829	0.8197	20	4 0 6
140.01	0.8831	0.8197	10	6 2 3
140.29	0.8846	0.8189	40	1 5 $\bar{2}$
140.37	0.8851	0.8187	5	3 1 $\bar{8}$
140.43	0.8854	0.8186	15	0 0 8
140.78	0.8873	0.8177	20	6 0 4
142.49	0.8966	0.8134	25	6 2 $\bar{6}$
142.56	0.8970	0.8133	50	4 0 $\bar{8}$, 5 1 5
143.04	0.8995	0.8121	20	8 0 0
144.60	0.9076	0.8085	25	8 0 $\bar{4}$
145.34	0.9113	0.8069	40	1 5 2
151.62	0.9399	0.7945	5	7 1 $\bar{6}$
152.52	0.9436	0.7929	25	1 3 $\bar{7}$
153.57	0.9477	0.7912	30	5 3 $\bar{6}$
153.90	0.9490	0.7907	35	7 3 $\bar{2}$
155.27	0.9542	0.7885	25	7 3 $\bar{1}$
155.52	0.9551	0.7882	60	3 5 0
156.83	0.9597	0.7863	60	4 4 3
156.94	0.9600	0.7861	20	2 2 7
157.73	0.9627	0.7850	25	3 3 $\bar{7}$
159.25	0.9676	0.7831	50	2 2 $\bar{8}$
159.30	0.9677	0.7830	70	4 4 $\bar{5}$
160.19	0.9704	0.7819	80	3 5 $\bar{2}$
160.57	0.9715	0.7815	35	7 3 $\bar{3}$
162.77	0.9776	0.7790	80	3 1 7
164.06	0.9808	0.7778	70	8 2 $\bar{2}$
166.40	0.9860	0.7757	15	1 1 8
166.58	0.9864	0.7756	100	7 1 3
166.90	0.9870	0.7753	85	7 3 0

[a] $a_0 = 6.691$ Å; $b_0 = 4.231$ Å; $c_0 = 6.744$ Å; $\beta = 103°50'$; $\mu r = 20.0$; space group No. 15; $\lambda(K\alpha_1) = 1.54051$ Å.

E. CHEMICAL REACTIVITY

Very pure Th metal is relatively immune to atmospheric attack, but the carbides, especially ThC, are so reactive to water vapor that they should be handled either in a nonreactive atmosphere or under a dry liquid. Both carbides can be dissolved by H_2O, 1:1 HCl, H_2SO_4, HNO_3, 25% tartaric acid, and 5% NaOH (Samsonov *et al.*, 1960). The reaction with water has been studied on a number of occasions, the most recent being a work by Kempter and Krikorian (1962).

ThC_2 forms only a thin coat of ThO_2 after 24 hours at 300° in pure O_2, while at 500° it is fully oxidized (N. Brett *et al.*, 1960). In moist air it reacts ten times faster than UC_2, being completely converted to the oxide after ~10 hours at 30°. The carbon-deficient material is somewhat less reactive. Although there is no reaction with nitrogen at room temperature, there is a slight reaction in dry air (Engle, 1961).

F. HARDNESS

The only reported measurement of microhardness was made by Kempter and Krikorian (1962). $ThC_{0.99}$ and ThC_2 gave 850 kg/mm^2 and 600 kg/mm^2 (200 g DPH), respectively.

G. THERMOCHEMICAL PROPERTIES

1. Heat of Formation

Huber and Holley (1962) measured the heat of formation of $ThC_{0.99}$ by combustion calorimetry and calculated a value of $\Delta H^\circ_{298} = -7 \pm 6$ kcal/mole. The large uncertainty was believed due to the high percentage of unburned material found after combustion. More recently, Huber and Holley (1966) report the following values for the heat of formation at 298.15°, based on a redetermination of the heats of combustion: -16.9 ± 1.6, -23.7 ± 0.9, -28.5 ± 1.9, -29.6 ± 1.1, and -29.7 ± 1.8 kcal/mole for $ThC_{0.75}$, $ThC_{0.81}$, $ThC_{0.91}$, $ThC_{1.00}$, and $ThC_{1.91}$, respectively. From the emf developed by the cell Th, $ThF_4/CaF_2/ThF_4$, ThC_{1-x}, Aronson and Sadofsky (1965) were able to determine the partial molar free energy of Th in ThC as a function of composition at 900°C. As has been observed for the other defect carbides, the partial free energy changes slowly until near the stoichiometric composition. By performing a Gibbs–Duhem integration and combining the result with $\Delta \bar{F}_{Th}$, a free energy of formation of -23.7 kcal/mole was calculated at 900°C for $ThC_{0.96}$.

Using the CO pressure measured by Prescott and Hincke (1927) over the ThO_2–CO–C system, combined with estimated free energy functions and a more recent value for the heat of formation of ThO_2, Lofgren and Krikorian (1964) calculated that $\Delta H^\circ_f(298°) = -31.6 \pm 1.2$ kcal/mole for ThC_2. A similar study using torsion effusion was undertaken by Hollahan and Gregory (1964). Such efforts are doomed from the start. Not only does this system dissolve oxygen, but the amount, hence the effect, will certainly change with temperature. Furthermore, attainment of solid-state equilibrium is difficult to demonstrate. There is little advantage in calculating thermochemical data from such measurements and none whatever in attributing the behavior to ThC_2. Egan (1964) calculated $\Delta H_f = -37.1$ kcal/mole and $\Delta F_f = -29.4 \pm 0.3$ kcal/mole, both at 800°C using emf values from the cell Th, $ThF_4/CaF_2/ThF_4$, ThC_2, C.

On the basis of equilibria in the Th–W–C system, Rudy *et al.* (1962a) gave a range of -32 to -23.3 kcal/mole for ΔF_f of ThC_2 at 1500°C.

2. Low Temperature Heat Capacity

Takahashi *et al.* (1965) have obtained the heat capacity for $ThC_{1.98}$* between 5° and 350°. The following values were calculated for 298.15°: $C_p = 13.59$ cal/mole-deg, $S° = 16.42$ cal/mole-deg, $H°_{298.15} - H°_0 = 2458$ cal/mole.

3. Vaporization

Using a mass spectrometer, Jackson *et al.* (1962) found a $Th_{(g)}$ pressure above $ThC_{2(s)} + C_{(s)}$ between 2000° and 2422°, which was somewhat less than that of $ThC_{2(g)}$. The pressures were described by the following equations:

$$ThC_{2(g)}, \log P(\text{atm}) = -39{,}364\,(\pm 163)/T + 7.20\,(\pm 0.65)$$

$$Th_{(g)}, \log P(\text{atm}) = -36{,}025\,(\pm 144)/T + 5.74\,(\pm 0.57)$$

The data points for $Th_{(g)}$ are shown in Fig. 57 with the value obtained from a Ag calibration as the upper end of the line while a Mo calibration gave the lower end.

Lonsdale and Graves (1962) and Kent (1963) studied this system using target collection. In view of the mass spectrometric work, their calculated thorium pressures were corrected for the vaporized ThC_2 and the result is shown in Fig. 57. After the latter work had been published, a negative temperature error in the NBS-calibrated pyrometer was discovered. When this is taken into account, the agreement with Lonsdale and Graves (1962) improves. Clearly, the mass spectrometer pressures are too low. The temperature error in the work of Lonsdale and Graves (1962), suggested by Lofgren and Krikorian (1964), is not the explanation for the difference. However, there is another possibility. The mass spectrometer calibration was based on a cross section of 89.5 for thorium. In view of a measured cross section of 50 for uranium, their thorium cross section was probably too high. This, of course, does not account for all of the difference between these measurements, but it helps. The probable pressure curve in Fig. 57, was drawn with these comments in mind.

* A detailed description of this sample and its preparation is given by Stout (1964).

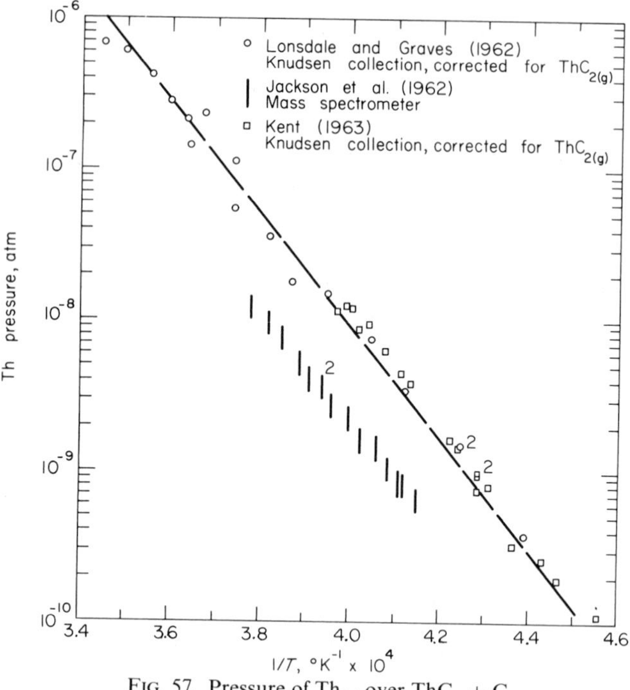

FIG. 57. Pressure of $Th_{(g)}$ over ThC_2 + C.

The free energy of formation for ThC_2 appears to be temperature independent at −29.5 kcal/mole, if the vapor pressure measurements are compared to values obtained from other techniques at other temperatures. If this is the case, the slope produced by the $Th_{(g)}$ pressure (Fig. 57) is too great. Since the phase limit of ThC_2 apparently moves to a lower stoichiometry as the temperature is raised, the $Th_{(g)}$ pressure would increase faster, as the temperature was raised, than would be expected if the composition remained fixed (see Chapter XIII, Section G). Indeed, at 2800°, the measured pressure appears to be too great by about a factor of two. Although this is not the only explanation, it should be considered when future measurements are made.

The pressure of Th over ThC_2 + C has been studied by emission spectrometric techniques (Lofgren and Krikorian, 1964). Although some difficulty was experienced in obtaining consistent data, a heat of formation value near −23 kcal/mole (third law) was reported.

The measured Th pressures indicate a preferential evaporation of carbon from ThC_2. Consequently, congruent evaporation in the carbon-deficient ThC region would be expected.

XI

THE URANIUM–URANIUM DICARBIDE SYSTEM

A. INTRODUCTION

An enormous amount of work has been directed, of late, to those properties of UC and UC_2 which are important to high temperature power reactor technology. Most studies have been made under conditions dictated by economy rather than purity, and much of the emphasis has been placed on the engineering aspects of the problem. While such information is necessary and valuable, it adds little to a basic understanding of the pure U–C system, and, therefore, is beyond the scope of this discussion.

In spite of this great interest, the complete phase diagram and many of the basic properties have remained in doubt until very recently. Although this is partly due to the complexity of the system, the main problem stems from the almost unavoidable presence of dissolved oxygen and nitrogen. These elements can seriously affect the properties of the carbides and, unless their presence is taken into account, there is little hope of consistency between independent measurements. It is therefore worthwhile to consider, first, the changes produced when carbon is replaced by these elements.

1. Nitrogen

Above 1200°, the lowest temperature reported, all or part of the carbon atoms in UC can be replaced by nitrogen. This substitution results in a contraction of the lattice (Austin and Gerds, 1958; J. T. Williams and Sambell, 1959). Indeed, if UC having a parameter of 4.9605 Å, indicating integral stoichiometry, is used, the lattice parameter versus nitrogen content is almost linear. On the other hand, by starting with UC having a parameter of 4.9544, a variation is produced which is almost independent of nitrogen content at first, but then approaches the value for UN as the nitrogen content is increased (J. T. Williams and Sambell, 1959). Thus, the effect of this impurity is influenced by the vacancy concentration in the nonmetal lattice. Magnier *et al.* (1964b) observed a positive deviation from Vegard's Law at low nitrogen concentrations for material which, according to the analysis, must have contained some UC_2. Austin and Gerds (1958) noted an equilibrium composition of about 35 mole % UN + 65 mole % UC at 1800° when UC_2 was present. They also found that nitrogen is essentially insoluble in UC_2 and U_2C_3. However, the presence of nitrogen is claimed to inhibit the formation of U_2C_3 (Henney *et al.*, 1963). According to Rough and Chubb (1959), nitrogen reacts with the molten carbide to displace carbon from the monocarbide to produce some UC_2. Such a contamination can result during arc-melting if N_2 is present in the gas (D. J. Brown, 1964). Chubb and Keller (1963) found 700 ppm nitrogen in $UC_{1.0}$, after melting in a partial pressure of 0.01 atm of N_2. The amount increased with nitrogen pressure and as the carbon content was reduced. Atoda *et al.* (1964) observed a reaction with N_2 (1 atm) starting at 600°. This increased rapidly up to 1100°, and became almost constant between 1100° and 1250°. The nitrogen combined with the uranium, producing free carbon and U_2N_3 with a composition between $UN_{1.4-1.6}$, depending on the temperature.

2. Oxygen

The solubility of oxygen in UC and the ease of its dissolution depend on a number of factors, the more important being the stoichiometry, the annealing temperature, and the CO pressure. Even though there is no agreement in the literature as to the role each plays, a brief discussion will be attempted, based largely on the excellent work of Anselin *et al.* (1964) and Brett *et al.* (1964). In order to simplify the presentation, the composition extremes of the UC phase will be handled separately beginning with hypostoichiometric UC.

Since UO_2 is insoluble in UC, the amount of dissolved oxygen in a particular sample will depend largely on the rate at which the UO_2 can be converted to the easily soluble but unstable UO. If free uranium is present, the reduction can take place above 1200° by the reaction $UO_2 + U = 2[UO]$.* Because no gas is evolved it makes no difference whether heating is carried out in vacuum or in argon. On the other hand, above 1600° in vacuum, the reaction $2UO_2 + UC = 3[UO] + CO$ can proceed with the removal of CO. Now the gaseous environment is

* Brackets are used to indicate that the material is dissolved in the carbide phase.

important. When heating is done in argon there is a less efficient removal of CO, partly because the sample will sinter and partly because the evolved CO will accumulate in the gas. If the CO pressure is sufficiently high to stop or reverse this reaction, the UC phase will contain less dissolved oxygen than if the CO pressure were lower. Thus, the proposal that a lower CO pressure leads to an apparently higher solubility of oxygen (Sano *et al.*, 1963; Brett *et al.*, 1964) can be explained. In the absence of UO_2, the reaction U(C, O) = [U] + CO can lower the oxygen content if the CO pressure is sufficiently low. This reaction can produce free U or just a lower stoichiometry, depending on the conditions. The CO pressure over $U(C_{0.75}O_{0.25}) + U + UO_2$ has been measured by Stoops and Hamme (1964). Evaporation of UO can also reduce the oxygen content.

When U_2C_3 or UC_2 are present with UO_2, the initial reaction in vacuum produces UC with the evolution of CO and the loss of the higher carbide. After all of the higher carbide has been removed, a reaction takes place between the UC and the remaining oxide (Harrison *et al.*, 1964). At high CO pressures, additional U_2C_3 might result above 1400° according to the reaction

$$3UC + UO_2 = 2[UO] + U_2C_3$$

Below 1400°, the terminal composition of U(C, O), in equilibrium with UO_2 and U, lies near $UC_{0.65}O_{0.35}$ (Anselin *et al.*, 1964; Brett *et al.*, 1964; Magnier *et al.*, 1964b). Values for this composition as low as $UC_{0.75}O_{0.25}$ (Stoops and Hamme, 1964) and as high as $UC_{0.2}O_{0.8}$ at 1600° (Namba *et al.*, 1962; Sano *et al.*, 1963; Robinson and Chiotti, 1964) have been reported. On the other hand, UC which is in equilibrium with U_2C_3 and UO_2, dissolves only a little oxygen, no more than 5 at. % at 1400° (Anselin *et al.*, 1964). U_2C_3 contains essentially no oxygen at room temperature, but UC_2 can go to $UC_{1.8}O_{0.15}$ (Henney *et al.*, 1963).

The effect of this impurity on the various properties is complicated by being dependent on the carbon content of the material as well as on the presence of vacancies (Magnier *et al.*, 1964b; Accary, 1963). This should be kept in mind when interpreting experimental data. Dissolved oxygen causes the lattice parameter of UC to go through a maximum at 4.9613 Å and 1800 ppm O. Witteman (1963) noted an increase to 4.9625 Å when a small amount of UO_2 was added to hyperstoichiometric UC. Maxima have also been reported recently by Brett *et al.* (1964) (4,9625 Å) and by Anselin *et al.* (1964) (4.956 Å). Uranium was present as the second phase in the latter work. As the oxygen content is increased beyond the maximum, the lattice parameter decreases rapidly to 4.9519 ± 0.0001 Å at saturation (Witteman, 1963; Stoops and Hamme, 1964). Values of 4.9476 Å (Anselin *et al.*, 1964) and 4.9490 Å (Vaughn *et al.*, 1957) have also been reported when uranium metal was present. Thus, in the presence of uranium, the vacancies in the carbon lattice can change the effect of dissolved oxygen.

The formation of U_2C_3 is apparently inhibited by the presence of dissolved oxygen as well as nitrogen according to Henney *et al.* (1963). Although U_2C_3 is the stable phase in contact with graphite below ~1500°, it did not form when the nitrogen–oxygen concentration was in excess of ~100 ppm. Instead, the samples consisted of $UC_{1-x}N_x$ and α-UC_2 containing a small amount of oxygen. In their case, self-purification was claimed when annealing was done at 1300° for times up to 70 hours in a vacuum of 10^{-5} torr. On the other hand, both Anselin *et al.* (1964) and Brett *et al.* (1964) observed the presence of U_2C_3 in their material even though an oxide phase was present.

A study of these carbides is made even more difficult because they hydrolyze so easily. For this reason, it is difficult to know whether the oxygen content is dissolved in the carbide or has been acquired as a surface film during handling. For example, Keller *et al.* (1962) report that 25-μ UC powder is pyrophoric and that a slightly coarser powder, stored in argon for 2 months, increased in oxygen content from 790 to 1200 ppm.

B. PREPARATION

A great deal of attention has been given to ways of preparing the carbides economically and in large quantities. These techniques are, in general, unsuitable for the preparation of small, pure research specimens, and will not be discussed in any detail except to acquaint the reader with their limitations.

Experience at Los Alamos and elsewhere has shown that the carbides of uranium can be prepared easily, and, under the proper conditions, to a high degree of purity by arc-melting the elements together. If a graphite electrode is used, the melt tends to pick up additional carbon, and, for this reason, a tungsten electrode is sometimes preferred. Reports of contamination by W or by Cu from the water-cooled hearth usually give low values, unless the melt was allowed to overheat and sputter. A satisfactory procedure is as follows: The proper amount of uranium, as a freshly cleaned rod, and graphite, as spectroscopic rods, are placed in a shallow depression in the copper hearth. Air is evacuated, and the system is back-filled with purified helium or argon. The use of helium, although it produces a more unstable arc, allows a shorter melting time which results in less carbon pickup from the electrode. A zirconium button is melted to further purify the gas, after which the arc is transferred to the uranium rod. By playing the arc over the melt, the carbon can be dissolved quite easily. The button is then turned on edge several times and remelted. A current between 400 and 600 amp is sufficient to melt a charge of about 100 g (P. L. Stone, 1962).

Uranium will react with hydrocarbon gases to produce UC at low temperatures and UC_2 when the temperature is raised. However, because carbon diffusion is slow through the initial carbide film, the metal is normally reduced to a fine powder by converting it to the hydride previous to carbiding.* Methane will give mainly UC below 650°, and mainly UC_2 above 900° (Kalish, 1960). Propane and butane will react much more rapidly than methane, but the conditions are more critical to prevent the deposition of free carbon. For these gases, UC is the major product below 750°. UC can even be produced at 10° in propane, if the system is exposed to a gamma flux (Sano *et al.*, 1960). In general, such methods have led to an impure product because of the difficulties in obtaining pure gases. Furthermore, the resulting fine powder is very reactive and must be handled with special care.

Economically, the reaction between the uranium oxides and carbon is very attractive. However, unless considerable time is invested in high vacuum purification or unless the product is arc melted, impure material is certain to result. For example, UO_2 + C pellets heated at 1700°–2000° in a vacuum of $<10^{-2}$ torr show a residual oxygen content of 0.1–0.5 wt % (Himmelstein *et al.*, 1963). There have been reports of a reduced oxygen level after heating in flowing argon (K. M. Taylor, 1960), but experience by others (Stoops and Hamme, 1962) has shown that there are many difficulties connected with this procedure. Unless great pains are taken to remove all oxygen (free or combined) from the argon, the net removal of oxygen from the carbide may be quite small.

The preparation of UC from a liquid metal system has been studied by Johnson *et al.* (1963). A mixture of powdered uranium and charcoal in liquid Mg–Zn alloy at 800° gave UC as a precipitate after 2–5 hours. However, they found oxygen was a serious impurity in the final product.

Not only are the powdered uranium carbides pyrophoric in air, but even if left in an inert atmosphere for any length of time, they will acquire

* In this connection, F. Brown *et al.* (1964) found that only H_2 which had been evolved from uranium hydride was sufficiently pure to produce the pure hydride.

what little oxygen is present in the gas. Crushing arc-melted UC in an Ar atmosphere containing 40 ppm O and 15 ppm H_2O results in at least a fivefold increase in oxygen content (B. L. Taylor *et al.*, 1964). It is advisable, therefore, to store the material as large pieces and then, only if absolutely necessary, make a powder immediately before use.

C. PHASE RELATIONSHIP

The three compounds, UC, U_2C_3, and UC_2, make up the U–C system. Fcc UC is stable from room temperature to its melting temperature; bcc U_2C_3 decomposes at about 1730° without melting; and UC_2 is stable from about 1500° to its melting point. UC_2 containing carbon converts from a tetragonal (α) to a cubic (β) lattice at about 1765°. An equilibrium phase diagram is shown in Fig. 58. The positions of several phase boundaries are still in doubt and they are, therefore, represented as dashed lines.

Pure uranium has at least three crystal forms. The various reported transition temperatures and melting points are compared in Table 64.

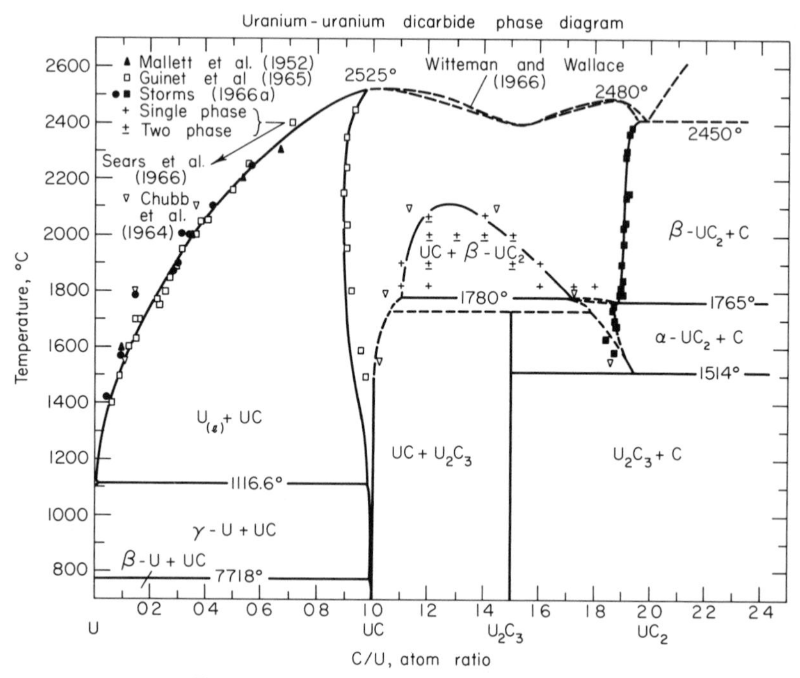

FIG. 58. Phase diagram of the U–UC_2 system.

TABLE 64

TRANSITION TEMPERATURES[a] AND MELTING POINT[a] OF URANIUM

α–β	β–γ	γ–Liquid	Investigator
667° ± 1.3°	774.8° ± 1.6°	1132.3° ± 0.8°	Blumenthal (1960)
—	—	1132° ± 10°	Udy and Boulger (1954)
657°–682°	754°–774°	1134°	Tadashi and Tadashi (1958)
657°	768°	1133°	Buzzard *et al.* (1953)
—	—	1133° ± 2°	Dahl and Cleaves (1949)
656.3°–665.3°	776.3°–770.8°	1130°	Baumrucker and Chiswik (1953)
645°–667°	764°–772°	—	Dahl and Van Dusen (1947)
662° ± 3°	—	—	Moore and Kelley (1957)

[a] Given in degrees Centigrade.

A low temperature phase change has been observed at 42°K (Fisher and McSkimin, 1961). The presence of carbon lowers the transition temperature to eutectoids at 665.9° and 771.8°, respectively, and the melting point of the metal is lowered slightly to 1116.6° (Blumenthal, 1960). This author also reports that the solubility of carbon in solid uranium is no higher than 185 ppm even at the eutectic temperature. Once liquid forms, however, the solubility of carbon increases rapidly with temperature, as can be seen in Fig. 58.

The formation of UC causes the melting point to rise to a maximum. Values of 2525° ± 30° (lower limit) at $UC_{0.98}$ (Witteman and Wallace, 1966); 2560° ± 50°C at $UC_{1.1}$ (Witteman and Bowman, 1963); 2590° ± 50° (Chiotti, 1952), 2350°–2400° (Mallett *et al.*, 1952); 2520° (Brownlee, 1958); 2275° (Rundle *et al.*, 1948); and 2280° (H. W. Newkirk and Bates, 1959) have been reported. This last measurement was made using a tungsten vee to hold the melt and the value is near those found in the W–UC system. Unlike the other cubic carbides, quenched UC has only a slight homogeneity range, which at first was thought to be negligible (Rundle *et al.*, 1948). With the lattice parameter behavior first noted by J. T. Williams *et al.* (1960), a composition range at higher temperatures was suspected. In an effort to clarify these observations, Buckley (1961) examined quenched alloys containing various impurities as well as various amounts of free uranium. He found the lattice parameter of quenched UC to go through a minimum when the total composition was reduced below $UC_{0.8}$, in agreement with J. T. Williams *et al.* (1960). When a sample containing a small amount of free uranium was quenched from various temperatures, a similar minimum was observed. An anneal at 1300° caused the lattice parameter to increase to 4.959 Å, and small cubic particles of uranium appeared within the grains. From this, Buckley (1961) concluded that rapidly cooled UC retains a defect structure which is characteristic of some higher temperature. By applying thermochemical arguments and reasoning from the behavior of the lattice parameter, he concluded that the solidus must be retrograde with a lower limit at $UC_{0.985}$* and about 2000°. Magnier and Accary (1964), and Kerr (1963) recently confirmed this observation, but the former workers placed the limit at $UC_{0.96}$* and 1700°. This "nose" in the low-carbon boundary was suggested to result from the peritectic formation of an unidentified compound at this temperature. No experimental support for this interpretation has been reported. In fact, efforts by Witteman (1966) to find this phase by thermal analysis were completely negative. These results have stimulated a number of recent efforts to measure this boundary more directly. Magnier and Accary (1965) revised their previous work by melting various compositions of UC using electron bombardment, then quenching. Metallographic examination and the variation in the lattice parameter were used to verify a single-phase region between $UC_{0.923\pm0.006}$ and $UC_{1.000\pm0.006}$. Since these limits must depend on how effectively the quench was made, the former must be treated as an upper limit to the low-carbon boundary. A study, which is not affected by this problem, was made by Guinet *et al.* (1965). They heated a piece of $UC_{1.0}$ in liquid uranium at various temperatures, hoping its composition would equilibrate with the liquid. In the absence of heating times or proof that equilibrium was, indeed, attained, their values, shown in Fig. 58, must also be considered an upper limit. As a consequence of a vaporization study, Storms (1966a) was able to determine this boundary by noting the composition at which the pressure over UC + $U_{(l)}$ equalled the pressure of uranium extrapolated from the single-phase UC region (Fig. 67). This measurement suffers only from the uncertain shape of the pressure vs. composition curve. The excellent agreement between this and the equilibration studies at high temperatures, where equilibrium is rapid, gives confidence that the pressure technique is reliable at the lower temperatures where agreement is not as good and equilibrium might not have occurred. The boundary in Fig. 58 was drawn on this basis. At 1300°, metallographic studies by Witteman and Bowman (1963) give $UC_{0.980\pm0.005}$ as the lower-phase boundary.

* Conflicting composition values were reported in the paper. A discussion of this problem was made by Ervin and Korst (1966).

The upper terminus of UC approaches $UC_{1.0}$ when material is cooled slowly, but an oil quench from 1700° has given $UC_{1.12}$ (Burdick *et al.*, 1955). This is consistent, within the expected error, with the vapor pressure studies by Storms (1966a), the metallographic observations of Sears *et al.* (1966), and the x-ray studies of Witteman and Bowman (1963).

In the region between UC and UC_2, the diagram shows several very interesting features which still have not been completely delineated. In 1952, Mallett *et al.* proposed a solid solution to exist between UC and UC_2 in the region between about 2020° and the melting point, and that this broke into a two-phase field of UC and UC_2 below 2020°. Their diagram shows termination of the miscibility gap at 1800° by the formation of U_2C_3. These conclusions were based on a metallographic examination of alloys quenched from between 1700° and the melting point. However, they were unaware of the α–β transition of UC_2. Nine years later, Chubb and Phillips (1961a), using the same technique, presented evidence to challenge this interpretation. Their diagram shows a miscibility gap which extends to the solidus, forming a eutectic between UC and β-UC_2. However, in the discussion to the paper (Chubb and Phillips, 1961b) they reported subsequent evidence for a single-phase region above 2100°C. Witteman and Bowman (1963) have confirmed this as well as the ideas of Mallett *et al.* (1952) by using thermal analysis techniques.* Alloys cooled from just below the melting temperature show a break in the cooling rate where the solid solution breaks into UC + β-UC_2, followed by a thermal arrest where cubic UC_2 converts to the tetragonal form. Thus, a hat-shaped miscibility gap was proposed with a critical temperature of 2050° ± 50°C at $UC_{1.35\pm0.05}$, and with a lower isotherm extending between $UC_{1.0-1.065}$ and $UC_{\sim1.6}$. A recent metallographic examination of quenched alloys in this region (Sears *et al.*, 1966) has placed better limits on the boundaries, but these are at odds with the position proposed by Storms (1966a) from pressure studies. The latter technique is sufficiently insensitive in this region that a curve can be drawn, as was done in Fig. 58, to be basically consistent with both measurements. Also Figs. 67 and 68 have been made to conform.

U_2C_3 has been a very elusive compound which is not normally found in material quenched from above 1800°. Early workers at Iowa State College suggested, as one explanation for the Widmänstatten structure exhibited by material quenched from the melt, that a U_2C_3 phase existed at high temperatures, but it could not be retained upon cooling (Rundle

* Details of this technique can be found in a paper by Rupert (1963).

et al., 1948; Wilhelm *et al.*, 1949). Later, Mallett *et al.* (1951) showed that the actual situation was just the opposite, that U_2C_3 was not stable at high temperatures but was formed only very slowly at lower temperatures. They found this phase to require some mechanical stress to initiate its formation. Later workers also noted this behavior. In fact, heating under pressure very quickly produces U_2C_3 (Witteman, 1966). Other factors, such as the influence of dissolved oxygen and nitrogen may play a role (Henney *et al.*, 1962). Using very pure material, Witteman and Bowman (1963) observed it to form easily during cooling, when the composition was near $UC_{1.5}$, and when the material had been cycled across the decomposition temperature several times. Heating within the solid solution region reduced its ability to reform upon cooling. Using material of unknown purity, Chubb and Dickerson (1963) found complete formation within 15 minutes at 1600°. Norreys *et al.* (1964) and Imoto *et al.* (1964) concluded that a time delay, depending on temperature, precedes its formation. The decomposition temperature was placed at 1840° by Wilson (1960), but this temperature is clearly too high. Chubb and Phillips (1961b) propose 1775°, while neutron diffraction studies show it to be near 1730°C (A. L. Bowman, 1966). The phase is very close to a line compound (Mallett *et al.*, 1951; Witteman and Bowman, 1963).

UC_2 has a melting point near 2500° and a transition from cubic to tetragonal at 1765° when carbon is present. It decomposes into U_2C_3 and carbon near 1500°. Each of these features will be discussed in the following section. Work at Los Alamos has shown a melting point minimum of $\sim$2450° between UC and UC_2 and melting of UC_2 at 2450° $\pm$ 50° in contact with graphite. In addition, metallographic examination of small beads of UC_2 + C, which were cooled very rapidly from the melting point, has revealed a eutectic structure (Hoffman; see Witteman and Bowman, 1963). Thus, the maximum melting point of the UC_2 phase must be in excess of 2450°. Congruent melting was found at $UC_{1.89}$ and 2477° $\pm$ 19°C (Witteman and Wallace, 1966). Mallett *et al.* (1952) gave a range of 2450°–2500°. The very low value of 2200°, reported by Wilson (1960), was probably due to tungsten contamination. The proposal that UC_2 melts peritectically in contact with carbon (Chubb and Phillips, 1961a) has not been supported.

The polymorphic transition between α- and β-UC_2 is too rapid to allow the cubic form to be retained to room temperature. Using a high temperature x-ray camera, Wilson (1960) observed the transition at 1820°. However, thermal arrest work at Los Alamos has placed this temperature at first near 1800° (Witteman, 1963; Rupert, 1963), then at 1785° $\pm$ 20°

(Wallace *et al.*, 1964), and finally, with a more sophisticated thermal arrest apparatus, 1765° ± 20° was obtained (Witteman, 1966). This was confirmed by Cook (1965), using thermal analysis, with a temperature of 1768° ± 25°. All of this work was done in the presence of graphite. There is no doubt the transition is 15°–20° higher when UC is the second phase (Wilson, 1960; Witteman, 1963).

Under equilibrium conditions UC_2 will decompose into U_2C_3 and carbon upon cooling. However, this reaction is very slow. Decomposition temperatures of 1500° (Leitnaker and Witteman, 1962); 1500°–1600° (Imoto *et al.*, 1964); 1750° (Henney *et al.*, 1963); 1600° (Rudy and Benesovsky, 1963); and $<1550°$ (Huddle *et al.*, 1962) have been reported. Using high temperature x-ray diffraction, Henney and Jones (1965a) observed only U_2C_3 in a sample of U_2C_3 + 20 wt. % C so long as the temperature was below 1680°. At higher temperatures α-UC_2 appeared and this converted to the β form at 1860°. Since the α–β transition temperature is well established at 1765°, there would appear to be an $\sim$100° temperature error in this measurement. Consequently, the conversion temperature of U_2C_3 into α-UC_2 might better be given as 1580°. Because this rather wide scatter might be due to dissolved oxygen or nitrogen, Witteman (1966) undertook a detailed study both with and without these impurities. A value of 1514° ± 10° resulted. Since the formation of U_2C_3 is also slow, it is not unusual to find the nonequilibrium mixture $UC_2 + C + U_2C_3 + UC$ as the decomposition product.

UC_2 is never obtained with an integral stoichiometry. This defect structure was first noted by Mallet *et al.* (1952) and by many others since then. The composition of this boundary as a function of temperature has been determined by Storms (1966a), using the classic technique of equilibrating unsaturated UC_2 with graphite at various temperatures and by vapor pressure measurements. He found β-$UC_{1.96}$ as the phase limit at the eutectic temperature and β-$UC_{1.89}$ at the α–β transition. Other workers have reported compositions centering around $UC_{1.88}$ and $UC_{1.95}$, depending on the amount of free carbon present and the thermal history. Witteman and Bowman (1963) showed that $UC_{1.94}$ could be retained from the melt provided free carbon was largely absent. With the presence of free carbon, $UC_{1.89}$ resulted. Finely divided graphite is thought to act as precipitation centers, allowing the β-UC_2 to acquire a lower composition which is representative of some lower temperature. During a rapid quench, the α–β transition takes place without a change in composition. However, the equilibrium composition of the α form at the transition is in some dispute. Imoto *et al.* (1964) found UC in slowly cooled $UC_{1.86}$ and assumed this had precipitated at the transition. From the relative amounts of UC_2 and UC, they calculated $UC_{1.96\pm0.04}$ as the composition of α-UC_2. However, Storms (1966a) found α-$UC_{1.86}$ at the transition with a trend to higher compositions at lower temperatures. To reconcile these two observations, the precipitation of UC must occur below the transition, from the α-UC_2 phase. This is indicated in Fig. 58 by a construction which allows metastable UC to precipitate from carbon-deficient α-UC_2. Thus, the composition found by Imoto *et al.* (1964) should apply to a temperature near 1500°.

D. LATTICE PARAMETER AND STRUCTURE

Uranium metal has three crystal forms: orthorhombic, tetragonal, and body-centered cubic. Only the first is stable at room temperature

TABLE 65
COPPER RADIATION, POWDER PATTERN FOR α-U[a]

2θ	$\sin^2\theta$	*d* spacing	Intensity	*h k l*
30.43	0.0689	2.9345	5	0 2 0
34.93	0.0901	2.5666	30	1 1 0
35.52	0.0931	2.5250	45	0 2 1
36.22	0.0966	2.4777	25	0 0 2
39.51	0.1142	2.2790	30	1 1 1
48.02	0.1655	1.8932	5	0 2 2
51.20	0.1867	1.7826	40	1 1 2
57.02	0.2279	1.6136	3	1 3 0
60.27	0.2520	1.5343	40	1 3 1
63.33	0.2756	1.4673	10	0 4 0
64.70	0.2863	1.4394	20	0 2 3
65.34	0.2914	1.4269	10	2 0 0
66.39	0.2997	1.4069	5	0 4 1
67.36	0.3075	1.3890	15	1 1 3
69.45	0.3245	1.3522	5	1 3 2
73.77	0.3603	1.2833	1	2 2 0
75.19	0.3722	1.2625	10	0 4 2
76.64	0.3844	1.2423	30	2 2 1
76.89	0.3866	1.2388	10	0 0 4
77.06	0.3880	1.2365	15	2 0 2
83.72	0.4453	1.1543	25	1 3 3
84.89	0.4555	1.1413	1	0 2 4
85.06	0.4569	1.1395	2	2 2 2
87.32	0.4766	1.1157	20	1 1 4
89.20	0.4930	1.0970	4	0 4 3

TABLE 65 (continued)

2θ	$\sin^2 \theta$	*d* spacing	Intensity	*h k l*
90.39	0.5034	1.0856	15	1 5 0
97.70	0.5670	1.0230	10	2 4 0
98.94	0.5777	1.0134	25	2 2 3
100.50	0.5911	1.0018	10	2 4 1
101.55	0.6001	0.9943	30	1 5 2
103.23	0.6144	0.9826	5	1 3 4
103.89	0.6201	0.9782	5	0 6 0
106.76	0.6442	0.9597	5	0 6 1
108.92	0.6622	0.9466	10	0 4 4
109.10	0.6636	0.9455	20	2 4 2
110.22	0.6728	0.9390	25	3 1 0, 0 2 5
110.85	0.6779	0.9355	15	2 0 4
112.84	0.6941	0.9245	10	1 1 5
113.20	0.6970	0.9226	10	3 1 1
115.68	0.7167	0.9098	10	0 6 2
119.58	0.7468	0.8913	5	2 2 4
112.61	0.7695	0.8781	25	3 1 2
124.67	0.7844	0.8697	10	2 4 3
128.40	0.8106	0.8555	5	3 3 0
131.59	0.8319	0.8445	40	1 3 5
132.03	0.8348	0.8430	40	3 3 1
132.45	0.8375	0.8417	10	0 6 3
137.70	0.8698	0.8259	10	0 0 6
139.39	0.8796	0.8213	10	0 4 5
141.26	0.8900	0.8165	55	1 5 4
141.31	0.8903	0.8163	20	3 1 3
144.54	0.9072	0.8087	10	3 3 2
145.37	0.9114	0.8068	20	2 6 0
146.47	0.9168	0.8044	1	1 7 0
150.60	0.9356	0.7963	35	2 6 1
151.33	0.9387	0.7950	5	0 2 6
151.88	0.9410	0.7940	80	1 7 1
155.10	0.9535	0.7888	65	2 4 4
156.88	0.9599	0.7862	65	1 1 6
158.21	0.9643	0.7844	100	2 2 5

[a] $a_0 = 2.8539$ Å; $b_0 = 5.8691$ Å; $c_0 = 4.9554$ Å; $\mu r = 15.0$; space group No. 63; $\lambda(K\alpha_1) = 1.54051$ Å.

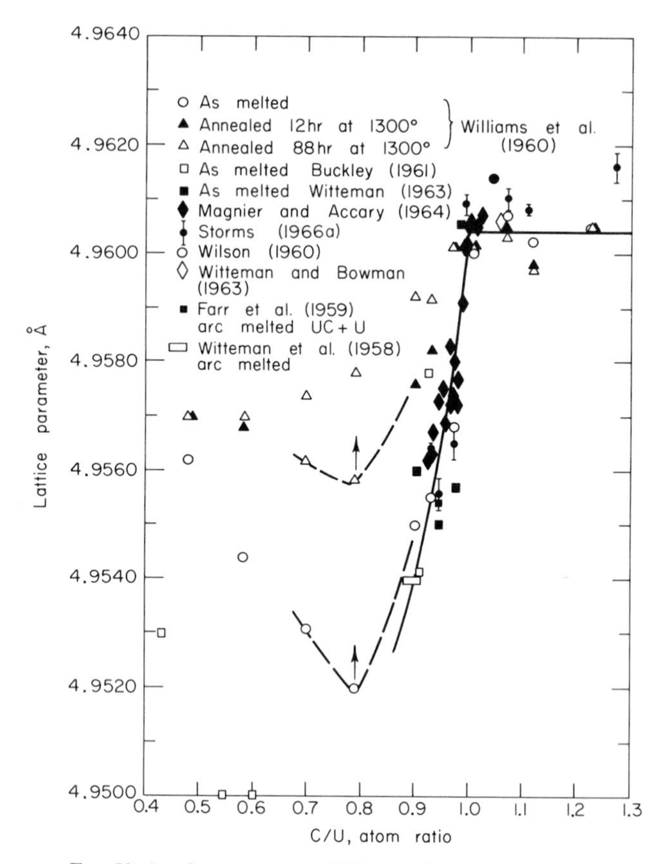

FIG. 59. Lattice parameter of UC as a function of composition.

and is seen in quenched material. A calculated powder pattern is listed in Table 65 based on the evaluation by Connolly (1962).

UC is fcc, as was first reported by Litz *et al.* (1948). According to Fig. 59, the best parameter for hyperstoichiometric UC is 4.9605 ± 0.0002 Å. Higher parameters reported by other workers are no doubt due to the effect of dissolved oxygen. At the low-carbon boundary, the parameter depends on the thermal history as well as on the almost unavoidable presence of oxygen. By removing the oxygen with Be, Anselin *et al.* (1964) obtained a value of 4.956 Å. Carniglia (1964) found the same parameter after zone-refining a single crystal reported to be $UC_{1.0}$ (Table 66). When the parameter curve of the oxycarbide was extrapolated to a zero oxygen content, a parameter of 4.9597 ± 0.0004 Å resulted (Magnier *et al.*,

TABLE 66
COPPER RADIATION, POWDER PATTERN FOR $UC_{1.0}$[a]

2θ	$\sin^2\theta$	d spacing	Intensity	$h\ k\ l$
31.20	0.0723	2.8639	35	1 1 1
36.19	0.0964	2.4802	25	2 0 0
52.10	0.1929	1.7538	30	2 2 0
61.99	0.2652	1.4956	40	3 1 1
65.08	0.2893	1.4320	15	2 2 2
76.79	0.3858	1.2401	10	4 0 0
85.19	0.4581	1.1380	25	3 3 1
87.96	0.4822	1.1092	25	4 2 0
99.05	0.5787	1.0126	25	4 2 2
107.58	0.6510	0.9546	30	5 1 1, 3 3 3
122.90	0.7716	0.8769	15	4 4 0
133.45	0.8439	0.8385	75	5 3 1
137.39	0.8680	0.8268	60	6 0 0, 4 4 2
158.26	0.9644	0.7843	100	6 2 0

[a] $a_0 = 4.9605$ Å; $\mu r = 11.0$; structure type $B1$, space group No. 225; $\lambda(K\alpha_1) =$ 1.54051 Å.

1964b). However, there is no assurance this applies to stoichiometric UC.

U_2C_3 was found to be bcc ($I\bar{4}3d$) from x-ray (Mallett *et al.*, 1952) as well as from neutron diffraction studies (Austin, 1959). A lattice parameter of 8.088 Å is usually found regardless of how it is prepared. From this data, a powder pattern for U_2C_3 was calculated and is listed in Table 67. The compound has a very narrow composition range as well as a low solubility for oxygen and nitrogen. Its formation has been suggested to result from a slight shift in the uranium positions (Gillam, 1962) with the movement of the carbon atoms by interstitial diffusion accounting for the slowness of formation. Magnier *et al.* (1964a) observed the phase to form from UC_2 by nucleation and growth.

The structure of α-UC_2 has been determined on three occasions by neutron diffraction (Atoji and Medrud, 1959; Austin, 1959; A. L. Bowman *et al.*, 1966). All assigned the CaC_2-type structure ($I4/mmm$). Numerous values for the lattice parameter have been reported but with rather poor agreement. This is primarily due to a variable composition. Rapidly cooled UC_2 containing little free carbon can have a composition as high as $UC_{1.94}$. When free carbon is present, the quenched material will be near $UC_{1.86}$. However, if the sample is cooled slowly, the $UC_{1.86}$ will

TABLE 67

COPPER RADIATION, POWDER PATTERN FOR U_2C_3[a]

2θ	$\sin^2 \theta$	d spacing	Intensity	$h\ k\ l$
26.98	0.0544	3.3019	10	2 1 1
31.25	0.0726	2.8595	30	2 2 0
35.05	0.0907	2.5577	35	3 1 0
41.75	0.1270	2.1616	40	3 2 1
44.78	0.1451	2.0220	5	4 0 0
53.06	0.1995	1.7244	35	3 3 2
55.62	0.2177	1.6510	10	4 2 2
58.10	0.2358	1.5862	45	4 3 1, 5 1 0
62.88	0.2721	1.4767	25	5 2 1
65.19	0.2902	1.4298	1	4 4 0
67.46	0.3084	1.3871	5	5 3 0
71.90	0.3446	1.3120	10	6 1 1, 5 3 2
74.07	0.3628	1.2788	5	6 2 0
76.22	0.3809	1.2480	35	5 4 1
80.47	0.4172	1.1925	5	6 3 1
82.57	0.4353	1.1674	10	4 4 4
84.66	0.4535	1.1438	15	7 1 0, 5 4 3
88.83	0.4898	1.1006	25	6 3 3, 7 2 1, 5 5 2
90.90	0.5079	1.0808	20	6 4 2
92.98	0.5260	1.0620	10	7 3 0
97.16	0.5623	1.0272	15	6 5 1, 7 3 2
99.26	0.5805	1.0110	5	8 0 0
101.37	0.5986	0.9956	5	7 4 1
105.65	0.6349	0.9667	5	6 5 3
107.82	0.6530	0.9532	10	6 6 0, 8 2 2
110.02	0.6711	0.9402	35	7 5 0, 7 4 3, 8 3 1
114.51	0.7074	0.9158	5	7 5 2
116.82	0.7256	0.9043	1	8 4 0
119.17	0.7437	0.8932	5	9 1 0
124.05	0.7800	0.8722	45	7 6 1, 9 2 1, 6 5 5
126.60	0.7981	0.8622	35	6 6 4
129.24	0.8163	0.8526	35	9 3 0, 7 5 4, 8 5 1
134.84	0.8525	0.8342	25	9 3 2, 7 6 3
137.85	0.8707	0.8255	15	8 4 4
141.04	0.8888	0.8170	20	9 4 1, 8 5 3
148.23	0.9251	0.8008	30	7 7 2, 10 1 1
152.43	0.9432	0.7931	100	10 2 0, 8 6 2
157.33	0.9614	0.7856	50	9 4 3, 9 5 0

[a] $a_0 = 8.088$ Å; $\mu r = 10.0$; space group No. 220; $\lambda(K\alpha_1) = 1.54051$ Å.

TABLE 68
STRUCTURE AND LATTICE PARAMETERS OF α-U, UC, AND α-UC_2

Phases present	Composition of first phase	Lattice parameter (Å)	Structure	Investigator
α-U	Pure	$a = 2.8539 \pm 0.0001$ $b = 5.8691 \pm 0.0001$ $c = 4.9554 \pm 0.0001$	$Cmcm\ D_{2h}^{17}$ Orthorhombic	Mueller and Hitterman (1960)
UC + U	$UC_{0.93}$	$a = 4.9563 \pm 0.0007$	fcc	Magnier and Accary (1964)
UC + UC_2	$UC_{1.0}$	$a = 4.9605 \pm 0.0002$	fcc	Figure 59
U_2C_3	U_2C_3	$a = 8.0889 \pm 0.0009$	bcc	Witteman and Bowman (1963)
α-UC_2 + C	$UC_{1.89}$	$a = 3.519 \pm 0.001$ $c = 5.979 \pm 0.002$	Tetragonal	Witteman and Bowman (1963)
α-UC_2	$UC_{1.94}$	$a = 3.5241 \pm 0.0005$ $c = 5.9962 \pm 0.0008$	Tetragonal	Witteman and Bowman (1963)

decompose into UC and $UC_{1.96}$. The latter reaction will also occur if the sample is initially a mixture of UC and UC_2. Thus, a change in cooling rate can produce some unexpected changes in the lattice parameter. Since this phase dissolves little oxygen or nitrogen, the lattice parameter is a good indication of the stoichiometry. Parameters for the extreme compositions as well as for the other phases are listed in Table 68, and a calculated powder pattern is given in Table 69.

Above 1765° the tetragonal structure converts to a cubic form. After Wilson (1960) proposed a CaF_2 structure, based on high temperature x-ray studies, most workers have argued for a FeS_2-type structure (Bredig, 1960; Chang, 1961). Recent work at Los Alamos, using high temperature neutron diffraction, has ruled out either possibility (A. L. Bowman *et al.*, 1966). The β form is structurally similar to KCN with the C_2 groups either as free rotators or randomly oriented along the [111] plane. It is interesting to note that, whereas the C–C distance in CaC_2 is equal to the triple bond, this distance in α-UC_2 is essentially that of a double bond.

E. CHEMICAL REACTIVITY

The very high reactivity of the uranium carbides has been a limitation to their application and a nuisance to those attempting to prepare pure

TABLE 69

COPPER RADIATION, POWDER PATTERN FOR α-$UC_{1.89}$[a]

2θ	$\sin^2\theta$	d spacing	Intensity	$h\ k\ l$
29.43	0.0645	3.0327	50	1 0 1
29.86	0.0664	2.9895	15	0 0 2
36.06	0.0958	2.4883	30	1 1 0
47.50	0.1622	1.9125	35	1 1 2
51.92	0.1916	1.7595	15	2 0 0
52.74	0.1973	1.7342	30	1 0 3
60.81	0.2561	1.5219	40	2 1 1
61.06	0.2580	1.5164	20	2 0 2
62.04	0.2655	1.4947	5	0 0 4
73.90	0.3614	1.2813	15	1 1 4
76.50	0.3833	1.2442	10	2 2 0
77.16	0.3889	1.2351	30	2 1 3
84.01	0.4478	1.1511	10	3 0 1
84.22	0.4497	1.1487	15	2 2 2
85.09	0.4572	1.1392	10	2 0 4
85.74	0.4628	1.1322	15	1 0 5
87.60	0.4791	1.1128	15	3 1 0
95.22	0.5455	1.0429	25	3 1 2
99.27	0.5806	1.0109	15	3 0 3
101.24	0.5975	0.9965	5	0 0 6
106.19	0.6394	0.9632	25	3 2 1
107.32	0.6488	0.9562	10	2 2 4
107.99	0.6545	0.9521	30	2 1 5
112.74	0.6933	0.9251	10	1 1 6
119.29	0.7446	0.8926	30	3 1 4
122.22	0.7666	0.8798	10	4 0 0
122.98	0.7722	0.8765	35	3 2 3
125.33	0.7891	0.8671	15	2 0 6
131.46	0.8311	0.8449	35	4 1 1
131.75	0.8330	0.8440	20	4 0 2
133.80	0.8461	0.8374	25	3 0 5
136.24	0.8611	0.8300	20	1 0 7
136.45	0.8624	0.8294	10	3 3 0
149.04	0.9288	0.7992	35	3 3 2
156.41	0.9582	0.7869	50	4 2 0
158.08	0.9638	0.7846	100	4 1 3
164.05	0.9808	0.7778	60	2 2 6

[a] $a_0 = 3.5190$ Å; $c_0 = 5.9790$ Å; $\mu r = 10.0$; space group D_{4h}^{17}, No. 139; $\lambda(K\alpha_1) = 1.54051$ Å.

materials. No attempt has been made to compile all of the chemical properties exhibited by these carbides; only those reactions which would hamper the production of pure materials are discussed. Additional information can also be found in the introduction.

Fine UC is pyrophoric and in larger pieces it will slowly react with water vapor or oxygen at room temperature. For example, the storage of powdered UC in Ar containing 200 ppm O_2 will result in a stable oxygen content of 0.2–0.4 wt % (Sowden *et al.*, 1964). Oxidation of arc-melted buttons by CO_2 is measurable above 350° and no protective film is formed up to at least 700° (D. J. Brown and Stobo, 1962; Atoda *et al.*, 1964). At low temperatures, free carbon accumulates as the uranium reacts to form UO_2. Although the reaction of UC with H_2O at room temperature is slow, at 95° the reaction becomes violent. $UC_{0.75}O_{0.25}$ is much more stable under these conditions (Stoops and Hamme, 1964). Grossman (1963) observed that the surface film which was produced when UC was exposed to air could be removed by heating to above 1530° in vacuum. Below 1430° this film would reform even in a vacuum of 5×10^{-7} torr. Low pressure oxygen (10^{-4}) at 900° produced a film of UO_2 and UC_2 on the surface of UC (Ervin and Miller, 1966). Dilute HCl completely dissolves UC and gives a gas composition which is insensitive to the concentration and temperature. It is suggested that the C/H ratio in the gas could be used as an indication of free uranium content (Besson *et al.*, 1964).

Mallett *et al.* (1952) observed no reaction between U_2C_3 and water at 75° unless the solution was made strongly acid. Borchardt (1959) found the reaction between $UC_{1.69}$ and oxygen between 150° and 680° to give UO_2 and carbon. At higher temperatures the reaction led to U_3O_8 and CO_2.

The reaction of UC_2 with water has been studied recently by Kempter (1962), and Bradley and Ferris (1963). UC_2 was found to hydrolyze faster than UC. Tripler *et al.* (1959) found a reaction rate with N_2, O_2, and H_2O which increased in this order. UC_2 is apparently slightly more reactive to oxidation by CO_2 than is UC (Atoda *et al.*, 1964). Above 600°, N_2 reacts giving graphite and the sesquinitride (Atoda *et al.*, 1964).

F. APPEARANCE

All of the uranium carbides are gray when powdered and metallic looking when seen as an arc-melted button.

G. HARDNESS

The apparent hardness of these carbides naturally depends on the composition and purity if cast materials are measured, and on the annealing temperature if the pieces were sintered from powders. Because these variables cannot be easily related to the fundamental property of the material, only microhardness values of reasonably well-characterized material have been listed.

A Knoop hardness of 935 kg/mm^2 (100-g load) has been reported for UC (Tripler *et al.*, 1959). This agrees well with 923 $\pm$ 56 kg/mm^2 obtained by Meerson *et al.* (1960). Measurements reported by Chubb and Dickerson (1962), although they show a good deal of scatter, center around 600 kg/mm^2. More recently, these authors (1963) gave 650 kg/mm^2 DPH as the room temperature value for both $UC_{1.02}$ and $UC_{0.98}$ with a decrease in hardness at higher temperatures.

Workers at Battelle have consistently reported 1100 kg/mm^2 (both Knoop and DPH) for U_2C_3 and 500 kg/mm^2 for UC_2 (Tripler *et al.*, 1959; Chubb and Dickerson, 1962, 1963; Chubb and Rough, 1960). Jones (1956) found 700 kg/mm^2 DPH for UC_2. Norreys *et al.* (1964) observed 1500 kg/mm^2 (50-g load) as the hardness of U_2C_3.

H. THERMOCHEMICAL PROPERTIES

Quite a few critical evaluations of this system have appeared, but, unfortunately, each was based on basic values which time has not treated kindly (Henney *et al.*, 1962; Rand and Kubaschewski, 1960; Huber *et al.*, 1963; Cunningham *et al.*, 1962; Vienna Panel, 1963). Without going into such a detailed treatment as was presented in the Vienna Report (Vienna Panel, 1963), a broad picture of the more reliable data and its implications will be attempted. There is, perhaps, still no universal agreement about the interpretation of the various measurements and the cause for their differences. Nevertheless, with appropriate apologies, some effort will be made to show why these conflicts might have occurred.

1. Uranium

To take advantage of some recent measurements, the high temperature thermal properties of uranium metal have been reviewed. Figure 60 shows a summary of the heat content data. The various studies are in excellent agreement except in the γ region. In the absence of any reason why this difference should exist, the reported values were combined and

TABLE 70
THERMAL FUNCTIONS OF URANIUM[a]

Form	T (°K)	$H_T^\circ - H_{298}^\circ$ (cal/mole)	C_p° (cal/mole-deg)	S_T° (cal/mole-deg)	$-(F_T^\circ - H_{298}^\circ)/T$ (cal/mole-deg)
α	298.15	0.0	6.61	12.00	12.00
	300	12.22	6.61	12.04	12.00
	400	672.3	6.80	13.94	12.26
	500	1391	7.63	15.54	12.76
	600	2200	8.56	17.01	13.34
	700	3099	9.40	18.40	14.00
	800	4076	10.09	19.70	14.60
	900	5111	10.58	20.92	15.24
	940.0	5537	10.72	21.38	15.49
β	940.0	6136	12.06	22.02	15.49
	1000	6859	12.06	22.77	15.91
	1048.0	7438	12.06	23.33	16.24
γ	1048.0	8441	10.24	24.29	16.24
	1100	8973	10.24	24.79	16.63
	1200	9997	10.24	25.68	17.35
	1300	11020	10.24	26.49	18.02
	1400	12040	10.24	27.26	18.65
	1405.5	12100	10.24	27.30	18.69
Liquid	1405.5	13780	11.45	28.49	18.68
	1500	14860	11.45	29.23	19.32
	1600	16010	11.45	29.97	19.97
	1700	17150	11.45	30.66	20.57
	1800	18300	11.45	31.32	21.15
	1900	19440	11.45	31.94	21.70
	2000	20590	11.45	32.53	22.23
	2100	21730	11.45	33.08	22.73
	2200	22880	11.45	33.62	23.22
	2300	24020	11.45	34.13	23.68
	2400	25170	11.45	34.61	24.13
	2500	26310	11.45	35.08	24.56

[a] α-U, $H_T^\circ - H_{298.15}^\circ = 1.2840 \times 10^3 - 4.1635T + 1.3526 \times 10^{-2}T^2 - 4.1234 \times 10^{-6}T^3 - 3.3863 \times 10^5/T$ (cal/mole, 298°–940°K, ±1.6%); β-U, $H_T^\circ - H_{298.15}^\circ = -5.2010 \times 10^3 + 12.060T$ (cal/mole, 940°–1048°K, ±0.8%); γ-U, $H_T^\circ - H_{298.15}^\circ = -2.2883 \times 10^3 + 10.238T$ (cal/mole, 1048°–1405.5°K, ±1.5%); liquid U, $H_T^\circ - H_{298.15}^\circ = -2.3163 \times 10^3 + 11.452T$ (cal/mole, 1405.5°–2500°K, ±0.2%).

fit by a linear equation. The same procedure was applied to the β and liquid regions. For α-U, the fitting function (the same as was used to treat the carbide system) was made to agree with the low temperature heat capacity

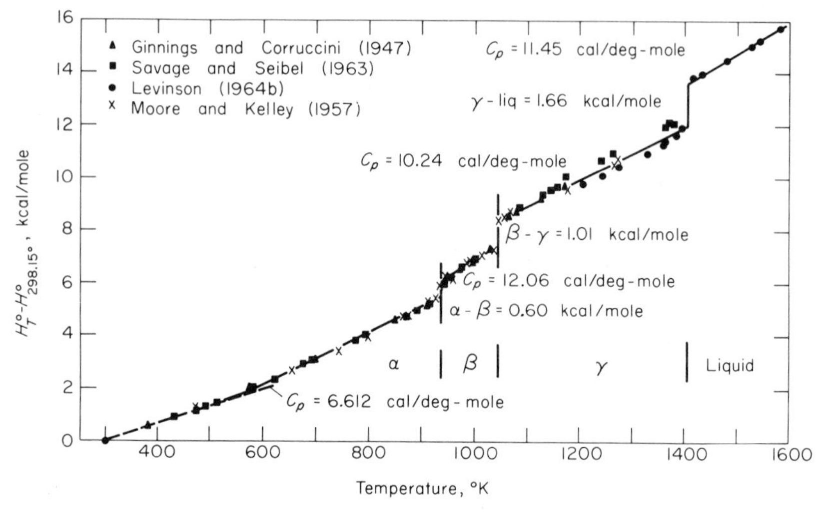

FIG. 60. High temperature enthalpy of U.

measurements of Flotow and Lohr (1960). The resulting thermal functions are listed in Table 70.

2. URANIUM MONOCARBIDE, UC

a. Heat of Formation

The heat of formation of UC has been measured by combustion calorimetry on three occasions. Farr *et al.* (1959) obtained -21.0 ± 1.0 kcal/mole after correcting for about 4% free uranium and 850 ppm oxygen. Droege *et al.* (1959) gave -20.0 ± 5.0 kcal/mole, after corrections were made for the 1450 ppm oxygen and the uranium metal present. If a common heat of formation for U_3O_8 is used, this value becomes -19.7 kcal/mole. A recent recalculation of the former measurement by Huber *et al.*, (1963) has led to -21.7 ± 1.0 kcal/mole. This was subsequently accepted by the Vienna Panel (1963). Based on a better estimation of the stoichiometry, this becomes -21.1 ± 0.9 kcal/mole for $UC_{0.96}$ (Storms and Huber, 1967).

The vaporization study by Storms (1966a) suggested that the heat of formation of carbon-deficient UC might be rather composition-sensitive. Since carbon-deficient material was used in both of the calorimetric studies, another combustion measurement was undertaken by Storms and Huber (1967) using $UC_{0.996}$ and $UC_{1.032}$. Values of -23.3 ± 0.9 kcal/mole and -23.0 ± 1.0 kcal/mole, respectively, were obtained for $\Delta H_f^\circ(298.15^\circ)$.

This is in excellent agreement with the vapor pressure measurements, as will be described later.

Thermochemical data for UC and various compositions of UC_xO_{1-x} have been determined by Robinson and Chiotti (1964, 1966) from the reaction between liquid Zn and UC, from the equilibrium involving UC–Zn–$ZnCl_2$–UCl_3–C, and from an electrolytic cell. In the first system, the disappearance of $UZn_{8.5}$ above ~700°C was used to obtain −22.7 kcal/mole (700°C) as the free energy for UC by applying the relationship $\Delta G°(U_2C_3) + \Delta G°(UZn_{8.5}) - 3\Delta G°(UC) = 0$. The absence of U_2C_3 in the system at room temperature was explained by assuming an oxygen stabilization of the UC phase which increased as the temperature was lowered, thereby causing the U_2C_3 to decompose. Since most of this work was done in a graphite crucible, unit carbon activity could have resulted. Under this condition, however, UC and U_2C_3 cannot exist together. In addition, the formation of U_2C_3 is so slow at this temperature that an equilibrium involving this phase would be unlikely. In the absence of proof that U_2C_3 actually formed at 700°, there is a serious doubt whether the claimed reaction actually occurred. When the chloride system was studied, considerable oxygen contamination was found. In the presence of UO_2 and graphite, the sum of the free energy of UC and the partial free energy of UC in UO_xC_{1-x} equalled −41.2 kcal/mole at 700°C. Apparently, dissolved oxygen has a pronounced effect on the stability of the UC phase. With this result in mind, these workers (Robinson and Chiotti, 1964) undertook to measure the free energy of various compositions within the oxycarbide system using the emf produced by the cell $U/LiCl$–KCl–$UCl_3/UO_xC_{1-x}, C$. By extrapolating to zero oxygen content, they obtained $\Delta F°_{(UC)} = -16{,}915 - 1.9T$ (460°–760°C) as an expression for the free energy of formation of pure UC. Unit carbon activity was assumed. When combined with the known thermal values (Tables 70 and 72), this equation gives −16.3 kcal/mole as the heat of formation at 298.15°. Such a low heat could result if unit carbon activity was not actually achieved at the oxycarbide–UCl_3 interface. According to the phase diagram and an extrapolation of vapor pressure studies, a very small change in the carbon content at this temperature can drastically alter the uranium activity. If this were the case, the above equation would give the partial free energy of uranium in UC_{1-x}, where x represents a very small but unknown defect in the carbon lattice.

Piazza and Sinnott (1962) have measured the CO pressure over a mixture of UO_2, $U(C, O)_2$, and $U(C, O)$. Although UC in contact with

UC_2 dissolves little oxygen, at least at low temperatures, the few listed lattice parameters for UC would suggest a variable and nonequilibrium oxygen content. Since oxygen stabilizes the UC phase, the CO pressure should not be used to obtain thermochemical information for pure UC.

b. *Low Temperature Heat Capacity*

A number of low temperature heat capacity studies have been made but with some differences. Westrum *et al.* (1965) used massive pieces broken from an arc-melted button. Provided a surface oxide was not formed during handling, this sample should have been at least oxygen and nitrogen free, although no analyses were given for these elements. An average composition for the three buttons used is $UC_{1.039}$, which means a small amount of UC_2 must have been present. No correction was apparently made. The thermal values at 298.15° are listed in Table 71. Andon *et al.* (1964a) made a similar measurement using arc-melted UC containing 2.5 mole % UC_2 for which corrections were made. The analyzed oxygen content of 0.12 wt % is rather high, but its effect on the

TABLE 71
A COMPARISON OF MEASURED LOW TEMPERATURE THERMAL VALUES FOR UC, U_2C_3, AND UC_2 AT 298.15°K

C_p° (cal/deg-mole)	S° (cal/deg-mole)	$H^\circ_{298.15} - H^\circ_0$ (cal/mole)	Assumed composition	Investigator
		UC		
12.11	14.28	2193	$UC_{1.0}$	Westrum *et al.* (1965)
11.84	14.03	2159	97.5 UC + 2.5 $UC_{1.9}$	Andon *et al.* (1964a)
		U_2C_3		
25.66	32.93	4829	U_2C_3	Farr *et al.* (1965)
26.55	32.91	4836	75.3 U_2C_3 + 10.6 UC +4.1 $UC_{1.9}$ + 9.9 C	Andon *et al.* (1964b)
		α-UC_2		
14.46	16.30[a]	2513	72.05 $UC_{1.90}$ + 10.03 UC + 17.9 C	Westrum *et al.* (1965)
14.52	16.33[a]	2521	$UC_{1.94}$	Farr *et al.* (1965)
14.50	16.31[a]	2522	4.7 UC + 95.3 $UC_{1.91}$	Andon *et al.* (1964a)

[a] Entropy of mixing between random C_1 and C_2 groups is not included. See Chapter XIII, Section G,2.

measurements is not known since its chemical form is unknown. These data are also listed in Table 71. The rather limited values given by de Combarieu *et al.* (1963) are significantly higher compared to the preceding studies, while the material was apparently much purer. For subsequent calculations, an average between the values reported by Andon *et al.* (1964a) and those of Westrum *et al.* (1965) will be used.

TABLE 72
THERMAL FUNCTIONS OF $UC_{1.0}$[a]

T (°K)	$H^\circ_T - H^\circ_{298}$ (cal/mole)	C°_p (cal/mole-deg)	S°_T (cal/mole-deg)	$-(F^\circ_T - H^\circ_{298})/T$ (cal/mole-deg)
298.15	0.0	11.98	14.15	14.15
300	22.18	12.00	14.22	14.15
400	1282	13.06	17.84	14.64
500	2618	13.59	20.82	15.58
600	3995	13.94	23.33	16.67
700	5402	14.19	25.50	17.78
800	6832	14.42	27.41	18.87
900	8285	14.64	29.12	19.91
1000	9760	14.86	30.67	20.91
1100	11260	15.08	32.10	21.87
1200	12780	15.32	33.42	22.77
1300	14320	15.58	34.66	23.64
1400	15890	15.85	35.82	24.47
1500	17490	16.13	36.92	25.26
1600	19120	16.44	37.98	26.03
1700	20780	16.77	38.98	26.76
1800	22470	17.11	39.95	27.46
1900	24200	17.48	40.88	28.15
2000	25970	17.86	41.79	28.81
2100	27780	18.27	42.67	29.45
2200	29620	18.69	43.53	30.07
2300	31520	19.14	44.37	30.67
2400	33450	19.61	45.20	31.26
2500	35440	20.10	46.01	31.83
2600	37470	20.60	46.81	32.39
2700	39560	21.13	47.59	32.94
2800	41700	21.68	48.37	33.48
2823	42200	21.81	48.55	33.60

[a] $H^\circ_T - H^\circ_{298.15} = -4.9624 \times 10^3 + 14.315T - 1.5130 \times 10^{-4}T^2 + 3.5038 \times 10^{-7}T^3 + 2.0828 \times 10^5/T$ (cal/mole, 298°–2823°K, ±0.4%).

c. High Temperature Heat Content

Within a short time of one another, two measurements of the heat content of UC were reported, one at lower temperatures and the other to near the melting point, both in excellent agreement.* By combining the data and forcing C_p at 298.15° to agree with the low temperature measurements, the equation for $H_T^\circ - H_{298}^\circ$, as well as thermal functions shown in Table 72, were obtained. The data and the equation are compared in Fig. 61.

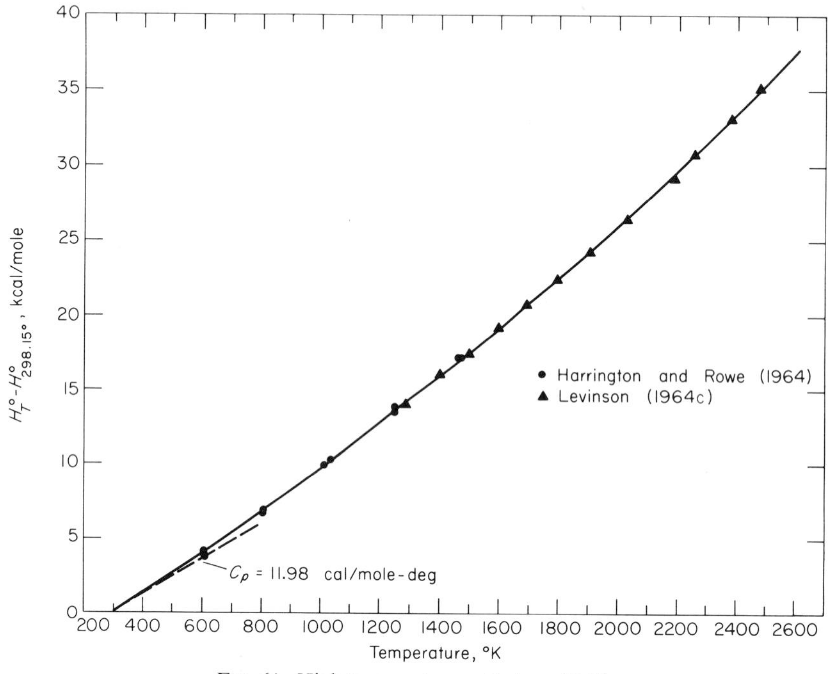

FIG. 61. High temperature enthalpy of $UC_{1.0}$.

In the absence of measurements, a number of estimations of the heat capacity have fluorished. Two of the more widely used attempts are compared to several direct measurements and the results of the present treatment in Fig. 62. Note that this system, like many of the other carbides, has an increasingly larger C_p as the melting point is approached. Also, like the other carbides, one would expect to find an important change in these

* To adjust to a common reference temperature (298°K), 300 cal were subtracted from the values of Harrington and Rowe (1964) and 170 cal were added to the values of Levinson (1964c). When the former data were reported at the Harwell Conference, this correction was omitted.

properties as the composition is changed. Unfortunately, only a very narrow composition range of UC can be quenched in, so any attempt to make such a measurement must be done at high temperatures where the difficulties are increased.

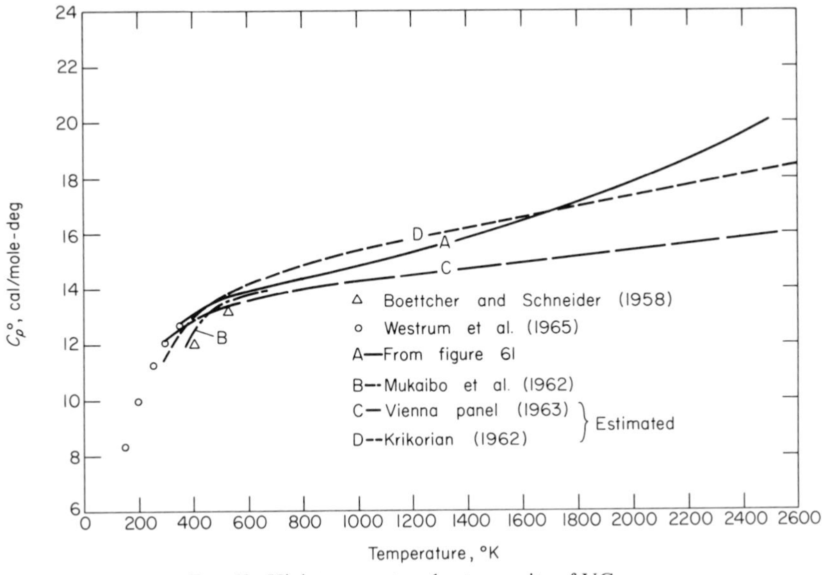

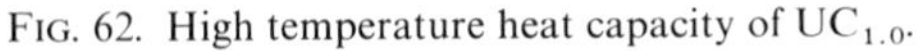
FIG. 62. High temperature heat capacity of $UC_{1.0}$.

3. U_2C_3

a. Heat of Formation

A heat of formation of -49 ± 4 kcal/mole of U_2C_3 was obtained by Huber and Holley (1962) from the heat of combustion. Galvanic measurements between 700° and 900°C gave the equation $F_f^\circ = -43{,}860 - 7T$ (cal/mole) (Behl and Egan, 1966). The absence of thermal data prevents a comparison of these measurements. However, since the phase decomposes into $UC_{\sim 1.05}$ and $UC_{\sim 1.8}$ near 2000°K, and the reaction $U_2C_3 + 0.92C = 2UC_{1.96}$ occurs at 1787°, the free energy can be calculated at these temperatures. If the free energy values obtained from the vapor pressure measurements are used and if the thermal functions of UC and UC_2 are assumed to be independent of composition, the respective reactions result in -51.9 kcal/mole at 2000° and -52.6 kcal/mole at 1787°. This compares to -51.4 kcal/mole at 1073° from the above emf study. These values can be fit by the equation $\Delta F_f^\circ = -50{,}760 - 0.6T$ (cal/mole).

b. Low Temperature Heat Content

Low temperature data for this compound has been provided by Farr *et al.* (1965) and by Andon *et al.* (1964a).* As is generally the case with this compound, the data, shown in Table 70, are in excellent agreement.

c. High Temperature Heat Content

No studies have been reported.

4. UC_2

a. Heat of Formation

A recent redetermination of the heat of combustion of $UC_{1.90}$ (Huber *et al.*, 1963) has yielded 21.1 ± 1.4 kcal/mole at 298.15°. The Vienna Panel (1963) adopted 23 ± 2 kcal/mole.

By measuring the emf developed by a cell involving C, UC_2, UF_3, and U, Behl and Egan (1966) obtained the equations $\Delta F_f^\circ = -15{,}820 - 8.2T$ (cal/mole, 973°–1145°) and $\Delta F_f^\circ = -18{,}980 - 5.2T$ (cal/mole, 1045°–1193°) for the free energy of UC_2. From the thermal values in Tables 70, 73,† and those given by the JANAF Panel (1963), an average third law heat of formation of -20.5 ± 0.5 kcal/mole can be calculated for $UC_{1.9}$ at 298.15°. There is, however, a trend in this quantity with temperature which is included in the indicated error. In view of such good agreement between these diverse measurements and with vaporization studies, which are discussed in a later section, a value of -20.0 ± 1.0 kcal/mole is recommended as the heat of formation of $UC_{1.9}$.

Besides these more or less direct measurements, thermodynamic information has been obtained from a number of ternary systems. The activity coefficient of uranium in UC_2 has been measured by equilibrating UC_2 with liquid Bi at 800°–1000°C. Good agreement with the calorimetric values is claimed (Balzhiser and Ragone, 1964). Alcock and Grieveson (1962) have attempted to measure the activity of uranium in various compositions between UC and UC_2 by equilibrating with liquid gold. The resulting activity of gold was determined by vapor pressure measurements, and this was used to obtain the uranium activity by combining a Gibbs–Duhem integration with the known activity of Au in the U–Au system. However, the uranium activity is almost a factor of 10 higher than that reported by Storms (1966a). The reason for this discrepancy is not clear. Benesovsky and Rudy (1961) have studied the systems UC–(Zr, Hf, Nb)–C from which a free energy of formation

* The reported values were subsequently amended slightly (Andon *et al.*, 1964b).

† A randomization entropy of 0.63 eu was included.

difference, $\Delta F_{(UC_2)} - \Delta F_{(UC)}$, of -2.1 ± 1 kcal/mole at 1700°C was calculated. This can be compared to -1.2 kcal/mole based on currently accepted values.

The CO pressure over an initial mixture of UC_2 and graphite has been measured and attributed to the equilibrium $UO_2 + 4C = UC_2 + 2CO$ (Piazza and Sinnott, 1962). While the solubility of oxygen in UC_2 is small at low temperatures, its presence at high temperatures will influence the stability of the UC_2 phase in an unknown way. Any attempt to use this equilibrium to obtain thermochemical values for pure UC_2 must, therefore, accept a rather large uncertainty.

b. Low Temperature Heat Capacity

UC_2 has been studied at two different compositions. For $UC_{1.90}$, Andon *et al.* (1964a) as well as Westrum *et al.* (1965) obtained essentially identical results. A study of single-phase $UC_{1.94}$, reported by Farr *et al.* (1965), also shows no significant difference from the lower composition. These values are compared in Table 71.

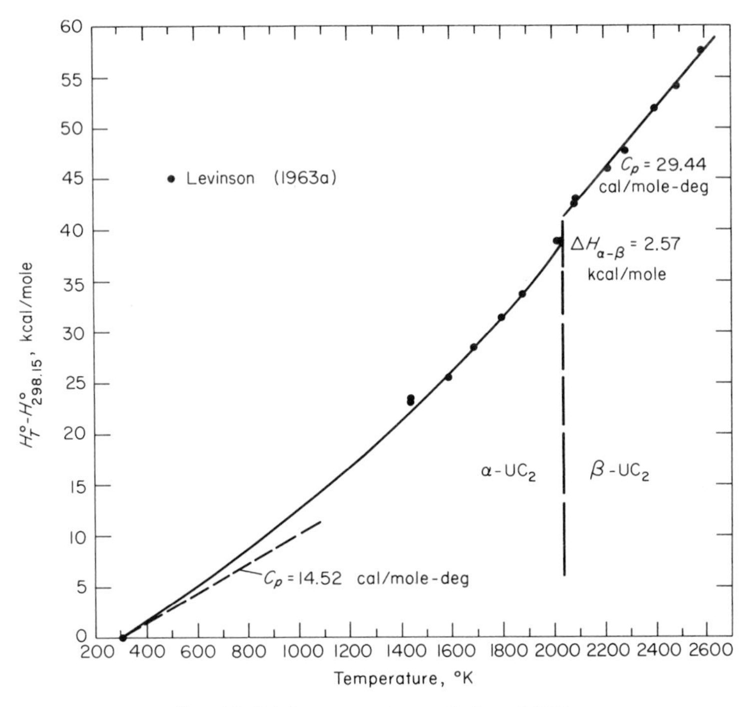

FIG. 63. High temperature enthalpy of $UC_{1.93}$.

c. *High Temperature Heat Content*

The one study of this property, which has been reported, is shown in Fig. 63. In the α region, the fitting equation was made to join smoothly the low temperature heat capacity and to give $H^\circ_T - H^\circ_{298.15} = 0.0$ at 298.15°. The β region was treated by a linear equation. The calculated thermal functions are shown in Table 73.

When the resulting heat capacity (Fig. 64) of α-UC_2 is plotted, a rather dramatic increase is found after about 1000°. Although most of the carbides show a similar behavior, the magnitude in this system is unusual. A number of difficulties attend this measurement, the most important of which is the changing composition at the phase boundary. When α-UC_2 is cooled slowly, a certain amount of UC can precipitate from it, the amount depending on the cooling rate. This would add to the amount of heat recovered in the calorimeter. In the β region, graphite precipitates upon cooling in a similar manner. As a result, the high temperature heat content and the heat capacity for both crystal forms may be too high. Avoiding this problem is not easy. Future studies should use single-phase $UC_{1.96}$ and then determine whether UC has formed upon cooling. If so, corrections can be made.

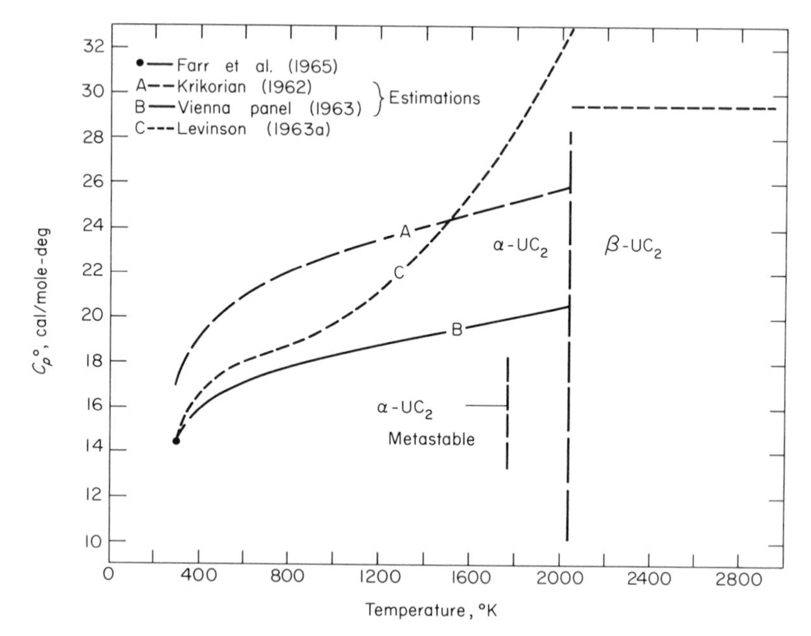

FIG. 64. High temperature heat capacity of $UC_{1.93}$.

TABLE 73
THERMAL FUNCTIONS OF $UC_{1.93}$[a]

T (°K)	$H_T^\circ - H_{298}^\circ$ (cal/mole)	C_p° (cal/mole-deg)	S_T° (cal/mole-deg)	$-(F_T^\circ - H_{298}^\circ)/T$ (cal/mole-deg)
α				
298.15	0.0	14.52	16.33	16.33
300	26.92	14.58	16.42	16.33
400	1606	16.67	20.95	16.93
500	3323	17.55	24.78	18.13
600	5104	18.05	28.02	19.52
700	6929	18.43	30.83	20.94
800	8791	18.82	33.32	22.33
900	10690	19.27	35.56	23.68
1000	12650	19.81	37.62	24.97
1100	14660	20.46	39.54	26.21
1200	16740	21.22	41.35	27.40
1300	18910	22.11	43.08	28.54
1400	21170	23.12	44.76	29.64
1500	23540	24.27	46.39	30.70
1600	26030	25.55	48.00	31.73
1700	28650	26.96	49.59	32.73
1800	31420	28.50	51.17	33.71
1900	34360	30.18	52.76	34.67
2000	37460	32.00	54.35	35.62
2038	38690	32.73	54.96	35.97
β				
2038	41260	29.44	56.22	35.97
2100	43090	29.44	57.10	36.58
2200	46030	29.44	58.47	37.55
2300	48980	29.44	59.78	38.49
2400	51920	29.44	61.03	39.40
2500	54860	29.44	62.23	40.29
2600	57810	29.44	63.39	41.16
2700	60750	29.44	64.50	42.00
2800	63690	29.44	65.57	42.82

[a] α-UC_2, $H_T^\circ - H_{298.15}^\circ = -8.0511 \times 10^3 + 22.352T - 4.4730 \times 10^{-3}T^2 + 2.3057 \times 10^{-6}T^3 + 5.1379 \times 10^5/T$ (cal/mole, 298°–2038°K, $\pm 0.5\%$); β-UC_2, $H_T^\circ - H_{298.15}^\circ = -1.8727 \times 10^4 + 29.436T$ (cal/mole, 2038°–2800°K, $\pm 1.0\%$); M.W. = 261.2. A randomization entropy of 0.50 eu is not included.

I. VAPORIZATION

1. Uranium

Early measurements of the uranium vapor pressure, as reviewed by Katz and Rabinowitch (1951), were very uncertain. To improve this situation, Rauh and Thorn (1954) (RT)* undertook a Knudsen measurement using partial collection from a Ta cell. During the study, the oxygen pressure was increased monotonically while a steady decrease in uranium pressure was observed. This was blamed on an increasing oxygen content which produced an increasingly impervious UO_2 film on the liquid surface. A number of calculations were made which supported this interpretation and, on this basis, the first run was assumed to be the more oxygen-free compared to the others. After corrections were applied for the apparent oxygen effect as well as for the dissolved Ta, the pressure was represented by $\log P(\text{atm}) = -(23{,}330 \pm 21)/T + 5.702$, and 116.6 kcal/mole was given as the heat of vaporization at 0°K. Good internal consistency was also noted. There is, however, no direct proof in this paper for an increasing oxygen content as the oxygen pressure was changed. Six years later, DeMaria *et al.* (1960) (DBDI), as part of a survey of several oxide systems, measured the pressure over $U_{(1)}$ in contact with Al_2O_3 in a Mo cell using a mass spectrometer. Uranium pressures considerably lower than those of RT were found. But this study also revealed two important properties of this system: a severe tendency for uranium to creep through and out of crucibles, which was suggested as the cause for the high pressures obtained by RT; and, under their conditions, UO was found as the major gaseous species. A heat of vaporization for uranium of 126.0 ± 5 kcal/mole was given, but, for numerous reasons, this value was not accepted (Rand, 1962). Shortly thereafter, Alcock and Grieveson (1961–1962) published the results of a collection study using a BeO cell with a tungsten lid. Their results, shown in Fig. 65, are in such good agreement with RT that the question might seem to be settled. However, since BeO is reduced by uranium to form UO_2 (Drowart *et al.*, 1964), the metal would have been saturated with oxygen. An attempt to resolve this discrepancy was next made by Ackermann *et al.* (1962) (ART). The creep of uranium was dismissed as the explanation based on the unreported observation of RT that, after an early run, an autoradiograph indicated no uranium on the crucible lid. Various arguments were developed involving an assumed rate of oxygen entry into the cell and the effect this would have on the formation of gaseous UO and solid UO_2.

* In the following discussion, the papers will be designated by the initials of the authors.

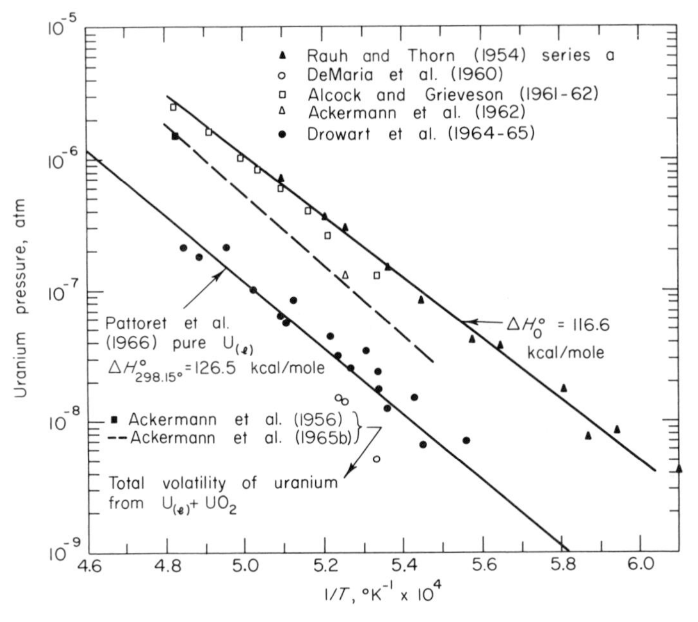

FIG. 65. Pressure of $U_{(g)}$ over $U_{(l)}$.

This reasoning eliminated the formation of a UO_2 film as an explanation. So, in order to reconcile all of the observations, it was necessary to conclude that, as oxygen dissolves in the U–Ta liquid, the pressure of uranium drops faster than the UO pressure increases. To test this idea, uranium contained in a Ta cell was observed by a mass spectrometer while the ambient oxygen pressure was changed. As expected, the uranium pressure apparently dropped while the UO pressure remained almost unaffected. However, a drop in the H_2O^+ peak was also observed. This made it necessary to assume a change in spectrometer sensitivity which caused the U intensity to drop, but which was exactly counterbalanced by an increase in the UO pressure. Consequently a direct test was prevented, so an indirect tack was taken. If oxygen does not change the activity of uranium, as was argued by DBDI, changing the oxygen pressure by a factor of 100 should produce a similar change in the UO pressure. The observed change, even allowing for the sensitivity problem, was much too small. Therefore, they proposed that a change must have occurred in the uranium activity. Since there is no assurance of even a slight similarity between the total pressure measured at the ion gauge and the oxygen pressure over the lid of the Knudsen cell, no conclusion can be derived from this observation. When a mixture of U and UO_2 was added to the cell, the U, UO, and UO_2 pressure ratios agreed with those reported by DBDI, with UO as the major species. At this point the question still remains, Does oxygen lower the pressure of uranium and raise that of UO by an equal amount?

During the last few years, the uranium pressures over a number of binary uranium systems were measured. In particular, the U–C system showed a basic conflict between the measured pressures and the heat of formation, if RT's heat of vaporization was used. Also, the observed congruently vaporizing composition at $UC_{1.1}$ is not consistent with the calculated uranium pressure. This is discussed in some detail by Alcock *et al.* (1964a,b) and Drowart *et al.* (1964) from opposite sides of the issue.

With this in mind, the latter workers (1965) attempted to duplicate the experimental conditions used by RT and to study the pressure of U both in the presence and absence of oxygen with a mass spectrometer. Two important points were made: after using RT's procedure, U, UO, and UO_2 were found in the vapor with DBDI's absolute pressures, and with a ratio reported by ART for the $U_{(l)} + UO_2$ system. At most, a change by a factor of 1.6 was observed in the uranium pressure during deoxidation, while the UO^+/U^+ ratio changed from 10 to 0.03. The experimental conditions of Alcock and Grieveson (1961–1962) were also duplicated and the presence of $UO_{2(s)}$ in the uranium was verified both visually and by the pressure measurements. In light of this evidence, an explanation was offered for RT's observations. Instead of an increase in the oxygen content with time, as RT proposed, the reduced uranium volatility was caused by a deoxidation which occurred independently of the ambient oxygen pressure. In answer to this explanation, Ackermann *et al.* (1965a) admit that the collection pressures might be too high, because of the $UO_{(g)}$, but point out they are already a factor of 2 higher than those measured over $U_{(l)} + UO_2$ (Ackermann *et al.*, 1956, 1965b) and the slope is 18 kcal/mole less. In addition, attempts to duplicate the previous measurements using a mass spectrometer have given erratic results. They state that "at this time, any further removal of remaining discrepancies cannot be effected" and suggest that an uncontrolled variable, possibly Ta, is obscuring a complete understanding of the system. If Ta leads to a higher oxygen activity, in the presence of $UO_{2(s)}$, hence a higher UO pressure, then RT's values would give the total volatility of the U–Ta–UO_2 system while Ackermann *et al.* (1965a) measured the U + UO_2 system. This does not explain why Alcock and Grieveson (1961–1962) also obtain higher pressures using a BeO crucible nor why the summation of the U, UO, and UO_2 partial pressures found by DBDI using an Al_2O_3 crucible are also higher than the total volatility from $U_{(l)} + UO_2$. In any case, the conclusions reached by RT have not been supported. Drowart *et al.* (1965) have continued their studies using W and Ta cells containing oxygen-free uranium as well as various compositions in the oxide system. Similar results were obtained from both cells. These measurements give $\log P(\text{atm}) = 5.77 - 2.54 \times 10^4/T$ as the pressure of pure uranium between 1720° and 2340°K. Using the thermal functions in Table 69 and those listed for $U_{(g)}$ by Feber and Herrick (1965), a heat of vaporization at 298.15°K of 126.5 kcal/mole (third law) and 126.8 kcal/mole (second law) were calculated. A value of 126.5 ± 0.5 kcal/mole is recommended. Further support for this will be presented in the next section.

2. Carbide System

Beginning with Leitnaker and Witteman (1962), a considerable effort has been devoted to proving that a composition near $UC_{1.1}$ is congruently vaporizing. Vozzella has consistently reported $UC_{1.1}$ (Vozzella *et al.*, 1963, DeCrescente and Miller, 1964; Vozzella and DeCrescente, 1965) for temperatures between 2325° and 2500°K. M. G. Bowman and Krupka (1963) and Witteman and Bowman (1963), reporting results of a continuing study being made at Los Alamos, found a composition of $UC_{1.065}$ between 2373° and 2573°K. Even a plug of $UC_2 + C$ ($UC_{2.2}$) heated at 2323°K has been found to lose carbon preferentially down to at least $UC_{1.3}$ (Krupka, 1966). This contrasts with the experience reported by Alcock *et al.* (1964a). They noted an increasing amount of graphite on the surface of an evaporating plug, but, unfortunately, the temperature was not given. Storms (1966a) has recently shown that below 2000°K the system will, indeed, lose uranium preferentially, but above 2300°K the congruent composition is near $UC_{1.1}$. Thus, these observations may not be inconsistent. The congruent studies have been done in a sufficiently good vacuum ($<10^{-6}$ torr) and with sufficiently pure materials that there is no doubt this behavior is real, and not caused by the evolution of CO as suggested by Alcock *et al.* (1964a).

A number of vapor pressure measurements have been made at several isolated compositions, i.e., over $UC_2 + C$ and over compositions near the congruent composition. Storms (1966a) has studied this system as a function of composition and has shown how the previous measurements relate to the general behavior. The following discussion will be based primarily on his work, starting at $UC_2 + C$. As can be seen in Fig. 66, the collection study of Leitnaker and Witteman (1962) and the mass

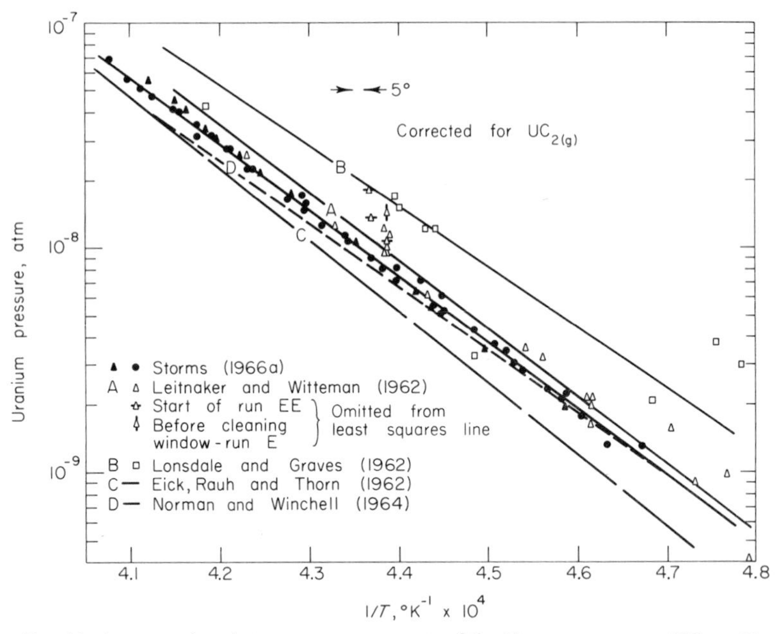

FIG. 66. A comparison between measurements of the $U_{(g)}$ pressure over UC_2 + C.

spectrometer studies of Norman and Winchell (1964) and Storms (1966a) are in good agreement, especially at the lower temperatures. The slightly lower pressures reported by Eick *et al.* (1962) coupled with the apparently low carbon content of their sample ($UC_{1.78}$) suggest an impurity besides the reported 0.1% Ta which lowered the activity of uranium.* A number of studies have given much higher pressures [Alcock and Grieveson, 1962 (weight loss); Fujishiro, 1961 (collection); Alexander *et al.*, 1964 (collection); Lonsdale and Graves, 1962 (collection)], but these were no doubt influenced by the effect of an oxide impurity. The use of fine powders and especially the grinding of the sample between measurements, as was done by several workers, is certain to result in oxide contamination, even if this is done in a dry box. There is very little oxygen removal below 1800° (Anselin *et al.*, 1964) and a complete purification will result only after extensive heating above 2000°. For example, after heating a powdered sample (<325 mesh) for 6 hours at 1900°, Leitnaker and Witteman (1962) measured a uranium pressure which was much higher than previous values and which dropped with time. Only after two additional hours of

* Indeed, this impurity alone might be responsible for the reduced pressure. Nevertheless, the two studies overlap within the random errors.

heating was agreement achieved. This behavior is indicated in Fig. 66 by points labeled "start of run EE." Besides evolving some UO and UO_2, which add to the collected uranium, the rapid loss of oxygen as CO can deplete the surface in carbon faster than it can be replaced by diffusion. As a result, the uranium pressure above the material will start high, then drop as the initial composition gradient is eliminated. This behavior was observed by Storms (1966a) in the UC region and accounts for a similar observation by Alcock *et al.* (1964a) which they attributed to the formation of a graphite diffusion barrier. Unless such problems are taken into account, a collection study of any refractory uranium compound will produce little of value.

The second law partial molar heat of vaporization for uranium from various compositions is shown in Fig. 67. A number of features deserve special comment. It has been the habit of those who have measured the U pressure over $UC_2 + C$ to assume a constant composition for the UC_2 phase throughout the temperature range of their measurements. Not only is the composition not constant, but its change has a marked effect on the slope of the uranium pressure, amounting to about 10 kcal/mole in the second law heat. Thus, any claimed agreement between the second and third law heats must have been coincidence. The effect of a composition change at a phase boundary is discussed in more detail in Chapter XIII, Section G,4. Within the single-phase region, $\Delta\bar{H}_U$ maximizes near $UC_{1.84}$, drops as more carbon is removed, then maximizes again near $UC_{1.2}$. The intervention of a two-phase region prevents an observed connection between the two maxima, but a dashed line indicates how this might occur at higher temperatures, within the single-phase region. Near $UC_{1.0}$, the heat drops rapidly and then remains essentially constant as the carbon atoms are removed, leaving vacancies in the carbon sublattice. Excellent agreement is found with the Langmuir studies of Vozzella *et al.* (1963), with the collection work of Krupka (1965) and Anselin and Poitreau (1966), and with the mass spectrometric study of Drowart *et al.* (1965). The apparent heat for $U_{(l)} + UC$ is higher than that in the adjacent single-phase UC region as the phase diagram requires. Since the two-phase, apparent $\Delta\bar{H}_U$ must be less than the heat of vaporization of pure uranium, a lower limit can be obtained for the latter value. A further refinement can be made by assuming the solution of carbon in liquid uranium to be ideal. The resulting heat is indicated by a ∇ on the uranium axis. One would expect the heat for pure uranium to fall near this value.

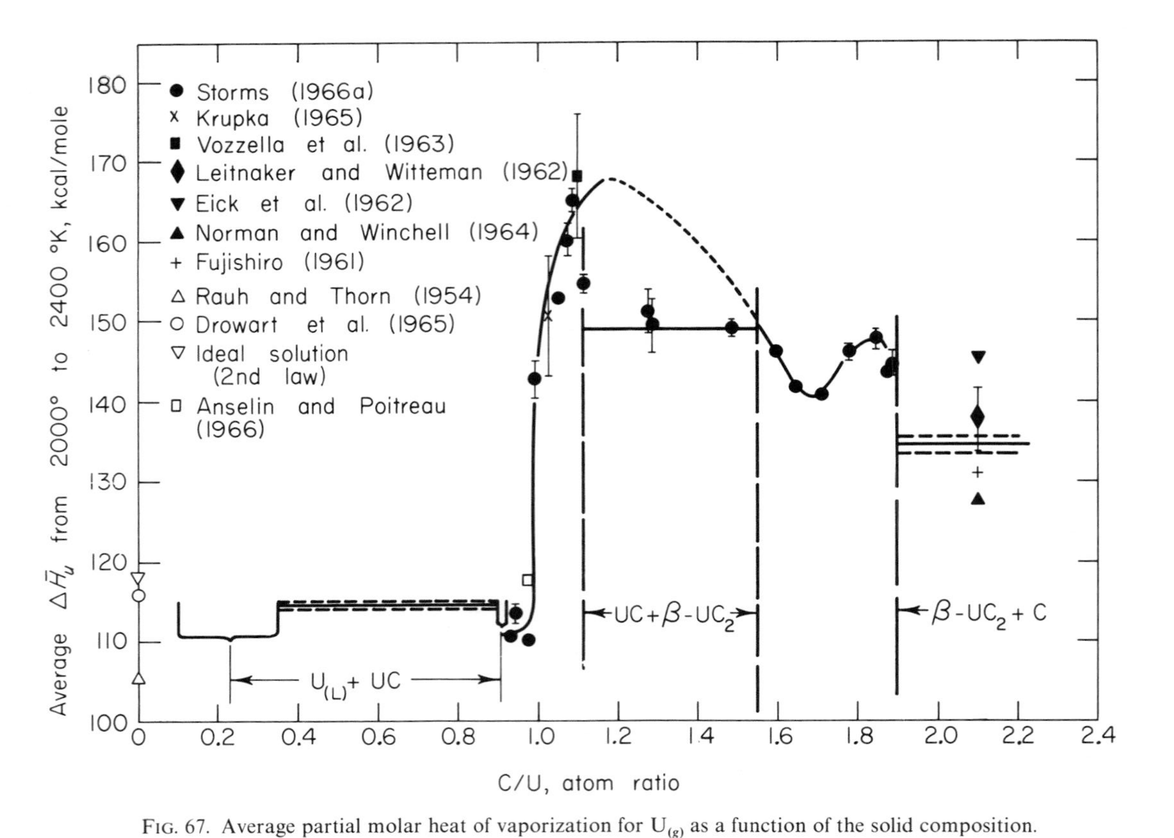

FIG. 67. Average partial molar heat of vaporization for $U_{(g)}$ as a function of the solid composition.

As can be seen in Fig. 67, a comparison with the direct measurements for uranium shows that this observation is clearly at odds with the value advocated by Rauh and Thorn (1954), but it supports the work of Drowart *et al.* (1965).

When the pressure is plotted as a function of composition, as was done in Fig. 68, the steepest change is found at $UC_{1.0}$. Good agreement in this region is found with the collection study of Krupka (1965) and Anselin and Poitreau (1966), but the Langmuir pressures given by Vozzella *et al.* (1963) are about a factor of 0.44 lower at $UC_{1.1}$. This may result from a nonunity evaporation coefficient, but such an explanation has not been proven. Within the UC_2 region, the pressure drops rapidly near the

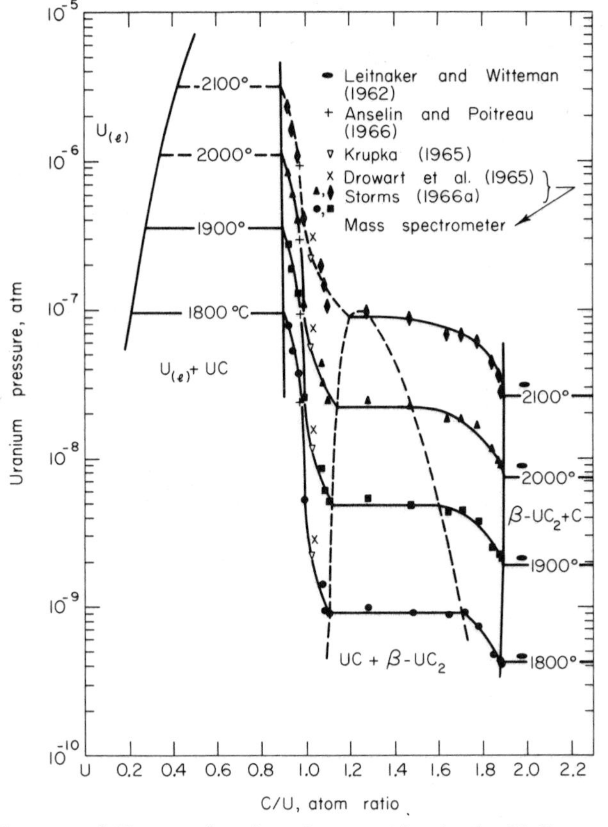

FIG. 68. Pressure of $U_{(g)}$ as a function of composition in the U–C system at various centigrade temperatures.

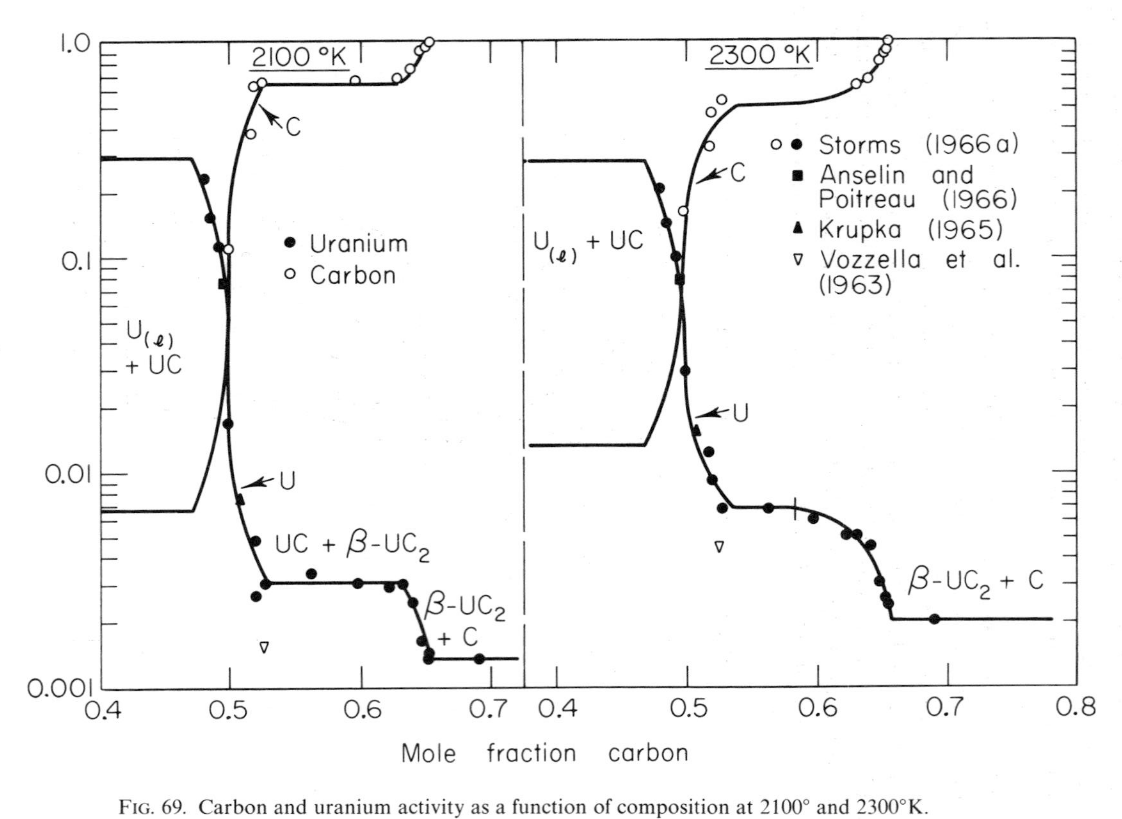

FIG. 69. Carbon and uranium activity as a function of composition at 2100° and 2300°K.

TABLE 74

ACTIVITY OF C AND U, FREE ENERGY OF FORMATION AND HEAT OF FORMATION AT VARIOUS COMPOSITIONS IN THE U–C SYSTEM[a]

Composition (C/U)	Third law							
	2100°K				2300°K			
	α_U[c]	α_C	$-\Delta F_f$ (kcal/mole)	$-\Delta H_f^\circ(298.15^\circ)$ (kcal/mole)	α_U[c]	α_C	$-\Delta F_f$ (kcal/mole)	$-\Delta H_f^\circ(298.15^\circ)$ (kcal/mole)
0.90	0.280	0.0068	23.70	—	0.26	0.0142	23.30	—
0.96	0.145	0.014	24.83	—	0.12	0.029	24.86	—
1.00	0.020	0.110	25.15	23.0	0.028	0.128	25.39	23.3
1.10	0.0036	0.560	25.82	—	0.0084	0.410	25.96	—
1.70	0.0031	0.630	27.13	—	0.0050	0.610	27.70	—
1.80	0.0023	0.770	26.98	—	0.0039	0.700	27.95	—
1.88	0.00138	1.000	27.13	19.0	0.0025	0.890	28.05	18.7[b]

[a] $\Delta H_{298}^\circ = RT(\ln \alpha_U + x \ln \alpha_C) - T\Delta$ fef for $U_{(1)} + xC_{(s)} = UC_{x(s)}$ (third law).

[b] Entropy of mixing between C_1 and C_2 groups is included.

[c] Values reported by Storms (1966a) were raised by 8% to improve agreement with absolute measurements.

$UC_2 + C$ phase boundary, with an increased slope at the higher temperatures. The collection study by Leitnaker and Witteman (1962) gives pressures which, on the average, are 16% higher than those reported by Storms (1966a).

The system evaporates $UC_{2(g)}$ as well as a small amount of $UC_{4(g)}$. Since the $UC_{2(g)}/U_{(g)}$ pressure ratio is proportional to the carbon activity squared, Storms (1966a) was able to determine the carbon activity directly by measuring this ratio at various temperatures and compositions. Thus, the carbon activity was obtained without measuring any pure carbon specie. The result is compared to the uranium activity in Fig. 69 and Table 74. A curve for the carbon activity was calculated by a Gibbs-Duhem integration of the uranium activity curve and the result is compared to the direct measurements in the figure.

With the above information and the assumption of unity evaporation coefficients for U, C_1, C_2, C_3, and UC_2, the congruently vaporizing composition can be calculated. This was done by plotting the log evaporation rate ratio, C/U, against the composition of the solid, C/U, in Fig. 70.

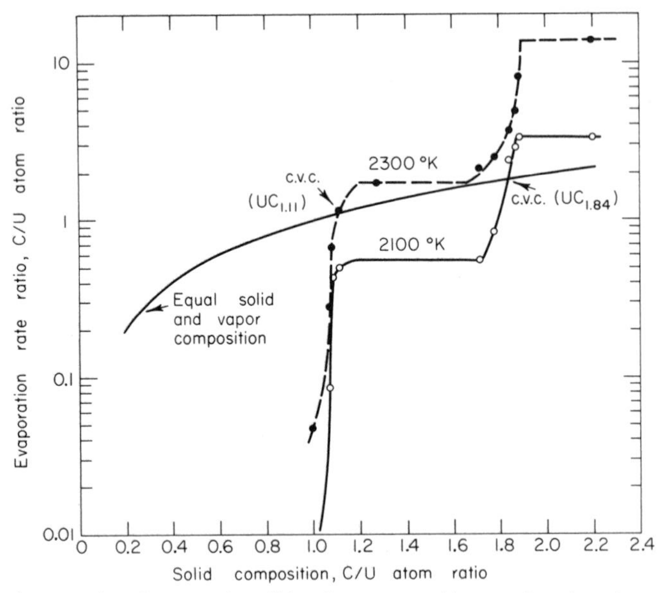

FIG. 70. A comparison between the solid and gas composition as a function of composition at 2100° and 2300°K.

Congruency for free evaporation occurs when these two quantities are equal. It is clear that above 2300°K the congruent composition lies near

$UC_{1.1}$ and does not change much as the temperature is increased. This is precisely what has been observed. At lower temperatures, it moves toward higher carbon contents until near 2230°K, and for a small temperature interval, it occurs in both the UC and UC_2 phases. As the temperature is lowered further, it finally moves to the $UC_2 + C$ phase boundary. Thus, below 2000°K $UC_2 + C$ will evaporate uranium preferentially. Of course, the evaporation of UO, UO_2, or CO can change this behavior.

In order to compare the pressure studies to the heat of combustion measurements, the heat of formation was calculated by the third law technique using 126.5 kcal/mole as the heat of vaporization of uranium. The results are listed in Table 74. When the mass spectrometric pressures are adjusted upward by 8% to average all of the absolute studies shown in Fig. 68, the resulting ΔH_f values are lowered by about 0.3 kcal/mole. On this basis, there is excellent agreement with the combustion measurement of Storms and Huber (1967) at $UC_{1.0}$. At UC_2, the agreement is not as good, but an explanation must await better thermal functions for this compound.

In view of the excellent agreement both between the vaporization studies, when the oxygen impurity was low, and with other independent measurements, there is no longer any doubt that the thermochemical behavior of this system is well known and that the heat of vaporization of uranium is very near 126.5 kcal/mole. A number of unfortunate properties are combined in this system which have required an inordinate effort before an understanding was achieved. The other refractory actinide compounds are probably cursed in a similar way and should be treated with a renewed respect.

XII

THE PLUTONIUM–PLUTONIUM DICARBIDE SYSTEM

A. PREPARATION

Arc melting, starting with either the elements or PuO_2 + C, has proven to be a satisfactory technique for making the carbides. The reaction between the elements is rapid and leads to an oxygen-free, dense carbide button which is relatively immune to atmospheric corrosion. However, compositions near Pu_2C_3 tend to shatter when cooled rapidly or when remelting is attempted (Mulford *et al.*, 1960; Kruger, 1962; Palfreyman and Russell, 1962).

Powder metallurgical techniques have been used but with only limited success. Reaction between the oxide and carbon in vacuum at temperatures as high as 1750° can give a product which is free of the oxide phase, but composition control is difficult (Ogard *et al.*, 1962). In addition, Pu_2C_3 was always present when the preparation of PuC was attempted even after the carbon content was varied over a wide range. The reaction in H_2 at 1600° always leaves some oxide phase (Palfreyman and Russell; 1962). Mulford *et al.* (1960) observed the reaction to become appreciable at 1100° and to be complete after the temperature had reached 1600°. Even when the oxide phase is absent, a considerable oxygen contamination can remain through the formation of PuC_xO_y (Anselin *et al.*, 1964; Skavdahl, 1963; Ainsley *et al.*, 1964; Brett *et al.*, 1964; Mulford *et al.*, 1965). Heating the hydride with carbon also results in the carbide (Drummond *et al.*, 1957; Pascard, 1962). In general, such products are porous, impure, and easily attacked by water vapor.

The powdered carbides are very reactive to water vapor, to a greater extent than UC, and are pyrophoric in some cases (Ogard *et al.*, 1962; Drummond *et al.*, 1957; Palfreyman and Russell, 1962; Kruger, 1962). Kruger (1962) noted that Pu_2C_3 is more reactive than PuC and a dry-box atmosphere of 1000 ppm (O_2 + H_2O) produced excessive surface corrosion within a few minutes.

PuC is very much like UC in that it forms an oxycarbide which can have a wide composition range. Much of the discussion in Chapter XI can, therefore, be applied here. As oxygen is added, the lattice parameter at first increases to 4.973 Å at 20 mole % PuO then decreases to 4.956 Å at 78 mole % PuO, where the oxycarbide, Pu_2O_3, and Pu are in equilibrium (Anselin *et al.*, 1964; Mulford *et al.*, 1965). As these authors suggest, the oxygen apparently goes into the empty carbon positions thereby increasing the parameter. Only then is carbon displaced from the lattice causing the parameter to decrease. The dissolution of nitrogen is expected to lower the parameter.

B. PHASE RELATIONSHIP

This system is composed of the following phases: plutonium metal with its six crystal forms; a zeta phase at Pu_3C_2; PuC with a defective cubic structure; another cubic compound at Pu_2C_3; and a tetragonal PuC_2 phase at high temperatures. This is summarized in a tentative phase diagram shown in Fig. 71.

Although the transition temperatures of the metal appear to be unaffected by dissolved carbon (Elliott and Larson, 1961; Mulford *et al.*, 1960), the melting point is depressed. Mulford *et al.* (1960) measured an 8° drop from 638° for the pure metal using thermal analysis, while Rosen *et al.* (1963) found incipient melting at 637° ± 1° compared to 641° ± 1°C for the element.

Above the eutectic, the solubility of carbon in liquid Pu follows the equation: log (mole fraction) = $0.50-23 \times 10^3/T$(700°–950°K); according to Bowersox and Leary (1963).

Each Pu allotrope transforms in contact with Pu_3C_2 (ζ phase). Thermal analysis studies by Mulford *et al.* (1960) have shown that Pu_3C_2 decomposes into ε-Pu + PuC at 575° while a metallographic technique places the temperature at 558° ± 2° (Rosen *et al.*, 1963). Pu_3C_2 is apparently a line compound which forms slowly during cooling (Rosen *et al.*, 1963).

Using metallographic and x-ray techniques, a number of workers have explored the single-phase region of PuC. The lower-phase boundary has been placed between $PuC_{0.832}$ and $PuC_{0.880}$ at 400° by Kruger (1963). Between 570° and 595°, the limit reaches $PuC_{0.77}$ with a trend to lower compositions at still higher temperatures (Rosen *et al.*, 1963). This is consistent with the range of $PuC_{0.698}$ to $PuC_{0.761}$ proposed by Ogard *et al.* (1965) for 575°. Burnham *et al.* (1964) give $PuC_{0.66}$ as the boundary at

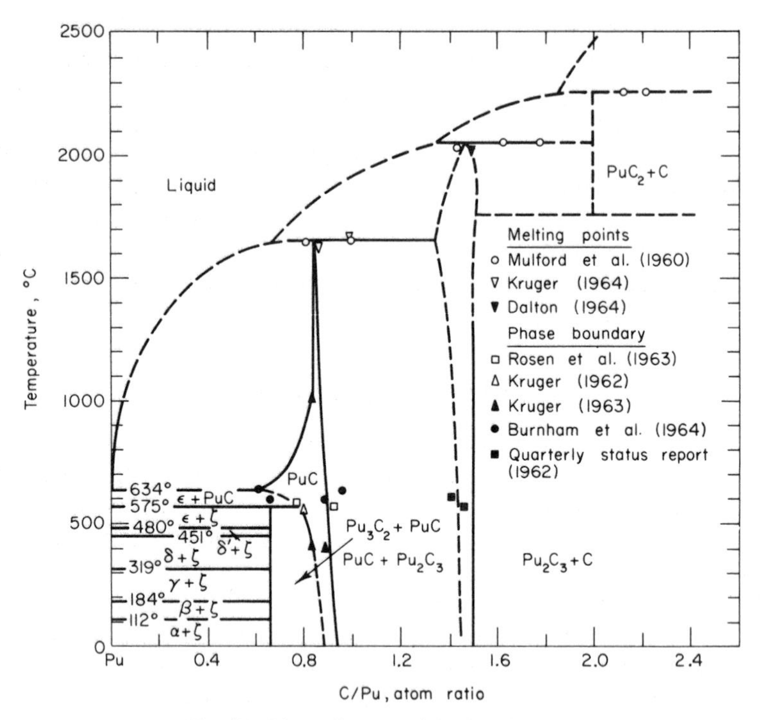

FIG. 71. Phase diagram of the Pu–C system.

600° and $PuC_{0.61}$ at the eutectic temperature, based on the variation in the lattice parameter. Above the eutectic, the composition increases to $PuC_{0.832}$ at 1000° (Kruger, 1963) with a trend to higher compositions as the peritectic temperature is approached (Rosen *et al.*, 1963). The high-carbon boundary at 600° has been reported at $PuC_{0.89}$ (Burnham *et al.*, 1964) while Rosen *et al.* (1963) gives $PuC_{0.92}$ at 570°C, both based on the lattice parameter variation. The use of as-cast material results in $PuC_{0.85}$ as the lower limit to this boundary at the peritectic temperature (Kruger, 1963). However, a metallographic study by Rosen *et al.* (1963) would place it near $PuC_{0.92}$. A trend to higher stoichiometry at lower temperatures is consistent with the behavior of the lattice parameter as the Pu_2C_3 content is increased. Kruger (1964) found that, although Pu_2C_3 was present in the as-cast material beyond $PuC_{0.85}$, the lattice parameter of PuC continued to increase until the overall composition exceeded $PuC_{0.92}$. This can be explained if the increased amount of Pu_2C_3 allowed the composition of the PuC phase to follow the phase boundary

TABLE 75

STRUCTURE AND LATTICE PARAMETER OF PLUTONIUM METAL AND ITS CARBIDES

Phases in equilibrium	Composition of first phase	Structure	Lattice parameters (Å)	Investigator
α-Pu	Pure at 21°	Simple monoclinic $P2_1/m$	$a = 6.183 \pm 0.001$ $b = 4.822 \pm 0.001$ $c = 10.963 \pm 0.001$ $\beta = 101.79° \pm 0.01°$	Zachariasen and Ellinger (1963a)
β-Pu	Pure at 190°	Monoclinic $I2/m$	$a = 9.284 \pm 0.003$ $b = 10.463 \pm 0.004$ $c = 7.859 \pm 0.003$ $\beta = 92.13° \pm 0.03°$	Zachariasen and Ellinger (1963b)
γ-Pu	Pure at 235°	Orthorhombic *Fddd*	$a = 3.159 \pm 0.001$ $b = 5.768 \pm 0.001$ $c = 10.162 \pm 0.002$	Zachariasen and Ellinger (1955)
δ-Pu	Pure at 320°	Face-centered cubic	$a = 4.6371 \pm 0.0004$	Ellinger (1956)
δ'-Pu	Pure at 465°	Body-centered tetragonal	$a = 3.327 \pm 0.003$ $c = 4.482 \pm 0.007$	Ellinger (1956)
ε-Pu	Pure at 490°	Body-centered cubic	$a = 3.6361 \pm 0.0004$	Ellinger (1956)
$PuC + Pu_3C_2$	$PuC_{0.74}$	fcc (NaCl type)	$a = 4.954$	Kruger (1962)
$PuC + Pu_2C_3$	$PuC_{0.94}$	fcc	$a = 4.9730 \pm 0.0001$	Kruger (1962)
$Pu_2C_3 + PuC$	$PuC_{\sim 1.5}$	Cubic, $I\bar{4}3d - T_d^6$	$a = 8.1210 \pm 0.0001$	Kruger (1962)
Pu_2C_3	$PuC_{\sim 1.5}$	Cubic	$a = 8.1258 \pm 0.0003$ $a = 8.1256 \pm 0.0001$	Mulford and co-workers (1960) Kruger (1962)
$Pu_2C_3 + PuC_2$	$PuC_{\sim 1.5}$	Cubic	$a = 8.1317 \pm 0.0003$	Mulford and co-workers (1960)
$Pu_2C_3 + C$	$PuC_{\sim 1.5}$	Cubic	$a = 8.1330 \pm 0.0010$	Chikalla (1962)
$PuC_2 + C$		Tetragonal $I4/mmm$	$a = 3.63$ $c = 6.094$	Chackraburtty and Jayadevan (1965)

to lower temperatures, hence to higher compositions, before equilibrium ceased during cooling. Peritectic melting of PuC has been measured by Mulford *et al.* (1960) and Kruger (1964) with good agreement. The microstructure of cast material suggests that the peritectic point might be near the liquid end of the peritectic isotherm (Kruger, 1963; Rosen *et al.*, 1963). This, according to the melting point measurements of Mulford *et al.* (1960), teminates at a composition no higher than $PuC_{0.82}$, but it might be as low as $PuC_{0.64}$ (Rosen *et al.*, 1963).

Pu_2C_3 also has a range of homogeneity, but one for which few data are available. Kruger (1963) noted a lattice parameter difference between

$PuC_{1.26}$ and $PuC_{1.47}$ while Mulford *et al.* (1960) and Chikalla (1962) found still higher parameters when the phase contacted graphite. These parameters are compared in Table 75. Work at Los Alamos (Quarterly Status Report, 1962) gave $PuC_{1.41}$ at 610° and $PuC_{1.46}$ at 555° for the low-carbon boundary. The upper boundary is assumed to lie at $PuC_{1.5}$, at least at low temperatures. This phase melts peritectically near 2050° according to Mulford *et al.* (1960).

A number of additional lines in the x-ray pattern have been observed in the composition region beyond Pu_2C_3. Drummond *et al.* (1957) then Mulford *et al.* (1960) published diffraction patterns which were attributed to PuC_2, but the patterns are different in many respects. Chackraburtty and Jayadevan (1965) obtained an additional pattern which contained many of the lines found by Mulford *et al.* (1960). Some lines could be indexed as tetragonal, isotypic with α-UC_2, but, as bound carbon increased beyond $PuC_{2.0}$, additional weak lines appeared which were identified as a mixture of graphite and a new phase. This was supported by measured bound carbon contents as high as $PuC_{2.2}$. A study of the PuC_2–α-UC_2 system by Leary (1966) has confirmed the existence of tetragonal PuC_2.

C. LATTICE PARAMETER AND STRUCTURE

The allotropic configurations of pure Pu metal are listed in Table 75 with their lattice parameters. In view of the low solubility of carbon in Pu, one would expect these parameters to remain unchanged in the carbide system.

No crystal structure has been assigned to Pu_3C_2.

PuC, with a NaCl-type lattice, shows a linear variation of lattice parameter with composition between the limits indicated in Table 75 (Kruger, 1963; Rosen *et al.*, 1963; Burnham *et al.*, 1964). The parameter at the low-carbon boundary is very sensitive to the cooling rate. A rapid quench suppresses the formation of Pu_3C_2 and causes the PuC phase to retain a low carbon content. When slow cooling is used, the PuC composition is higher, but this and the resulting lattice parameter are influenced by the amount of Pu metal present. Burnham *et al.* (1964) were able to retain a parameter as low as 4.950 Å when $PuC_{0.61}$ was quenched from the melt, but the parameter increased as the composition was reduced. Slow cooling from 600° produced a low of 4.964 Å, but this also rose as the Pu content was increased. Thus, free Pu metal apparently acts as a precipitation center, allowing the PuC phase to follow the phase boundary more effectively when it is present in large excess. Pu_3C_2 is very slow to form, but when it does it can influence the lattice parameter or dilatometric measurements in a discontinuous way near 575° (Ogard *et al.*, 1965; Kruger, 1962). On the other hand, Rand and Street (1964) observed an irreversible and discontinuous increase in the parameter of $PuC_{0.62}$ when the temperature reached 200°, 215°, 320°, and 400° with no sign of Pu_3C_2. The parameter can also be influenced by dissolved oxygen, which causes it to increase at first then to decrease as more oxygen is added (Anselin *et al.*, 1964; Mulford *et al.*, 1965), and by radiation damage, which slowly increases the parameter with time (Burnham *et al.*, 1964; Rand *et al.*, 1962). A calculated powder pattern for $PuC_{0.92}$ is given in Table 76.

Pu_2C_3 is also cubic, isotypic with U_2C_3 (Zachariasen, 1952). Although the composition range is uncertain but narrow, a higher lattice parameter has been observed when the second phase is graphite instead of PuC, as shown in Table 75. This phase, like its uranium equivalent, does not dissolve oxygen (Mulford *et al.*, 1965). A calculated powder pattern is given in Table 77.

A PuC_2 phase apparently exists at high temperatures, and it is isotypic with tetragonal α-UC_2 (Chackraburtty and Jayadevan, 1965; Leary, 1966). These workers as well as others (Mulford *et al.*, 1960; Drummond *et al.*,

TABLE 76

COPPER RADIATION, POWDER PATTERN FOR $PuC_{0.92}$[a]

2θ	$\sin^2\theta$	*d* spacing	Intensity	*h k l*
31.12	0.0720	2.8712	40	1 1 1
36.09	0.0960	2.4865	30	2 0 0
51.96	0.1919	1.7582	35	2 2 0
61.82	0.2639	1.4994	45	3 1 1
64.90	0.2879	1.4356	15	2 2 2
76.57	0.3838	1.2432	10	4 0 0
84.93	0.4558	1.1409	25	3 3 1
87.68	0.4798	1.1120	30	4 2 0
98.72	0.5758	1.0151	30	4 2 2
107.19	0.6477	0.9571	35	5 1 1, 3 3 3
122.37	0.7677	0.8791	20	4 4 0
132.79	0.8397	0.8406	80	5 3 1
136.66	0.8636	0.8288	60	6 0 0, 4 4 2
156.81	0.9596	0.7863	100	6 2 0

[a] $a_0 = 4.9730$ Å; $\mu r = 11.0$; structure type *B*1, space group No. 225; $\lambda(K\alpha_1) = 1.54051$ Å.

TABLE 77

COPPER RADIATION, POWDER PATTERN FOR Pu_2C_3[a]

2θ	$\sin^2\theta$	*d* spacing	Intensity	*h k l*
26.83	0.0538	3.3199	5	2 1 1
31.08	0.0718	2.8751	15	2 2 0
34.86	0.0897	2.5716	15	3 1 0
41.51	0.1256	2.1734	20	3 2 1
44.53	0.1435	2.0330	1	4 0 0
52.75	0.1974	1.7337	20	3 3 2
55.29	0.2153	1.6599	5	4 2 2
57.76	0.2333	1.5948	20	5 1 0, 4 3 1
62.50	0.2692	1.4847	10	5 2 1
67.05	0.3050	1.3946	1	5 3 0
71.45	0.3409	1.3192	5	5 3 2, 6 1 1
73.60	0.3589	1.2858	1	6 2 0
75.74	0.3768	1.2548	20	5 4 1
79.94	0.4127	1.1990	5	6 3 1
82.03	0.4306	1.1738	5	4 4 4
84.10	0.4486	1.1500	10	7 1 0, 5 4 3
88.22	0.4845	1.1066	10	5 5 2, 7 2 1, 6 3 3
90.28	0.5024	1.0867	10	6 4 2
92.33	0.5204	1.0678	5	7 3 0
96.46	0.5562	1.0328	5	7 3 2, 6 5 1
98.53	0.5742	1.0165	1	8 0 0
100.62	0.5921	1.0010	5	7 4 1
104.84	0.6280	0.9720	5	6 5 3
106.97	0.6460	0.9584	5	6 6 0, 8 2 2
109.14	0.6639	0.9453	15	7 4 3, 7 5 0, 8 3 1
113.55	0.6998	0.9208	5	7 5 2
118.12	0.7357	0.8980	1	9 1 0
122.90	0.7716	0.8769	20	9 2 1, 7 6 1, 6 5 5
125.38	0.7895	0.8669	15	6 6 4
127.94	0.8075	0.8572	15	9 3 0, 7 5 4, 8 5 1
133.37	0.8433	0.8388	10	7 6 3, 9 3 2, 7 6 3
136.27	0.8613	0.8300	10	8 4 4
139.33	0.8792	0.8215	10	9 4 1, 8 5 3
146.12	0.9151	0.8052	10	10 1 1, 7 7 2
150.01	0.9331	0.7974	40	10 2 0, 8 6 2
154.42	0.9510	0.7898	20	9 5 0, 9 4 3
166.85	0.9869	0.7754	100	10 3 1, 7 6 5, 9 5 2

[a] $a_0 = 8.1320$ Å; $\mu r = 9.0$; space group No. 220; $\lambda(K\alpha_1) = 1.54051$ Å.

1957) observed additional lines which suggest the existence of other phases in this composition region.

D. APPEARANCE

All compositions in the Pu–C system appear to be gray metallic.

E. CHEMICAL REACTIVITY

According to Drummond *et al.* (1957), PuC will oxidize slowly when heated to 200°–300° in air, and will burn brightly in O_2 at 400°. A clean, dense surface was observed to remain bright after 2 months in air at room temperature. It was not attacked by cold water but effervesced steadily in hot water. Cold, dilute HCl or H_2SO_4 caused hydrolysis, although HNO_3 showed only a slight action.

Pu_2C_3 was somewhat more stable to acids than PuC.

The above authors also observed that PuC_2 was much less stable in moist air than the other carbides but was more stable to oxidation.

If metal is present or if the material is porous, chemical attack will be much more rapid.

F. HARDNESS

The hardness of PuC has been observed to vary between 600 and 1000 DPH as the carbon content of the phase increases (Quarterly Status Report, 1962). Mulford *et al.* (1960) reported a hardness for PuC in contact with Pu_3C_2 of between 500 and 600 DPH, and between 70 and 90 DPH for the Pu_3C_2 phase. Palfreyman and Russell (1962) give 750 and 900 kg/mm^2 (DPH) for PuC and Pu_2C_3, respectively. Kruger (1962) reported that arc-melted PuC has a hardness of 860 $\pm$ 25 DPH (200 g).

G. THERMOCHEMICAL PROPERTIES

1. Heat of Formation

Huber and Holley (1962) have measured the heat of formation of PuC and Pu_2C_3 by combustion calorimetry. Assuming that the PuC phase had a composition of $PuC_{0.77}$ and contained ~10% Pu_2C_3, they calculated a value of $\Delta H_f^\circ = +3.7 \pm 3.1$ kcal/mole. However, the lattice parameter ($a = 4.9646$ Å) indicates a composition near $PuC_{0.82}$, while at the measured composition, the phase can not contain Pu_2C_3. These discrepancies suggest a very large error in this measurement. The vapor pressure measurements, as described in a later section, indicate that the heat of formation is near −12 kcal/mole.

Their very preliminary measurement for Pu_2C_3 gives $\Delta H_f^\circ = -1.7$ kcal/mole. This value must also be much more negative in view of the pressure measurements.

2. HEAT CONTENT

Using $PuC_{0.869}$. Kruger and Savage (1964) measured the heat content between 400° and 1300° and described the result by the equation $H_T^\circ - H_{298.15}^\circ = -5035 + 13.08T + 5.718 \times 10^{-4}T^2 + 3.232 \times 10^5/T$ (kcal/mole of $PuC_{1.0}$). No discontinuities were observed in this property.

An entropy of 17.0 cal/mole-deg is estimated for PuC at 298.15° from the method of Kaufman (1962). This is combined with the heat content values to give the thermal functions listed in Table 78.

TABLE 78
THERMAL FUNCTIONS OF $PuC_{0.87}$

T (°K)	$H_T^\circ - H_{298.15}^\circ$ (cal/mole)	C_p° (cal/mole-deg)	$S_T^{\circ b}$ (cal/mole-deg)	$-(F_T^\circ - H_{298.15}^\circ)/T$ (cal/mole-deg)
298.15	0	—	17.00[a]	17.00
400	1097	11.52	20.16	17.42
500	2296	12.36	22.83	18.24
600	3559	12.87	25.13	19.20
700	4865	13.22	27.15	20.20
800	6201	13.49	28.94	21.19
900	7562	13.71	30.52	22.12
1000	8943	13.90	32.01	23.07
1100	10340	14.07	33.34	23.94
1200	11760	14.23	34.57	24.77
1300	13190	14.38	35.68	25.54
1400	14630	14.51	36.77	26.32
1500	16090	14.66	37.77	27.04
1600	17560	14.78	38.72	27.74
1700	19050	14.92	39.61	28.40
1800	20550	15.04	40.47	29.05
1900	22060	15.16	41.30	29.69

[a] Estimate. [b] Randomization entropy not included.

3. VAPORIZATION

a. Plutonium Metal

The vapor pressure of plutonium has been measured on two occasions with excellent agreement (Phipps *et al.*, 1956; Mulford, 1966a). The more recent and extensive study by Mulford (1966a), using Knudsen collection, gives $\log P(\mathrm{atm}) = -17{,}420/T + 4.913$ between 1133° and 1782°. Although different crucibles and ambient pressures were used without effect, the uncertainty in the vapor composition, i.e., the possible presence of PuO and PuO_2, makes the measurement an upper limit. Consequently, the third law heat of vaporization, 82.14 kcal/mole (298.15°), is a lower limit.

b. Plutonium Carbide System

Based on the measured weight loss from a graphite Knudsen cell, Mulford *et al.* (1962) gave the following equation to express the pressure of Pu over $PuC_2 + C$:

$$\log P(\mathrm{atm}) = -17{,}920/T + 2.779 \ (2000°\text{–}2500°\mathrm{K})$$

Starting with $PuC_{0.898}$, Palfreyman and Potter (1964) used a transpiration method to obtain pressures which were fitted by the equation

$$\log P(\mathrm{atm}) = -51{,}100/T + 22.3 \ (1773°\text{–}1838°\mathrm{K})$$

These workers assumed that PuC was the evaporating species, which is most unlikely. However, very little error is created if the evaporation produced only $Pu_{(g)}$. Mulford (1966b) has continued his studies of this system using the Knudsen collection technique and has obtained the total volatility of Pu from $PuC + Pu_2C_3$ and from $Pu_2C_3 + C$. The resulting pressures are compared in Fig. 72 at 1800° and the apparent partial heat of vaporization is indicated. If plutonium liquid forms an ideal solution as carbon is added, its pressure would decrease as indicated in the figure. Thus, the dashed curve gives an upper limit to the pressure in this region. This curve is continued through the composition range of PuC and Pu_2C_3 with a shape based on the behavior of the other carbides. Since the apparent partial heat from $PuC + Pu_2C_3$ is greater than the heat of vaporization for the pure liquid, the decomposition of PuC into $Pu_{(l)}$ (saturated with C) + Pu_2C_3 at a higher temperature is predicted, in agreement with the phase diagram. Pu_2C_3 shows itself to be the most stable phase in this system by accepting the major pressure change. This phase has a free energy at 1800° of -17.6 kcal/mole $PuC_{1.5}$ while a Gibbs–Duhem integration and a third law treatment of the data in Fig. 72 gives -12.4 kcal/mole for $PuC_{0.85}$. The resulting carbon activity within each two-phase region is also indicated in the figure.

Since the system loses Pu preferentially, a study of material which is not in equilibrium with carbon may produce low values as the evaporating

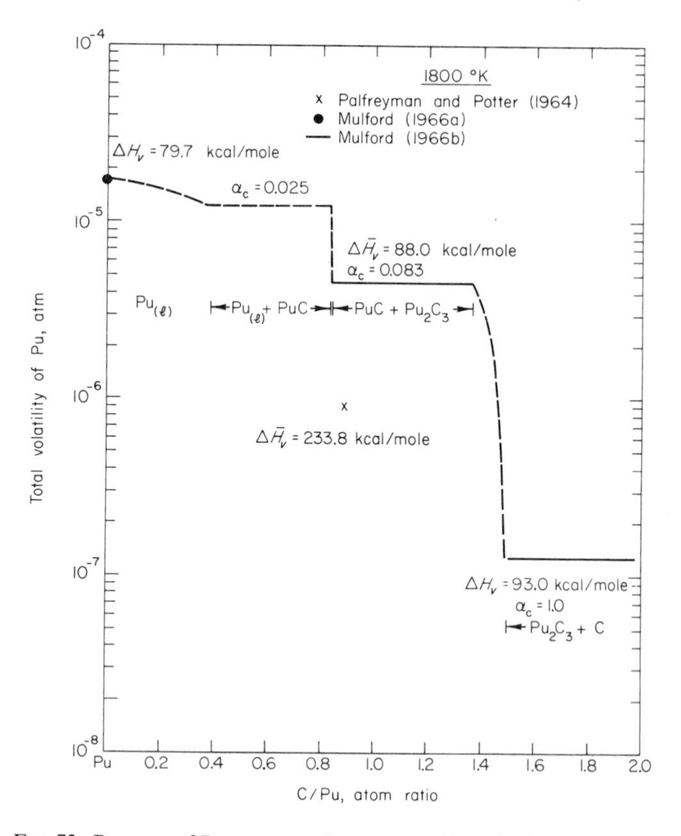

FIG. 72. Pressure of $Pu_{(g)}$ over various compositions in the Pu–C system.

surface acquires a higher carbon content. Thus, the pressures given by Palfreyman and Potter (1964) for $PuC_{0.898}$ might have been produced by a composition near the high-carbon boundary of Pu_2C_3. The competition between carbon diffusion and the evaporation of Pu would produce a variable surface composition which could account for the unreasonably high partial heat of vaporization.

It is important to remember that all of the above measurements have been interpreted assuming only $Pu_{(g)}$ as the evaporating specie. PuC_2 is probably a minor contributor from Pu_2C_3 while PuO may be important under certain conditions. Until a mass spectrometric examination is made, the reported pressures must be considered as upper limits.

XIII

DISCUSSION

A. PREPARATION

Preparation of the carbides is relatively easy, but to make them oxygen-free is a difficult and subtle process which many investigators have failed to appreciate. Even a few hundred parts per million of this impurity can have a noticeable effect on the physical and chemical properties while a few thousand parts per million can render the measurements worthless. Since the chemistry involving oxygen is very similar in these systems, the following discussion has a general application.

The carbides can dissolve considerable oxygen by its substitution for carbon. This can occur readily when the lattice is not fully saturated with carbon or through a process which removes carbon from the lattice. For example, $MC_{0.7}$, when exposed to the oxide will form $MC_{0.7}O_{0.3}$, but $MC_{1.0}$ under the same conditions will remain pure unless CO is removed from the system. Either process can result in lattice defects, i.e., $MC_{0.7}O_{0.1}$, for example, can be an end product under some circumstances. Thus, the behavior of the oxycarbide systems depends on two and sometimes three composition variables. The effect of nonmetal defects becomes particularly important when the preparation of a pure, carbon-deficient carbide is attempted.

Another way to examine this problem is to picture the oxycarbide as a solution between MC and MO. In order for oxygen to dissolve, the oxide phase must be reduced to the unstable but soluble MO. In many cases, the amount of dissolved oxygen will depend on whether this reaction can occur at a sufficient rate. When compositions near the high-carbon boundary are exposed to the oxide, the reaction

$$\text{Oxide} + \begin{matrix}\text{Carbon dissolved in}\\ \text{the carbide}\end{matrix} = \begin{matrix}\text{MO dissolved in}\\ \text{the carbide}\end{matrix} + \text{CO}$$

can lead to an increasing amount of dissolved oxygen as CO is pumped away. At the low-carbon boundary, the reaction

$$\text{Oxide} + \text{M in carbide} = \text{MO dissolved in carbide}$$

can proceed independently of the CO pressure.

There are two ways to remove oxygen from the lattice. In the presence of excess graphite, a high CO pressure will result in a purer and more nearly stoichiometric carbide. This can be attributed to a reaction such as $MC_{0.7}O_{0.3} + CO = MC_{0.9}O_{0.1}$ + oxide phase, and it depends on an increasing CO pressure as oxygen is replaced by carbon in the fully saturated oxycarbide. While a partial purification of the saturated carbide will result, this technique can not be applied to carbides which are not in equilibrium with graphite. The other method requires a very low CO pressure and the use of high temperatures. Its success will depend on a number of factors, including the stability of the oxycarbide, the annealing temperature and time, and the ambient CO pressure. In general, the stability of the oxycarbides decreases in the order: Group 4, actinides, Group 5, and Group 6. The Group 4 carbides are very difficult to purify by any treatment short of melting, and heating at low temperatures (1000°–2000°) will usually result in recontamination unless the vacuum is better than $\sim 10^{-6}$ torr. The U–C and Th–C systems can be purified at temperatures in excess of 2000°, but very little oxygen removal occurs from the oxycarbide below ~1600°. Except for vanadium carbide, which is discussed in Chapter IV, Groups 5 and 6 purify easily at temperatures above 1800°. The result of such a treatment naturally depends on allowing sufficient time for the oxygen to diffuse to the surface and be removed from the system.

When unsaturated carbides are sought, the purification problem becomes even worse. Since the CO pressure depends on the product of the carbon and oxygen activities, the CO pressure will drop rapidly as the carbide is made more defective. As a result, carbon-deficient carbides or the subcarbides are not only more difficult to purify, but they require a much better vacuum to remain pure if they are heated.

Because oxygen is so reluctant to leave these materials, the normal analytical methods are difficult to apply, especially in Group 4. Pt bath fusion (Smiley, 1955) and fusion in graphite (M. E. Smith *et al.*, 1963) have been used with mixed success. It is doubtful that a reliable chemical method exists for the determination of oxygen in the carbon-deficient Group 4 carbides.

Besides oxygen purity, composition uniformity is a serious problem when carbon-deficient carbides are made. The diffusion of carbon is so slow, in several of these systems, that evaporation or the presence of such gases as CO, CH_4, or flowing H_2 can lead to gradients which are difficult to detect. Since each system behaves differently in this respect, no general rules can be suggested except to emphasize the importance of taking this effect into account. Often the final treatment, the sharpness of the x-ray pattern, or the lattice parameter will given an indication of the homogeneity.

A number of techniques have been used to prepare the carbides, a few of which will be discussed in the following paragraphs. However, in most cases a final purification, as described above, is necessary.

It has been the common practice of early workers, and a few even now, to use the oxide and graphite as starting materials. Although this method has economic advantages, it seldom results in a purity sufficient for basic studies, and it is totally unacceptable for producing carbon-deficient compositions. The product should be used only after it has been further purified by arc melting or by a suitable high vacuum anneal.

The application of powder metallurgical techniques using mixtures of the elements or the metal hydride and graphite have resulted in relatively pure carbides of various compositions. This is a particularly useful method when defective compounds in Groups 5 and 6 are needed. The powdered metals or hydrides in Group 4 and the actinide series are sufficiently reactive to air that the introduction of oxygen is hard to avoid.

Arc melting is very useful when purity is the primary consideration. However, such a treatment often produces severe composition inhomogeneity, depending on the system and its stoichiometry. For example, TaC can not be successfully arc melted without a preferential loss of carbon, but Ta_2C can be made quite easily. The technique, in general, can be applied to all compositions in Group 6 and the actinide series. Other single-phase carbides can be made in this way, if a subsequent anneal is used.

The reactions between metal chlorides and graphite, and the metal with hydrocarbon vapors have been used to obtain coatings of the carbides. Bulk quantities can also be made by the latter reaction. Both techniques suffer from the difficulties in obtaining pure gases. The advantage in the latter method for bulk production, over the direct reaction with carbon, is the lower temperature needed. In order to fully use this advantage, however, the metal must be finely powdered. Thus, the chance for oxygen contamination is increased. Since hydrogen can dissolve in the defect carbides, any treatment involving H_2 or a hydrocarbon should be followed by a vacuum anneal.

B. PHASE RELATIONSHIP

The transition metal carbides show a regular change in behavior in going from one group to the next, and within a group the systems are quite similar. The same is true within the actinide series. A comparison is made in Table 79, between the melting point of the element, the minimum and the maximum melting temperatures within the system, and the melting temperature when graphite is present. The general trends in this property will be discussed in the following section.

Group 4 is characterized by a single cubic compound having a very wide range of composition which extends almost to $MC_{1.0}$. In each system, the phase melts congruently at a substoichiometric composition and at a temperature which is much higher than the melting point of the

TABLE 79
MELTING POINT COMPARISON[a]

	Group 4			Group 5		
	Ti	Zr	Hf	V	Nb	Ta
Pure element (°C)	1668° ± 8°	1855° ± 15°	2222° ± 10°	1888° ± 10°	2467° ± 10°	3014° ± 10°
Minimum m.p. (°C)	1645° ± 5°	1825° ± 15°	2200° ± 50°	1630° ± 20°	2335° ± 10°	2850° ± 25°
Maximum m.p. (°C)	3067° ± 20°	3420° ± 20°	3950° ± 20°	2700° ± 50°	3600° ± 50°	4000° ± 75°
M.p. in the presence of graphite (°C)	2776° ± 10°	2850° ± 50°	3180° ± 50°	2700° ± 50°	3300° ± 50°	3400° ± 50°
Composition at maximum m.p. (atom ratio)	0.8	0.83	0.95	0.85	0.82	0.88

	Group 6			Actinide		
	Cr	Mo	W	Th	U	Pu
Pure element (°C)	1915° ± 15°	2620° ± 10°	3410° ± 20°	1725° ± 10°	1132° ± 1°	639° ± 2°
Minimum m.p. (°C)	1500° ± 10°	2205° ± 3°	2710° ± 10°	<1725° ± 20°	1117° ± 2°	634° ± 4°
Maximum m.p. (°C)	1875° ± 25°	≥2580°	≥2780°	2670° ± 25°	2550° ± 25°	2050° ± 50°
M.p. in the presence of graphite (°C)	1875° ± 25°	2580° ± 10°	2780° ± 30°	2500° ± 15°	2450° ± 25°	2050° ± 50°
Composition at maximum m.p. (atom ratio)	0.68	0.72	0.75	1.8	0.98	2.0

[a] Error based on probable reproducibility between independent measurements.

element. The phase is normally found between $MC_{0.5}$ and $MC_{0.97}$, depending on the quenching rate and temperature. Although TiC and ZrC form eutectics with the metal, the situation with HfC is uncertain.

Within Group 5, the phase relationship becomes more complex. Between the metal and the MC compound, a M_2C phase forms with a narrow composition range at room temperature. This decomposes peritectically into a liquid and the MC phase with a composition near $MC_{0.6}$. The cubic phase extends only to $MC_{0.88}$ in the V–C system, but NbC and TaC approach $MC_{1.0}$ as the temperature is lowered. Melting of NbC and TaC is congruent at a substoichiometric composition. In fact, $TaC_{0.88}$ is the highest melting substance known.

Group 6 shows an increased complexity with only a slight similarity between the members. The chromium carbides are more like the manganese carbides rather than like the V–C system, and they have none of the features common to the Mo–C and W–C systems. Even the latter carbides have only a few similarities. Both form a M_2C compound having an allotropic transition, and both have a cubic MC phase which is only stable at high temperatures. While this group contains the highest melting metal (tungsten), the carbides melt at much lower temperatures than the respective elements.

The actinide carbides are different in many respects from the preceding systems. A cubic MC compound forms which, in the Th and U systems, can convert to cubic MC_2 at high temperatures by the substitution of C_2 groups for single carbon atoms. Such a continuous transition has not been found in the Pu–C system. On the other hand, the Pu–C and U–C systems share a M_2C_3 compound which is not found in the Th–C system. In each case, the melting point of the carbide is much higher than that of the element. The melting points decrease, however, in going from Th to U to Pu. One would expect Pa and Np, which fall within this series, to follow the same trend.

From these brief comments, some general conclusions are suggested. These common properties define a region of the periodic table as indicated below, in which strong M—C and M—M bonds dominate.

Sc	Ti	V	Cr	Mn
Y	Zr	Nb	Mo	Tc
La	Hf	Ta	W	Re

To the left of this region an acetylene-type bond can form, while to the right the carbides are very unstable, when they exist at all. If the melting point of the metal can be used as a measure of the M—M bond strength, then the increased melting temperature when the carbide forms can be taken as an indication of the M—C bond strength. This, of course, assumes no interaction between the bonds and a neglectable contribution by the C—C bonds. On this basis, Group 4 shows a relatively weak M—M bond, but a very strong interaction between the metal and carbon. In Group 5, both types of bond are strong, while Group 6 has only a strong M—M bond, which is weakened by the addition of carbon. Apparently the M—C bond, which is strongest in Group 4, weakens as the M—M bond strength increases in moving to the right, and it is weakened by C—C interactions as one moves to the left. The single fcc compound in Group 4 can be viewed as an attempt to maximize the number of strong M—C contacts and minimize the number of weak M—M bonds. In Group 5, the M—M bonds are sufficiently strong that hexagonal M_2C, with increased M—M contact, can form, although it is not as stable as the MC compound. On the other hand, the M_2C compound is the more stable phase in Group 6. Bonding in the actinide carbides is different in many respects, but the presence of C=C bonds in addition to strong M—C bonds is indicated. Both MC and MC_2 compounds are found with C=C groups occupying lattice positions in the latter case. The other properties, which will be discussed in order, also fit this general picture.

C. LATTICE PARAMETER AND STRUCTURE

The cubic (NaCl-type) carbide, when it forms in the transition metal systems, can exist over a very wide composition range by the removal of carbon atoms from the carbon sublattice. Attempts by a number of workers to find metal atom vacancies in the lattice have been unsuccessful. There is also no reason to believe that the carbon vacancies are anything but randomly located. While more careful, future measurements might reveal such behavior, the present understanding of these compounds would not suffer. On the other hand, the subcarbides, which are basically hexagonal, have an ordered carbon lattice which disorders upon heating. The ordering is apparently different in each system. This form can not tolerate carbon vacancies, but the disordered form has an increasingly wider composition range as the temperature is increased up to the M-M_2C eutectic.

In the actinide systems, the crystal chemistry is more complex. Cubic ThC can be very carbon-defective even at room temperature; UC is a line compound at room temperature, but at high temperatures the lattice becomes defective, resulting in retrograde melting; and PuC has a defective structure even at its high-carbon boundary. At high temperatures, C=C groups can replace carbon atoms at the cubic lattice sites in UC and ThC, and can lead to the MC_2 compound without a structure change. Apparently this can not happen in the Pu–C system. As the material is cooled, these groups orient in different ways with the result that UC_2 is tetragonal at room temperature, while ThC_2 becomes tetragonal then monoclinic upon cooling. Both UC_2 and PuC_2 are unstable at low temperatures. An M_2C_3 phase increases in stability in going from Th, where it has not been observed, to Pu, where it is the most stable phase in the system. If one had an interest in making a carbide of americium, Am_2C_3 would probably be the only stable phase at room temperature.

The removal of carbon causes the lattice parameter to change, usually to decrease. However, the parameter of TiC and ZrC maximizes, but HfC is uncertain in this respect. As yet, an explanation for this rather unexpected behavior can only be suggested.

An understanding of this property must take into account the effect of dissolved oxygen. Oxygen lowers the parameter in Group 4, while in Group 5 the parameter is raised. The effect in Group 6 is uncertain. UC and PuC exhibit a maximum, but the behavior of ThC has not been studied. However, impure samples generally show a smaller parameter. If used properly, the lattice parameter can be given an approximate indication of the impurity content. From this, it is clear that many measurements, even in recent years, have been based on very impure materials.

The lattice parameters, if viewed on a common basis, can give an indication of the bonding character. If, as Umanskii (1943) suggested, the carbon is in the metallic state, after having transferred electrons to the metal atoms, then the carbon atom size should be reduced in proportion to the number of electrons transferred. Indeed, Frantsevich and Kovens'kii (1961) find, from electrotransport studies, that carbon has a +4.0 charge in TiC, is +2.8 in TaC, and +0.6 in WC. With this in mind, the volume per carbon atom site was calculated assuming no change in the metal atom volume in forming the carbide. Of course, the metal should increase in size, but to a lesser extent. Consequently, the calculated carbon volumes must be viewed as an upper limit. When this quantity is plotted as a function of the number of vacant carbon sites, as was done in Fig. 73, the carbide systems fall into a pattern. The carbon atom volume, in the fully saturated cubic lattice, is smallest in Group 4, Group 5

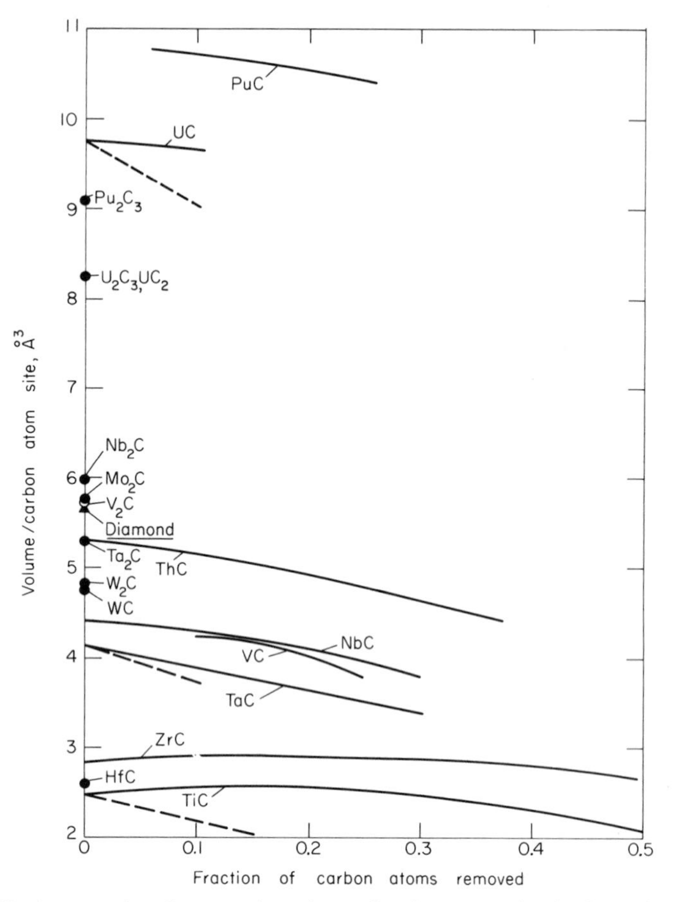

FIG. 73. A comparison between the volume of carbon atom sites in the various carbide structures.

is intermediate, and the M_2C compounds tend to lie near the volume found in diamond. It is tempting to assume a progressively smaller degree of ionization in this sequence, with diamond representing the unionized atom. Such a treatment would suggest a M—C bond strength which is proportional to the ionic state of the carbon atoms. The M_2C and Group 6 carbides, in general, show little ionic character on this basis. On the other hand, the carbon volume in the U–C and Pu–C systems is larger than that in diamond, and, consequently, a transfer of electrons from the metal to the carbon is indicated. ThC is apparently an exception to this behavior.

If the removal of carbon atoms involved no other process but the removal of volume from the lattice, one would expect the volume/carbon site to follow the dashed lines in Fig. 73, i.e., obey Vegard's Law. Since all systems deviate in a positive way, a repulsive force between the vacancies is indicated. This may account for the lattice parameter maximum observed in the TiC and ZrC phases.

Although this discussion does not exhaust all of the correlations or conclusions which this treatment suggests, it does give additional evidence for some ionic character to the bond in these systems.

D. HARDNESS

The introduction of carbon vacancies produces a marked reduction in the microhardness in the Group 4 cubic carbides. A maximum has been observed in the TaC phase and if the latter behavior is typical of Group 5, the high value for $VC_{0.88}$ (see Table 80) could result because the phase boundary composition happens to fall near the maximum hardness value. If NbC has a maximum, a composition near $NbC_{0.9}$ could be the hardest carbide. Clearly, there are theoretical and practical reasons to pursue this observation further.

There is no clearly defined trend in the hardness values and that which does appear does not correlate with the stability of the compound. Until this measurement is made both as a function of composition and crystallographic axis, an understanding will be difficult to achieve.

E. APPEARANCE

Of the transition metal carbides, only NbC and TaC have a color. The former is lavender, and the latter is yellow, but in both cases, this occurs only near the stoichiometric composition. Other compositions and the other carbide phases have a silver-metallic appearance. Only ThC_2 in the actinide series deviates from this pattern with a very pale yellow color for newly cleaved surfaces.

F. CHEMICAL REACTIVITY

A discussion of this property is complicated by the broad composition range exhibited by the carbides. As a result, the activity of both the metal and carbon can change by several orders of magnitude without a

TABLE 80

MICROHARDNESS OF THE TRANSITION AND ACTINIDE CARBIDES[a]

$TiC_{1.0}$	$ZrC_{1.0}$	$HfC_{1.0}$	$VC_{0.88}$	$NbC_{1.0}$	$TaC_{1.0}$	Cr_3C_2	MoC_{1-x}	α-WC	ThC_2	UC_2	PuC_2
2900	2700	2300	3000	2400	1600	1300	—	2200	600	500	—
			β-V_2C	Nb_2C	α-Ta_2C	Cr_7C_3	?-Mo_2C	?-W_2C	ThC	U_2C_3	Pu_2C_3
			2150	—	950	1600	1600	3000	850	1100	700
										UC	PuC
										900	900

[a] Values given as kg/mm^2 for a 50–100-g load.

change in crystal structure or even, in many cases, a change in outward appearance. In addition, they can dissolve the reacting substances in some cases. A selective attack of the metal or carbon can cause the composition, and with it the chemical behavior, to change with time at high temperatures.

1. Hydrogen

An example of this behavior occurs during the reaction with H_2. All of the carbon-saturated carbides will lose carbon as hydrocarbons at high temperatures. This lowers the carbon concentration, hence its activity, and raises the hydrocarbon concentration in the gas. At some point, depending on the carbide system and the temperature, these processes will come to equilibrium, but at a reduced carbide stoichiometry. If, on the other hand, the H_2 is made to flow and the hydrocarbons are swept away, the carbide will continue to lose carbon at a rate which will depend on the diffusion rate of carbon through the carbide. Fortunately for many applications, this rate is small. At low temperatures, H_2 can dissolve in the defect lattice forming a carbohydride.

2. Oxygen

The reaction with oxygen is somewhat more complicated. Both CO and a metal oxide phase are produced at an equal rate in the stoichiometric MC phase, so that no composition change occurs. At lower compositions, where the carbon activity is lower, one would expect the initial reaction to produce mainly the metal oxide phase, and a very low CO pressure. As the reaction continues to remove metal, the carbon activity under the oxide layer would increase, producing an increased CO pressure. This would remove carbon by diffusion through or by rupturing the oxide film. In either case, oxidation should proceed without a change in the overall carbide composition, i.e., without accumulating carbon or metal, and with a rate nearly equal to that exhibited by the stoichiometric composition. The situation is further complicated by the dissolution of oxygen in the carbide. This can lower the activity of both components and can reduce the overall oxidation rate. Thus, the oxycarbide may prove to be a more useful material under oxidizing conditions than the pure carbide.

3. Nitrogen

Except in Group 6, the reaction between a carbide and N_2 or a nitrogen-containing gas will result in the nitride. In some cases, this reaction is facilitated by the presence of H_2. Since the cubic nitrides and carbides are completely miscible in each other, the reaction product, under certain conditions, will be the carbonitride. Unfortunately, once nitrogen has been dissolved, it is very difficult to remove. Were it not for the smaller effect this impurity has on the carbide properties, it would be a more serious problem than the oxygen impurity.

4. Carbon Monoxide

A number of workers have measured the CO pressure over various carbide–oxide–graphite systems and attempted to obtain thermochemical information. With few exceptions the results have been irreproducible and in poor agreement with other techniques. This is especially true of Group 4 and the actinide carbides. Group 5 can apparently be studied in this way, but the situation in Group 6 is still in doubt. Even so, the effect of dissolved oxygen can be so important that such measurements should not be used to generate primary data unless the ternary system is well understood.

In this regard, a number of factors must be taken into account. Oxygen can only dissolve in the MC compound by substituting for carbon. A stoichiometric carbide which is in equilibrium with graphite will contain very little oxygen. Equilibrium, however, is difficult to achieve and maintain because carbon diffuses so very slowly in the carbides. Thus, the removal or addition of CO to the system can create important concentration gradients. If the CO pressure measurement is to have any validity at all, there must be a large excess of intimately mixed elemental carbon in the sample and many hours must be allowed for the system to reach equilibrium. At lower carbon contents, hence lower carbon activities, the oxygen content and its activity can be higher. If so, this will lead to a higher or lower CO pressure, depending on the system. Apparently, most of the carbide systems show a decrease in the CO pressure as the oxygen content is increased.

The actinide systems are somewhat different. UC_2, for example, does not have a fully saturated lattice when graphite is present, especially near 1765°. To this extent, oxygen can dissolve in the structure, especially at high temperatures. To a lesser extent, ThC_2 would behave in the same way. When this behavior is added to the possibility of concentration gradients, the CO pressure ceases to have any simple significance.

5. Aqueous Solutions

In general the Group 4 carbides are immune to attack by acids and bases, except when very strong oxidizing agents are present. This inertness decreases as one moves through Groups 5 and 6. The actinides are attacked simply by water. A mixture of HF and HNO_3 will dissolve all the carbides, especially when heated slightly.

All of the carbides yield CO_2 when oxidizing agents are used. On the other hand, the subcarbide gives free carbon, if it can be dissolved by a nonoxidizing acid such as HCl, as is the case with V_2C. The actinide carbides yield hydrocarbons, but little acetylene, under similar conditions. Thus, the chemical state of the carbon in the transition metal subcarbide is probably metallic, while the actinide systems appear to contain covalent single- and double-bonded carbon atoms.

G. THERMOCHEMICAL PROPERTIES

1. Low Temperature Heat Capacity

With only one exception (NbC), all low temperature measurements, hence values for $S^\circ_{298.15}$, have been based on material near the stoichiometric composition. The absence of information at other compositions is a severe limitation to a thermodynamic understanding of these systems.

TABLE 81

Entropy of Mixing Between Carbon Atoms and Vacancies

Composition, C/M	S_m^a, (cal/mole-deg)
1.0	0.00
0.9	0.65
0.8	0.99
0.7	1.21
0.6	1.34
0.5	1.38

[a] Based on $S_m = -R(n_1 \ln x_1 + n_2 \ln x_2)$ where x is the mole fraction and n, the number of moles (Lewis and Randall, 1961).

While measurement of the absolute entropy is straightforward at the stoichiometric composition, the presence of randomly positioned carbon defects at the lower compositions can produce an entropy term which can not be measured by this technique. If the vacancies are completely random in the lattice, as they seem to be, an entropy of mixing can be calculated. This is listed for several compositions in Table 81. Although the contribution is not large, it can make a significant error in high temperature calculations.

2. High Temperature Enthalpy

It has become common practice to treat enthalpy data by the arbitrary equation

$$H_T^\circ - H_{298.15}^\circ = A + BT + CT^2 + D/T$$

as suggested by Maier and Kelley (1932) and later refined by Shomate (1944). Inherent in the equation is a linearly increasing derivative, i.e., C_p, at high temperatures. This has proven to be satisfactory for most materials at relatively low temperatures, but the carbides and several of the associated elements can reach temperatures where this treatment breaks down. For example, a number of workers have observed, from direct heat capacity measurements, that several of the refractory elements appeared to have a rapidly increasing heat capacity near their melting points. In general, heat content measurements failed to show this behavior. If the above equation is expanded, quite arbitrarily, to include a T^3 term, and then applied to these elements, agreement with the heat capacity measurements greatly improves. This can be seen in the appropriate figures in the text. With this in mind, all of the heat content data were treated by the modified equation with two restraints. The expression was forced to equal zero at 298.15°, and C_p at 298.15° was made equal to a value obtained from low temperature measurements.

As a result of this treatment, a number of the carbides were also found to have an increasing C_p value near their melting temperatures. When an explanation is attempted, it should be borne in mind that many of the carbides, TiC for example, precipitate carbon from the stoichiometric composition upon cooling. The heat thus generated would add to the heat content and increase the heat capacity at high temperatures. On the other hand, some carbides precipitate carbon upon heating. As a result, the measured sample would consist of a mixture of graphite and a carbide of a reduced stoichiometry.

The absence of thermal data as a function of composition for all but one of the carbide systems makes an estimation technique desirable. An examination of the various free energy function values, listed in the text, reveals some convenient patterns between the stoichiometric compositions of the MC compounds. Above 1500°K, the *fef* vs. *T* curves of Groups 4 and 5 are nearly parallel and the adjacent carbides, TiC–VC and ZrC–NbC, have values which are very close at corresponding temperatures. A comparison between HfC and TaC is less satisfactory, but within 5%. If this trend is followed by the defect compositions, values for the other Group 4 and 5 carbides can be estimated from the measurements in the NbC system.

3. Heat of Formation

The heat of formation is most negative at HfC (Table 82), with a decrease in the absolute value in going to lower periods and higher groups. If this trend is followed to its extreme, the chromium carbides should be the least stable. This appears to be the case although measurements in Group 6 are very uncertain.

The heat of formation of the TaC, NbC, VC, and HfC phases has been measured as a function of composition. In all cases, the value per mole of metal becomes less negative as carbon is removed, as one would expect. The Group 5 carbides show the greatest change with composition, but the value per atom is nearly constant.

In the actinide system, the heat of formation as a function of composition has been measured recently for ThC and UC. A single value is available for PuC, but this is apparently much too positive. The thorium carbides

TABLE 82

Heat of Formation, Heat Capacity, and Entropy at 298.15°K for the Transition and Actinide Carbides

Compound	$S°$ (cal/mole-deg)	C_p (cal/mole-deg)	Composition (atom ratio)	$-\Delta H_f$ (kcal/mole)	Composition (atom ratio)
TiC	5.79	8.08	1.0	44.1 $+0, -1.0$	1.0
ZrC	7.927	9.016	0.96	47.0 ± 0.6	0.93
HfC	9.431	8.955	0.968	50.08 ± 0.35	0.958
V_2C	—	—	—	16.5 ± 0.6	0.5
VC	6.61[c]	7.72	0.88	24.5 ± 0.6[a]	0.88
β-Nb_2C	7.66	7.59	0.5	23.3 ± 0.6	0.5
NbC	8.29	8.79	0.98	33.6 ± 0.5	1.0
Ta_2C	—	—	—	24.9 $+0, -1.0$	0.5
TaC	10.1	8.764	1.0	34.1 ± 0.5	1.0
Cr_3C_2	6.81	7.84	2/3	5.5 ± 1.0[a]	2/3
Mo_2C	—	—	—	5.5 ± 0.3	0.5
MoC	—	—	—	3.0 ± 2.0	0.7
α-W_2C	—	—	—	6.3 ± 0.6	0.5
α-WC	—	—	—	9.67 ± 0.4	1.0
ThC	—	—	—	29.6 ± 1.1	1.0
ThC_2	16.42	13.59	1.98	29.7 ± 1.8	1.91
UC	14.15[a]	11.98[a]	1.0	23.3 ± 0.9	0.996
UC_2	16.33[a,c]	14.52[a]	1.93	20.0 ± 1.0[a]	1.9
PuC	17.0[b,c]	—	—	12[b]	0.85
Pu_2C_3	—	—	—	19[b]	1.5

[a] Probable value based on several independent measurements.

[b] Estimate.

[c] Randomization entropy not included.

appear to be the most stable members of the series with a regular but small decrease between adjacent systems.

While there are a number of techniques for obtaining this quantity, each with its own limitations and errors, the heat of combustion remains the most satisfactory for these systems. As accurate thermal values become available, vapor pressure measurements may prove to give results of greater accuracy. Equilibrium studies at lower temperatures are too susceptible to oxygen contamination and concentration gradients to be reliable, in most cases. This is especially true for defect compositions.

4. Vaporization

The measurement of vapor pressures is potentially the single most useful technique for high temperature research. It provides practical engineering information concerning the limitations imposed by this property, and it gives free energy information in an interesting temperature range which, when combined with thermal values, can give accurate heats and entropies of formation at room temperature. If the study is made as a function of composition, partial molar quantities can be obtained as well as the accurate location of phase boundaries. Since the actinide and rare earth carbides evaporate metal atoms as well as species which contain both carbon and metal, measurement of their partial pressures allows a direct determination of the carbon activity. Many other systems also allow a similar analysis. Lastly, melting points and other transition temperatures can be determined, in some cases, as a part of the study. This is done by cooling or heating slowly through the transition and noting the temperature at which the smoothly changing pressure shows an arrest or a break.

A number of techniques have been developed for pressure measurements. These include the absolute methods involving Knudsen collection, free evaporation (Langmuir), torsion effusion, and mass spectrometry. Optical absorption has also been used with mixed success. Each of these is not equally useful and their limitations must be understood when vapor pressure measurements are contemplated or evaluated. In this regard, a short description of each technique will be undertaken in the following paragraphs.

Knudsen collection involves the use of a cell containing a knife edge orifice from which the vapor is allowed to impinge on a suitable target. In order to obtain sufficient sensitivity as the temperature is reduced, the heating time must be increased. This requires that the effusion cell be very inert to the sample and that two-phase systems be studied. While the total volatility of the species containing the element of interest can be determined, the individual partial pressures can not. As a result, this technique has only a limited application and the pressure must be interpreted as an upper limit.

The Langmuir technique has been applied successfully to measuring the vapor pressure of the solid elements. When applied to compounds, the congruently evaporating composition must be used. Even if one is fortunate enough to find this behavior in the system of interest, several other problems arise. The method gives only the total evaporation rate which must be combined with the vapor composition to obtain the pressures. Frequently, because of an activation energy for vaporization, the evaporation rate is less than would be predicted from the equilibrium pressure. For this reason, an evaporation coefficient has been defined as the ratio between the Langmuir and Knudsen pressures. Even when these factors have been taken into account, the usual attempts at a thermodynamic analysis are frustrated by the fact that the congruent composition is not fixed, but changes with temperature. This is especially true as the measurements are pushed to increasingly higher temperatures. Added to this is the irritating tendency for this composition to lie at compositions for which other thermodynamic data are not available. As a result, the Langmuir technique tends to create more questions than it answers when applied to defect compounds.

Torsion effusion obtains the total pressure from the measured twist produced in a suspension system by radial vaporization under Knudsen conditions. While absolute pressures can be obtained in principle, many workers have found it expedient to calibrate with a material of known vapor pressure. When this is done, an accurate, continuous monitor of the total pressures can be made. However, if the vapor contains more than two species, the partial pressures can not be determined.

The mass spectrometer is the only technique which allows the vapor composition to be determined, and this can be done rapidly and with great sensitivity. Beyond that, its usefulness for pressure measurements depends on how accurately the apparatus can be calibrated. In this regard, it has been common practice to use the known vapor pressure of Ag, Au, or sometimes Mo combined with the measured or calculated ionization cross sections for the various species. While this method and its variations can give satisfactory answers, a comparison with an absolute determination using the system of interest is better. For example, the pressure of many metallic elements is known or can be determined by the Langmuir technique. If the elements of the system of interest fall into this category, their use for the calibration introduces fewer uncertainties. A comparison with an absolute measurement, made at some convenient temperature and composition in the system, can be used for further confirmation. With sufficient care, the mass spectrometer is potentially the best method for pressure measurements at high temperatures.

Regardless of the method used, a number of often ignored factors must be taken into account when the data is interpreted. Most vapor pressure studies of compounds are made using a two-phase mixture. A thermodynamic analysis of the result is always made on the basis of a fixed composition. At low temperatures this assumption is usually justified, but, as the measurements are carried closer to the melting point, the equilibrium phase composition will change significantly. Even if this change is small, a rapid change in the pressure with composition in this region can magnify the effect. As a result, agreement between a second and third law treatment will be poor. If sufficient information is available, the second law value can be corrected for this effect. This, however, involves a study at different single-phase compositions near the phase boundary, which is more than most workers care to undertake.

If such a study is contemplated, the phase diagram provides a number of predictions as to how the pressures must behave. A simple phase diagram, which contains some features common to many refractory systems, is shown in Fig. 74. Although a carbide will be described, it should be understood that all systems can be handled in this way. Starting with vaporization of the pure element, an essentially straight line is observed when the log of the metal pressure is plotted against $1/T$(Fig. 74B) with a slope, i.e., a second law heat of vaporization, as indicated by point A in Fig. 74C. When the two-phase region at B is examined, the pressure will follow a curved line, B, as the increasing amount of dissolved carbon in the metal lowers its pressure as the temperature is increased. In actual practice, the curvature is usually so slight that a straight line can be drawn. The slope, however, will be smaller than that of the pure metal, giving an *apparent* heat of vaporization shown as line B. If a composition at C is next examined, the resulting pressure line must intersect the two-phase curves at T_c, while, above this temperature the metal pressure over the single-phase region must be less than that over the two-phase region at all temperatures. Consequently, the partial heat of vaporization falls at point C (Fig. 74C) below that for the two-phase region. As the composition of the single-phase compound is moved to the right, the metal pressure must drop until, near the stoichiometric composition, another phase appears, in this case graphite. This is coupled with a

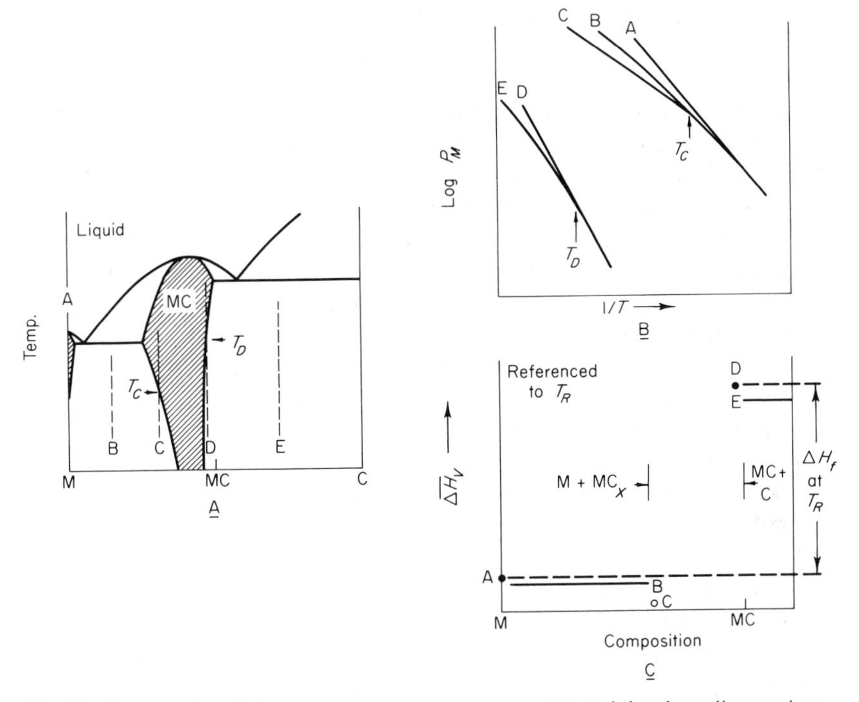

FIG. 74. A comparison between vapor pressure measurements and the phase diagram in a general system.

corresponding change in $\Delta\overline{H}_v$. At the phase boundary with carbon, point D can be obtained independently by simply adding the heat of formation at this temperature to the heat of vaporization of the metal, i.e., point A. Applying the same reasoning to this boundary as was used before, one finds that the two-phase material has an apparent partial heat of vaporization (E) which is smaller than that of the single phase near the boundary. On the other hand, if the phase boundary had moved to lower compositions as the temperature was raised, as is often the case with carbides, E would have been higher than D. The magnitude of this difference can be significant as mentioned earlier.

The problem remains as to how the pressure and the partial heats of vaporization change within the single-phase regions. As yet, this can not be predicted accurately, but certain restrictions exist. For example, the second law partial heats of vaporization in a carbide system can be related to the heat of formation by the formula

$$\Delta H_f^\circ = -\Delta \overline{H}_{\mathrm{m}} + \Delta H_{\mathrm{m}}^\circ + \mathrm{C/M}(\Delta H_{\mathrm{C}}^\circ - \Delta \overline{H}_{\mathrm{C}})$$

Since the heat of formation (ΔH_f°) decreases regularly, but slowly, as carbon is removed from the lattice, a change in the partial heat for the metal ($\Delta \overline{H}_{\mathrm{m}}$) under the same circumstances must be reflected as an opposite change in the partial heat for carbon ($\Delta \overline{H}_{\mathrm{C}}$). Thus, if the partial heat for the metal decreases monotonically as carbon is removed, as was found in the TiC and ZrC phases, the partial heat for carbon must be greater than the heat of vaporization of graphite ($\sim$170 kcal/mole) at all defect compositions.

If these partial heats are different at the congruently vaporizing composition, this composition will change with temperature. A change to lower carbon contents as the temperature is increased means that the partial heat for carbon is greater than that for the metal. This, of course, follows only if other vapor species are negligible. Of the transition metal carbides which are congruently vaporizing (ZrC, HfC, NbC, Ta_2C, and Mo_2C), only ZrC has been studied sufficiently to demonstrate a completely consistent pattern. In the actinide system, the congruent behavior of UC–UC_2 is well known and shows several interesting features. Above 2000°K the composition is very temperature-sensitive, moving from the UC_2 + C boundary as the temperature is raised. Over a small temperature interval near 2300°K, congruency occurs at two compositions, and as the temperature is raised further, it moves to $UC_{1.1}$ and remains relatively fixed. This behavior is consistent with the changes in the partial heats. A similar pattern should be found in the Th–C system.

An examination of the trends in the heat of vaporization from the metallic element compared to the partial heat of vaporization of the metal atom from the carbon-saturated carbides, shown in Table 83, allows several interesting conclusions to be drawn. These quantities give the energy to remove an atom to infinity and are related to the total bonding energy experienced by the metal atoms within the lattice. On this basis, the heat of vaporization of the element can be taken as the energy to form M—M bonds, while the partial heat from the carbide would be proportional to the total energy from M—M as well as M—C bonds in the lattice. If this view is taken, the M—M bond strength is, in general, weaker in Group 4 than in Groups 5 and 6. Tungsten apparently has very strong metal bonds. On the other hand, Group 4 has the strongest M—C bonds, Group 5 is intermediate, while in Group 6 they are very weak. From this one could conclude that the very high melting temperatures,

TABLE 83

A COMPARISON BETWEEN THE HEATS OF VAPORIZATION OF THE ELEMENTS AND THE PARTIAL HEATS OF VAPORIZATION FOR THE METALS FROM THE CARBON-SATURATED COMPOUNDS[a,b]

	Ti	Zr	Hf	V	Nb	Ta	Cr	Mo	W	Th	U	Pu
Element, ΔH_v° (kcal/mole)	113.2	145.4	144.9	122.8	172.1	186.5	94.9	157.0	203.1[c]	137.7[d]	126.5	82.1
Carbon-saturated compound, $\Delta\bar{H}_m$(kcal/mole)	157.3	192.4	195.0	146.8	205.5	220.5	99.9	~160	212.8	168	147.7	—
Composition (atom ratio)	1.0	0.96	1.0	0.88	1.0	1.0	0.67	0.67	1.0	2.0	1.87	—

[a] Values at 298.15°K.

[b] Except where noted otherwise the sources of the values are as discussed in the text.

[c] Barriault *et al.* (1961).

[d] Darnell *et al.* (1960).

which reach their peak at TaC, are related to the sum of the M—M and M—C bond energies. Although neither bond is as strong in TaC as elsewhere in these groups, the sum is greater. The actinides show a decrease in both the M—M and M—C bond strengths as one proceeds further into the series. This rather general picture does not take into account a weakening of the M—M bonds with the introduction of carbon, nor does it recognize the existence of C—C or C=C bonds. Nevertheless, it is consistent with the other properties of these materials.

When the partial molar heat for the metal is examined as a function of composition, Group 4 is found to have an increase in this value as the carbon content of the MC phase is increased. This is shown in Figs. 8 and 15. In terms of the above model, this would suggest that the addition of carbon increases the strength and/or number of M—C bonds, as one would expect. On the other hand, the Mo–C system, which is probably typical of Group 6, shows an increasing $\Delta\overline{H}_m$ only in the Mo_2C phase. The addition of carbon to cubic MoC_{1-x} causes a weakening of the bonds holding the metal atoms to the lattice, as can be seen in Fig. 49. Group 5 has not been investigated, but one would expect $\Delta\overline{H}_m$ to increase in both the M_2C and MC phases as carbon is added.

Of the actinides, only the U–C system has been studied in this way. Like the MC structure in Group 4, the addition of carbon to defective UC causes $\Delta\overline{H}_U$ to increase. Once the vacancies have been filled, the formation of C=C groups causes $\Delta\overline{H}_U$ to decrease. This results in a maximum near $UC_{1.15}$. A similar maximum in $\Delta\overline{H}_U$ is observed at $UC_{1.85}$, but the explanation must await further study.

BIBLIOGRAPHY*

Abrahamson, E. P., and Grant, N. J. (1956). *J. Metals* **8**; *Trans. AIME* **206**, 975.

Accary, A. (1963). *4th Uranium Carbide Meeting, East Hartford, Connecticut*, May 1963, TID-7676.

Ackermann, R. J., Gilles, P. W., and Thorn, R. J. (1956). *J. Chem. Phys.* **25**, 1089.

Ackermann, R. J., Rauh, E. G., and Thorn, R. J. (1962). *J. Chem. Phys.* **37**, 2693.

Ackermann, R. J., Rauh, E. G., and Thorn, R. J. (1965a). *J. Chem. Phys.* **42**, 2630.

Ackermann, R. J., Rauh, E. G., and Chandrasekhariah, M. S. (1965b). ANL-7048, Argonne National Laboratory, Lemont, Illinois.

Adams, R. P., and Beall, R. A., (1963). BM-RI-6304, Bureau of Mines (Reports of Investigations).

Adenstedt, H. K. (1952). *Trans. Am. Soc. Metals* **44**, 949.

Agte, C., and Alterthum, H. (1930). *Z. Tech. Physik* **11**, 182.

Ainsley, R., Wood, D. C., and Sowden, R. G. (1964). *In* "Carbides in Nuclear Energy, Vol. 2: Preparation Fabrication/Irradiation Behavior" (L. E. Russell, ed.), p. 540. Macmillan, New York.

Alcock, C. B., and Grieveson, P. (1961–1962). *J. Inst. Metals* **90**, 304.

Alcock, C. B., and Grieveson, P. (1962). *In* "Thermodynamics of Nuclear Materials," p. 563. Intern. At. Energy Agency, Vienna; see also Grieveson, P., Ph.D. Thesis, University of London.

Alcock, C. B., Eick, H. A., Rauh, E. G., and Thorn, R. J. (1964a). *In* "International Symposium on Compounds of Interest in Nuclear Reactor Technology" (J. T. Waber, P. Chiotti, and W. N. Miner, eds.), p. 257. Met. Soc. Am. Inst. Mining, Met. Petrol. Engrs.

Alcock, C. B., Eick, H. A., Rauh, E. G., and Thorn, R. J. (1964b). *In* "Carbides in Nuclear Energy, Vol. 1; Physical and Chemical Properties/Phase Diagrams" (L. E. Russell, ed.), p. 330. Macmillan, New York.

Alekseev, V. I., and Shvartsman, L. A. (1960). *Dokl. Akad. Nauk SSSR* **133**, 1327.

Alekseev, V. I., and Shvartsman, L. A. (1961). *Fiz. Metal. i Metalloved.* **11**, 545.

Alekseev, V. I., and Shvartsman, L. A. (1962). *Izv. Akad. Nauk SSSR, Otd. Tekhn. Nauk, Met. i Toplivo* **6**, 171.

Alekseev, V. I., and Shvartsman, L. A. (1963). *Izv. Akad. Nauk SSSR, Met. i Gorn. Delo Met. i Toplivo* No. 6, p. 171.

Alekseev, V. I., and Shvartsman, L. A. (1963). *Izv. Akad. Nauk SSSR, Met. i Gorn. Delo* p. 91.

Alexander, C. A., Ward, J. J., Ogden, J. S., and Cunningham, G. W. (1964). *In* "Carbides in Nuclear Energy, Vol. 1: Physical and Chemical Properties/Phase Diagrams" (L. E. Russell, ed.), p. 192. Macmillan, New York. Revised data is presented in BMI-X-10023 (1963).

Allen, B. C., Maykuth, D. J., and Jaffee, R. I. (1961–1962). *J. Inst. Metals* **90**, 120.

* The availability of reports can be determined by consulting Nuclear Science Abstracts, Report No. Index. Most of the reports are available from the Clearinghouse for Federal Scientific and Technical Information, National Bureau of Standards, U.S. Department of Commerce, Springfield, Virginia for $3.00 for a full-size copy.

Allten, A. G., Chow, J. G. Y., Simon, A. (1954). *Trans. Am. Soc. Metals* **46**, 948.

Alyamovskii, S. I., Gel'd, P. V., and Matveenko, I. I. (1961). *Zh. Strukt. Khim.* **2**, 445.

Alyamovskii, S. I., Shveikin, G. P., and Gel'd, P. V. (1963). *J. Inorg. Chem. USSR* **8**, 1042.

Anderson, C. T., Hayes, E. T., Roberson, A. H., and Kroll, W. J. (1950). BMI-RI-4658, Battelle Memorial Institute, Columbus, Ohio.

Andon, R. J. L., Counsell, J. F., Martin, J. F., and Hedger, H. J. (1964a). *Trans. Faraday Soc.* **60**, 1030.

Andon, R. J. L., Counsell, J. F., Martin, J. F., and Hedger, H. J. (1964b). Private communication to J. Farr.

Andrews, M. R. (1923). *J. Phys. Chem.* **27**, 270.

Andrews, M. R., and Dushman, S. (1921). *J. Franklin Inst.* **192**, 545.

Anselin, F., and Poitreau, J. (1966). CEA-R-2961, Centre d'etudes Nucléaires de Fontenay-Aux-Roses, La Documentation Française, Secrétariat Général du Gouvernement, Direction de la Documentation, 16, rue Lord Byron, Paris VIIIème.

Anselin, F., Dean, G., Lorenzelli, R., and Pascard, R. (1964). *In* "Carbides in Nuclear Energy, Vol. 1: Physical and Chemical Properties/Phase Diagrams" (L. E. Russell, ed.), p. 113. Macmillan, New York.

Arkharov, V. I., Konev, V. N., and Gerasimov, A. F. (1960). *Fiz. Metal. i Metalloved.* **9**, 695.

Arnold, J. O., and Read, H. A. (1912). *J. Iron Steel Inst.* (*London*) **85**, 215.

Aronson, S., and Sadofsky, J. (1965). *J. Inorg. & Nucl. Chem.* **27**, 1769; see also BNL-8039 (1965), Brookhaven National Laboratory, Upton, L.I., New York.

Atoda, T., Kobayashi, M., Sasa, Y., Takahashi, Y., and Higashi, I. (1964). *In* "Carbides in Nuclear Energy, Vol. 2: Preparation/Fabrication/Irradiation Behavior" (L. E. Russell, ed.), p. 496. Macmillan, New York.

Atoji, M., and Medrud, R. C. (1959). *J. Chem. Phys.* **31**, 332; see also Atoji, M. (1961). *J. Chem. Phys.* **35**, 1950–1960.

Austin, A. E. (1959). *Acta Cryst.* **12**, 159.

Austin, A. E., and Gerds, A. F. (1958). BMI-1272, Battelle Memorial Institute, Columbus, Ohio.

Avarbe, R. G., Avgustinik, A. I., Vilk, Iu. N., Omelchenko, Iu. A., and Ordanian, S. S. (1962). *Zh. Prikl. Khim.* **35**, 1976.

Badaeva, T. A., and Kuznetsova, R. I. (1963). *Stroenie i Svoistva Splavov Urana, Toriya i Tsirkoniya, Sb. Statei* p. 227.

Baenziger, N. C. (1950). Quoted by Wilhelm and Chiotti (1950).

Balzhiser, R. E., and Ragone, D. V. (1964). *Meeting Electrochem. Soc., Washington*, Oct. 11–15, 1964.

Bannister, G. H., and Thomson, J. R. (1963). AERE-R 4428, Great Britain Atomic Energy Research Establishment, Reactor Div., Harwell, Berks., England.

Barnes, B. T. (1929). *J. Phys. Chem.* **33**, 688.

Barriault, R. J., Bender, S. L., Dreikorn, R. E., Einwohner, T. H., Feber, R. C., Gannon, R. E., Hanst, P. L., Ihnat, M. E., Phaneuf, J. P., Schick, H. L., and Ward, C. H. (1961). ASD-TR-61-260, Part I, Vol. 1, Air Force Systems Command, Aeronautical Systems Div., Wright-Patterson A.F.B., Ohio.

Bartlett, R. W. (1963). Ph.D. Dissertation University of Utah, Salt Lake City, Utah; see also Bartlett, R. W., Wodsworth, M. E., and Cutler, I. B. (1963). *Trans. AIME* **227**, 467.

Baumruker, J. E., and Chiswik, H. H. (1953). ANL-5234, Argonne National Laboratory, Lemont, Illinois.

Beaumont, R. H., Chihara, H., and Morrison, J. A. (1960). *Phil. Mag.* [8] **5**, 188.

Becker, K. (1928). *Z. Physik* **51**, 481.

Becker, K., and Ewest, H. (1930). *Z. Tech. Physik* **11**, 148 and 216.

Bedford, R. (1964). UCRL-7520, University of California, Lawrence Radiation Laboratory, Livermore, California.

Behl, W. K., and Egan, J. J. (1966). *J. Electrochem. Soc.* **113**, 376.

Benesovsky, F., and Rudy, E. (1960). *Plansbeer. Pulvermet.* **8**, 66; see also translation (GA-tr-2611) General Atomics Div., General Dynamics Corp., San Diego, California.

Benesovsky, F., and Rudy, E. (1961). *Planseeber. Pulvermet.* **9**, 65–76; translated in GA-tr-2801, General Atomics Div., General Dynamics Corp., San Diego, California.

Benesovsky, F., and Rudy, E. (1963). DP-Report-132.

Bentle, G. G. (1958). NAA-SR-2069, North American Aviation, Inc.

Berkowitz-Mattuck, J. (1963). ASD-DR-62-203, Part II, A. D. Little, Inc., Cambridge, Massachusetts.

Berkowitz-Mattuck, J., Larson, J. T., Quigley, R. F., and Christiansen, W. (1963). ASD-TDR-62-203, Part II, A. D. Little, Inc., Cambridge, Massachusetts.

Besson, J., Blum, P., and Spitz, J. (1964). *In* "Carbides in Nuclear Energy, Vol. 1: Physical and Chemical Properties/Phase Diagrams" (L. E. Russell, ed.), p. 273. Macmillan, New York.

Bickerdike, R. L., and Hughes, G. (1959). *J. Less-Common Metals* **1**, 42.

Bittner, H., and Goretzki, H. (1962). *Monatsh. Chem.* **93**, 1000.

Bloom, D. S., and Grant, N. J. (1950). *Trans. AIME* **188**, 41.

Bloom, D. S., Putman, J. W., and Grant, N. J. (1952). *Trans. AIME* **194**, 626; see also (1952). *J. Metals* **4**, 626.

Blumenthal, B. (1960). *J. Nucl. Mater.* **2,** 197; see also (1959). ANL-5958, Argonne National Laboratory, Lemont, Illinois.

Blumenthal, B., Baumrucker, J. E., and Lloyd, L. T. (1960). *J. Nucl. Mater.* **2**, 23–30; see also ANL-5957, Argonne National Laboratory, Lemont, Illinois.

Boettcher, A., and Schneider, G. (1958). *Proc. 2nd U.N. Intern. Conf.* United Nations, New York. *Peaceful Uses At. Energy, Geneva, 1958* Vol. 6, p. 561.

Bolgar, A. S., Verkhoglyadova, T. S., and Samsonov, G. V. (1961). *Izv. Akad. Nauk SSSR, Otd. Tekhn. Nauk, Met. i Toplivo* p. 142.

Borchardt, H. J. (1959). *J. Inorg. & Nucl. Chem.* **12**, 113.

Bowersox, D. F., and Leary, J. A. (1963). LAMS-2832, Los Alamos Scientific Laboratory, New Mexico.

Bowman, A. L. (1961). *J. Phys. Chem.* **65**, 1596.

Bowman, A. L. (1965). Private communication.

Bowman, A. L. (1966). To be published.

Bowman, A. L., Wallace, T. C., Yarnell, J. L., Wenzel, R. G., and Storms, E. K. (1965). *Acta Cryst.* **19**, 6.

Bowman, A. L., Arnold, G. P., Witteman, W. G., Wallace, T. C., and Nereson, N. G. (1966). *Acta Cryst.* **21**, 670.

Bowman, M. G., and Krupka, M. C. (1963). *4th Uranium Carbide Meeting, East Hartford, Connecticut*, TID-7676, Technical Information Div., U.S.A.E.C.

Bradley, M. J., and Ferris, L. M. (1963). ORNL-TM-462, Oak Ridge National Laboratory, Oak Ridge, Tennessee.

Bradshaw, W. G., and Matthews, C. O. (1959). LMSD-2466, Lockheed Aircraft Corp., Missile Systems Div., Sunnyvale, California.

Brantley, L. R., and Beckman, A. O. (1930). *J. Am. Chem. Soc.* **52**, 3956.

Brauer, G., and Lesser, R. (1959a). *Z. Metallk.* **50**, 8; see also Brauer, G., Renner, H., and Wernet, J. (1954). *Z. Anorg. Allgem. Chem.* **277**, 249.

Brauer, G., and Lesser, R. (1959b). *Z. Metallk.* **50**, 487.

Brauer, G., and Schnell, W. D. (1964). *J. Less-Common Metals* **7**, 23; see also Schnell, W. D. (1960). Ph.D. Thesis, University of Freiburg, Freiburg im Breisgau, Germany.

Bredig, M. A. (1960). *J. Am. Ceram. Soc.* **43**, 493; see also ORNL-865 (1950) and ORNL-1260 (1951), Oak Ridge National Laboratory, Oak Ridge, Tennessee.

Brett, N. H., Law, D., and Livey, D. T. (1960). *J. Inorg. & Nucl. Chem.* **13**, 44; see also (1958). AERE-M/R-2574, Great Britain Atomic Energy Research Establishment, Harwell, Berkshire, England.

Brett, N. H., Harper, E. A., Hedger, H. J., and Pottinger, J. S. (1964). *In* "Carbides in Nuclear Energy. Vol. 1: Physical and Chemical Properties/Phase Diagrams" (L. E. Russell, ed.), p. 162. Macmillan, New York.

Brown, D. J. (1964). *In* "Carbides in Nuclear Energy, Vol. 2: Preparation/Fabrication/Irradiation Behavior" (L. E. Russell, ed.), p. 711. Macmillan, New York.

Brown, D. J., and Stobo, J. J. (1962). *In* "Powder Metallurgy in the Nuclear Age," Plansee Proceedings, p. 279. Metallwerk Plansee A.G., Reutte/Tirol, Austria.

Brown, F., Dennard, F. S., Ellis, P., Good, P. T., and Lapage, R. (1964). *In* "Carbides in Nuclear Energy, Vol. 2: Preparation/Fabrication/Irradiation Behavior" (L. E. Russell, ed.), p. 692. Macmillan, New York.

Brown, J. F., and Clark, D. (1951). *Nature* **167**, 728.

Browning, L. C., and Emmett, P. H. (1952). *J. Am. Chem. Soc.* **74**, 4773.

Brownlee, L. D. (1958). *J. Inst. Metals* **87**, Part 2, 58.

Buckley, S. N. (1961). AERE-R 3872. Great Britain Atomic Energy Research Establishment, Harwell, Berkshire, England.

Bückle, H. (1955). *Metall* **9**, 1067.

Bumps, E. S., Kessler, H. D., and Hansen, M. (1953). *Trans. Am. Soc. Metals* **45**, 1008.

Burdick, M. D., Parker, H. S., Roth, R. S., and McGandy, E. L. (1955). *J. Res. Natl. Bur. Std.* **54**, 217.

Burgers, W. G., and Basart, J. C. M. (1934). *Z. Anorg. Allgem. Chem.* **216**, 209.

Burlakov, V. D. (1957). *Phys. Metals Metallog.* (*USSR*) (*English Transl.*) **5**, 72.

Burnham, J. B., Skavdahl, R. E., and Chikalla, T. D. (1964). *In* "Carbides in Nuclear Energy, Vol. 1: Physical and Chemical Properties/Phase Diagrams" (L. E. Russell, ed.), p. 51. Macmillan, New York. See also (1962). HW-SA-3131.

Butorina, L. N. (1960). *Kristallografiya* **5**, 233.

Butorina, L. N., and Pinsker, Z. G. (1960). *Soviet Phys. Cryst.* (*English Transl.*) **5**, 560.

Buzzard, R., Liss, R. B., and Fickle, D. P. (1953). *J. Res. Natl. Bur. Std.* **50**, 209.

Cadoff, I., and Nielsen, J. P. (1953). *J. Metals* **5**, 248.

Cadoff, I., and Palty, A. E. (1952). WAL-401/14-30, Watertown Arsenal Laboratory, Watertown, Massachusetts.

Cadoff, I., Nielsen, J. P. and Miller, E. (1955). *Plansee Proc., 2nd Seminar, Reutte/Tyrol, 1955* p. 50. Pergamon Press, Oxford.

Campbell, I. E., Powell, C. F., Nowicki, D. H., and Gonser, B. W. (1949). *J. Electrochem. Soc.* **96**, 318.

Carlile, S. J., Christian, J. W., and Hume-Rothery, W. (1949). *J. Inst. Metals* **76**, 169.

Carniglia, S. C. (1964). *In* "Carbides in Nuclear Energy, Vol. 1: Physical and Chemical Properties/Phase Diagrams" (L. E. Russell, ed.), p. 403. Macmillan, New York. See also (1963). NAA-SR-Memo-9015.

Chackraburtty, D. M., and Jayadevan, N. C. (1965). *Acta Cryst.* **18**, 811.

Chang, R. (1961). *Acta Cryst.* **14**, 1097.
Charlton, M. G., and Davis, G. L. (1955). *Nature* **175**, 131.
Chikalla, T. D. (1962). HW-74024, General Electric Co., Hanford Atomic Products Operation, Richland, Washington.
Chiotti, P. (1950). AECD-3072, Ames Laboratory, Ames Iowa, ISC-103.
Chiotti, P. (1952). *J. Am. Ceram. Soc.* **35**, 123.
Chiotti, P. (1954). *J. Electrochem. Soc.* **101**, 567.
Chiotti, P. (1955). ISC-531, p. 14, Iowa State University, Ames, Iowa.
Chubb, W., and Dickerson, R. F. (1962). *Ceram. Bull.* **41**, 564.
Chubb, W., and Dickerson, R. F. (1963). *4th Uranium Carbide Meeting, East Hartford, Connecticut*, TID-7676.
Chubb, W., and Keller, D. L. (1963). BMI-X-258, Battelle Memorial Institute, Columbus, Ohio.
Chubb, W., and Phillips, W. M. (1961a). *Trans. Am. Soc. Metals* **53**, 465.
Chubb, W., and Phillips, W. M. (1961b). *Trans. Am. Soc. Metals* **53**, 938.
Chubb, W., and Rough, F. A. (1960). *2nd Uranium Carbide Meeting, Battelle Mem. Inst., Columbus, Ohio*. TID-7589, Technical Information Div., U.S. Atomic Energy Commission.
Chubb, W., Getz, R. W., and Townley, C. W. (1964). *J. Nucl. Mater.* **13**, 63.
Chupka, W. A., Berkowitz, J., Giese, C. F., and Inghram, M. G. (1958). *J. Phys. Chem.* **62**, 611.
Clougherty, E. V., Lothrop, K. H., and Kafalas, J. A. (1961). *Nature* **191**, 1194.
Cockett, G. H., and Watt, W. (1950). RAE-TN-MET-124, Great Britain Royal Aircraft Establishment, Farnborough, Hants, England.
Coffman, J. A., Kibler, G. M., Riethof, T. R., and Watts, A. A. (1960). AD 236-160. Flight Propulsion Laboratory Department, General Electric, Cincinnati, Ohio; (1961) WADD-TR-60-646, Part I, p. 40.
Coffman, J. A., Kibler, G. M., Lyon, T. F., and Acchione, B. D. (1963). WADD-TR-60-646, Part II, Wright Air Develop. Div., Wright-Patterson A.F.B., Ohio (work done at General Electric Co., Cincinnati, Ohio). See also Lyon (1962).
Connolly, D. E. (1962). TRG Report 359(S), United Kingdom Atomic Energy Authority, Risley, Warrington, Lancashire, England.
Cook, J. L. (1965). ORNL-TM-1188, Oak Ridge National Laboratory, Oak Ridge, Tennessee.
Copeland, M. I. (1962). BM-U-952, Bureau of Mines.
Coriou, H., Gauduchau, J., Grall, L., and Hure, J. (1959). *Mem. Sci. Rev. Met.* **56**, 693.
Costa, P., and Conte, R. R. (1964). *In* "International Symposium on Compounds of Interest in Nuclear Reactor Technology" (J. T. Waber, P. Chiotti, and W. N. Miner, eds.), p. 3. Met. Soc. Am. Inst. Mining, Met. Petrol. Engrs.
Cotter, P. G., and Kohn, J. A. (1954). *J. Am. Ceram. Soc.* **37**, 415.
Crafts, W., and Lamont, J. L. (1949). *Trans. AIME* **185**, 957.
Cunningham, G. W., Ward, J. J., and Alexander, C. A. (1962). BMI-1601, Battelle Memorial Institute, Columbus, Ohio.
Curtis, C. E., Doney, L. M., and Johnson, J. R. (1954). *J. Am. Ceram. Soc.* **37**, 458.
Dahl, A. I., and Cleaves, H. E. (1949). *J. Res. Natl. Bur. Std.* **43**, 513.
Dahl, A. I., and Van Dusen, M. S. (1947). *J. Res. Natl. Bur. Std.* **39**, 53.
Dalton, J. T. (1964). *In* "Carbides in Nuclear Energy, Vol. 1: Physical and Chemical Properties/Phase Diagrams" (L. E. Russell, ed.), p. 77. Macmillan, New York.
Darnell, A., McCollum, W., and Milne, T. (1960). *J. Phys. Chem.* **64**, 341.

Dawihl, W. (1950). *Z. Anorg. Allgem. Chem.* **262**, 212.
Deadmore, D. L. (1964). *NASA* (*Natl. Aeron. Space Admin.*), *Tech. Memo.* **TMX-52014**.
Deadmore, D. L. (1965). *J. Am. Ceram. Soc.* **48**, 357.
Deardorff, D. K., and Hayes, E. T. (1956). *Trans. AIME* **206**, 509.
Deardorff, D. K., and Kato, H. (1959). *Trans. AIME* **215**, 876.
deBoer, J. H., and Fast, J. D. (1930). *Z. Anorg. Allgem. Chem.* **187**, 193.
de Combarieu, A., Costa, P., and Michel, J. C. (1963). *Compt. Rend.* **256**, 5518.
DeCrescente, M. A., and Miller, A. D. (1964). *In* "Carbides in Nuclear Energy, Vol. 1: Physical and Chemical Properties/Phase Diagrams" (L. E. Russell, ed.), p. 342. Macmillan, New York.
Deem, H. W., and Winn, R. A. (1955). BMI-1052, p. 104, Battelle Memorial Institute, Columbus, Ohio.
DeMaria, G., Burns, R. P., Drowart, J., and Inghram, M. B. (1960). *J. Chem. Phys.* **32**, 1373.
DeSorbo, W. (1953). *J. Am. Chem. Soc.* **75**, 1825.
Dolloff, R. T., and Sara, R. V. (1961). WADD-TR-60-143, Part II, Wright Air Develop. Div., Wright-Patterson A.F.B., Ohio.
Domagala, R. F., and McPherson, D. J. (1954). *Trans. AIME* **200**, 238.
Donohue, J. (1963). *J. Am. Chem. Soc.* **85**, 1238.
Downing, J. H., Colton, N. B., and Chadwick, C. G. (1961). British Patent 870,930.
Droege, J. W., Lemmon, A. W., Jr., and Filbert, R. B., Jr. (1959). BMI-1313, pp. 38 and A-5, Battelle Memorial Institute, Columbus, Ohio.
Drowart, J., Pattoret, A., and Smoes, S. (1964). *J. Nucl. Mater.* **12**, 319.
Drowart, J., Pattoret, A., and Smoes, S. (1965). *J. Chem. Phys.* **42**, 2629; see also (1964). EURATOM Report, Contract No. 003-63-3DIRB.
Drummond, J. L., McDonald, B. J., Ockenden, H. M., and Welch, G. A. (1957). *J. Chem. Soc.* No. IV, p. 4785.
Dubrovskaya, L. B., Shveikin, G. P., and Gel'd, P. V. (1964). *Fiz. Metal. i Metalloved.* **17**,
Duwez, P. (1951). *Trans. AIME* **191**, 765.
Edwards, J. W., Johnston, H. L., and Blackburn, P. E. (1951a). *J. Am. Chem. Soc.* **73**, 4727.
Edwards, J. W., Johnston, H. L., and Blackburn, P. E. (1951b). *J. Am. Chem. Soc.* **73**, 172.
Edwards, J. W., Johnston, H. L., and Ditmars, W. E. (1953). *J. Am. Chem. Soc.* **75**, 2467.
Egan, J. J. (1964). *J. Phys. Chem.* **68**, 978. See also Bracker, J., and Egan, J. (1960). BML-659.
Ehrlich, P. (1949). *Z. Anorg. Allgem. Chem.* **259**, 1.
Eick, H., Rauh, E., and Thorn, R. (1962). *In* "Thermodynamics of Nuclear Materials," pp. 549–560. Intern. At. Energy Agency, Vienna.
Ellinger, F. H. (1943). *Trans. Am. Soc. Metals* **31**, 89.
Ellinger, F. H. (1956). *Trans. AIME* **206**, 1256.
Elliott, R. P. (1959). ARF-2120-4, Armour Research Foundation of the Illinois Institute of Technology, Technology Center, Chicago, Illinois. See also (1961). *Trans. Am. Soc. Metals* **53**, 13.
Elliott, R. P., and Larson, A. (1961). "The Metal Plutonium," Chapter 24. Am. Soc. Metals.
Elyutin, V. P., Merkulova, P. F., and Pavlov, Yu. A. (1958). *Proizv. i Obrabotka Stali i Splavov, Moskov. Inst. Stali im I. V. Stalina, Sb.* **38**, 79.
Engelke, J. L., Halden, F. A., and Farley, E. P. (1960). WADC-TR-59-654, Wright Air Develop. Center, Wright-Patterson A.F.B., Ohio.
Engle, G. B. (1961). GA-2068, General Atomics Div., General Dynamics Corp., San Diego, California.

Ervin, G., Jr., and Korst, W. L. (1966). *J. Nucl. Mater.* **19**, 193.
Ervin, G., Jr., and Miller, K. T. (1966). *Acta Met.* **14**, 222.
Evans, D. S., and Raynor, G. V. (1959). *J. Nucl. Mater.* **1**, 281.
Farr, J. D. (1962). Private communication.
Farr, J. D. (1965). Private communication.
Farr, J. D., Huber, E. J., Jr., Head, E. L., and Holley, C. E., Jr. (1959). *J. Phys. Chem.* **63**, 1455.
Farr, J. D., Witteman, W. G., Stone, P. L., and Westrum, E. F., Jr. (1965). *3rd Symp. Thermophys. Properties, Papers, La Fayette, Ind.*, Thermophysical Properties at Extreme Temperatures and Pressures (S. Gratch, ed.) p. 162. Am. Soc. Mech. Engrs. (1965).
Fast, J. D. (1952). *J. Appl. Phys.* **23**, 350.
Feber, R. C., Jr., and Herrick, C. C. (1965). LA-3184, Los Alamos Scientific Laboratory, New Mexico.
Ferguson, I. F., Ainscough, J. B., Morse, D., and Miller, A. W. (1964). *Nature* **202**, 1327.
Fesenko, V. V., and Bolgar, A. S. (1963). *Poroshkovaya Met., Akad. Nauk Ukr. SSR* **3**, 17.
Few, W. E., and Manning, G. K. (1952). *Trans. AIME* **194**, 271.
Fieldhouse, I. B., Hedge, J. C., and Lang, J. I. (1958). WADC-TR-58-274, Wright Air Develop. Div., Wright-Patterson A.F.B., Ohio.
Fieldhouse, I. B., Hedge, J. C., Lang, J. I., Takata, A. N., and Waterman, T. E. (1956). Develop. Div., Wright-Patterson A.F.B., Ohio.
Fieldhouse, I. B., Hedge, J. C., Lang, J. I., Takata, A. N., and Waterman, T. E. (1956). WADC-TR-55-495, Part I, Wright Air Develop. Div., Wright-Patterson A.F.B., Ohio.
Fisher, E. S., and McSkimin, H. J. (1961). *Phys. Rev.* **124**, 67.
Flotow, H. E., and Lohr, H. R. (1960). *J. Phys. Chem.* **64**, 904.
Foster, L. S., Forbes, L. W., Friar, L. B., and Moody, L. S. (1950). *J. Am. Ceram. Soc.* **33**, 27.
Frantsevich, I. N., and Kovens'kii, I. I. (1961). *Dopovidi Akad. Nauk Ukr. RSR* **1961** (11), 1471; translated in NASA-TTF-263.
Friederich, E., and Sittig, L. (1925). *Z. Anorg. Allgem. Chem.* **144**, 169.
Friemann, E., and Sauerwald, F. (1931). *Z. Anorg. Allgem. Chem.* **203**, 64.
Fries, R. J. (1962). *J. Chem. Phys.* **37**, 320.
Fries, R. J. (1966a). To be published.
Fries, R. J. (1966b). LA-3423, Los Alamos Scientific Laboratory, New Mexico.
Fries, R. J., and Kempter, C. P. (1960). *Anal. Chem.* **32**, 1898.
Fromm, E., and Roy, U. (1965). *J. Less-Common Metals* **8**, 73.
Fujishiro, S. (1961). *J. At. Energy Soc. Japan* **3**, 913.
Fujishiro, S., and Gokcen, N. A. (1961a). *Trans. AIME* **221**, 275.
Fujishiro, S., and Gokcen, N. A. (1961b). *J. Phys. Chem.* **65**, 161.
Fujishiro, S., and Gokcen, N. A. (1962). *J. Electrochem. Soc.* **109**, 835.
Gaev, I. S. (1953). *Zh. Neorgan. Khim.* **2**, 193.
Gantzel, P. K., and Baldwin, N. L. (1964). GA-4869, General Atomics Div., General Dynamics Corp., San Diego, California.
Gantzel, P. K., Langer, S., Baldwin, N. L., and Kester, F. L. (1965). *Advan. X-Ray Anal.* **8**, 78; see also Langer, S., Hancock, C., and Kester, F. (1962). *141st Am. Chem. Soc. Meeting, Washington, D.C.*; Langer, S., Baldwin, N. L., Gantzel, P. K., Kester, F. L., and Hancock, C. (1964). GA-5204, General Atomics Div., General Dynamics Corp. San Diego, California.

Geissen, B. C., Rump, I., and Grant, N. J. (1962). *Trans. AIME* **224**, 60.

Gel'd, P. V., and Kusenko, F. G. (1960). *Izv. Akad. Nauk SSSR, Otd. Tekhn. Nauk, Met. i Toplivo* No. 2, p. 79.

Gibson, C. D., Loomis, B. A., and Carlson, O. N. (1958). *Trans. Am. Soc. Metals* **50**, 348.

Gillam, E. (1962). *Acta Cryst.* **15**, 1183.

Gilman, J. J., and Roberts, B. W. (1961). *J. Appl. Phys.* **32**, 1405.

Ginnings, D. C., and Corruccini, R. J. (1947). *J. Res. Natl. Bur. Std.* **39**, 309.

Giorgi, A. L., Szklarz, E. G., Storms, E. K., Bowman, A. L., and Matthias, B. T. (1962). *Phys. Rev.* **125**, 837.

Gleiser, M. (1965). *J. Phys. Chem.* **69**, 1771.

Gleiser, M., and Chipman, J. (1962a). *J. Phys. Chem.* **66**, 1539.

Gleiser, M., and Chipman, J. (1962b). *Trans. AIME* **224**, 1278.

Godin, Yu. G., Evstyukhin, A. I., Emel'yanov, V. S., Rusakov, A. A., and Suchkov, I. I. (1961). *Met. i Metalloved. Chistykh Metal., Sb. Nauchn. Rabot* **1961**(3), 284.

Goldschmidt, H. J. (1948). *J. Iron Steel Inst.* (*London*) **160**, 345.

Goldschmidt, H. J., and Brand, J. A. (1963). *J. Less-Common Metals* **5**, 181; see also ASD-TDR-62-25, Part I, Air Force Systems Command, Aeronautical Systems Div., Wright-Patterson A.F.B., Ohio.

Goldschmidt, H. J., Catherall, E. A., Ham, W. M., and Oliver, D. A. (1963). ASD-TDR-62-25, Part II, Air Force Systems Command, Aeronautical Systems Div., Wright-Patterson A.F.B., Ohio.

Gorbunov, N. S., Shishakov, N. A., Saidkov, C. G., and Babad-Zakhryapin, A. A. (1961). *Izv. Akad. Nauk SSSR, Otd. Khim. Nauk* p. 2093.

Goretzki, H., Bittner, H., and Nowotny, H. (1964). *Monatsh. Chem.* **95**, 1521.

Grdina, Yu. V., and Lykhin, I. D. (1965). *Izv. Vysshikh Uchebn. Zavedenii, Chernaya Met.* **8**, 101.

Greenaway, H., Johnstone, S. T. M., and McQuillan, M. K. (1951). *J. Inst. Metals* **80**, 109.

Grigor'ev, A. T., Sokolovskaya, E. M., Simanov, Yu. P., Sokolova, I. G., Pavlov, V. N., and Maksimova, M. V. (1960). *Vestn. Mosk. Univ., Ser. II: Khim.* **15**, No. 4.

Grigor'eva, V. V., and Klimenko, V. N. (1959). *Issled. po Zharoproch. Splavam, Akad. Nauk SSSR, Inst. Met.* **4**, 317.

Grossman, L. N. (1963). *J. Am. Ceram. Soc.* **46**, 264.

Grossman, L. N. (1965). *J. Am. Ceram. Soc.* **48**, 236.

Grube, G., and Knabe, R. (1936). *Z. Elektrochem.* **42**, 793.

Guinet, P., Vaugoyeau, H., and Blum, P. L. (1965). *Compte. Rend.* **261**, 1312.

Gulbransen, E. A., and Andrew, K. F. (1952). *J. Electrochem. Soc.* **99**, 402.

Gurevich, M. A. (1963). *J. Inorg. Chem. USSR* (*English Transl.*) **8**, 1387.

Gurevich, M. A., and Ormont, B. F. (1954). *Dokl. Akad. Nauk USSR* **96**, 1165.

Gurevich, M. A., and Ormont, B. F. (1957). *Zh. Neorgan. Khim.* **7**, 1566.

Gurevich, M. A., and Ormont, B. F. (1958). *J. Inorg. Chem. USSR* (*English Transl.*) **3**, 404.

Hägg, G. (1931). *Z. Physik. Chem.* **B12**, 33.

Hägg, G., and Schönberg, N. (1954). *Acta Cryst.* **7**, 351.

Hansen, M., and Anderko, K. (1958). "Constitution of Binary Alloys." McGraw-Hill, New York.

Hansler, R. L. (1965). *J. Electrochem. Soc.* **112**, 881.

Hardy, G. F., and Hulm, J. K. (1954). *Phys. Rev.* **93** No. 5, 1004.

Harrington, L. C., and Rowe, G. H. (1964). PWAC-426, Pratt and Whitney Aircraft Div., United Aircraft Corp.; see also DeCrescente and Miller (1964).

Harrison, J. D. L., Isaacs, J. W., Roberts, W. G., and Russell, L. E. (1964). *In* "Carbides in Nuclear Energy, Vol. 2: Preparation/Fabrication/Irradiation Behavior" (L. E. Russell, ed.), p. 629. Macmillan, New York.

Hatsuta, K. (1931). *Kinzoku-no-Kenyu* **8**, 81.

Hawkins, D. T., and Orr, R. L. (1964). *J. Chem. Eng. Data* **9**, 505.

Hegedüs, A. J., and Gadó, P. (1960). *Z. Anorg. Allgem. Chem.* **305**, 227.

Hegedüs, A. J., and Neugebauer, J. (1960). *Z. Anorg. Allgem. Chem.* **305**, 216.

Hellström, K., and Westgren, A. (1933). *Svensk Kem. Tidskr.* **45**, 141.

Henney, J., and Jones, J. W. S. (1964). AERE-R 4619, Great Britain Atomic Energy Research Establishment, Harwell, Berkshire, England.

Henney, J., and Jones, J. W. S. (1965a). AERE-R 4992. Great Britain Atomic Energy Research Establishment, Harwell, Berkshire, England.

Henney, J., and Jones, J. W. S. (1965b). AERE-R 4993, Great Britain Atomic Energy Research Establishment, Harwell, Berks., England.

Henney, J., Hill, N. A. and Livey, D. T. (1962). AERE-R 4175, Great Britain Atomic Energy Research Establishment, Harwell, Berkshire, England.

Henney, J., Livey, D. T., and Hill, N. A. (1963). AERE-R 4176, Great Britain Atomic Energy Research Establishment, Harwell, Berkshire, England.

Henney, J., Jones, J. W. S., and Hill, N. A. (1964). *In* "Carbides in Nuclear Energy, Vol. 1: Physical and Chemical Properties/Phase Diagrams" (L. E. Russell, ed.), p. 69. Macmillan, New York. See also (1963). AERE-R-4456, Great Britain Atomic Energy Research Establishment, Harwell, Berkshire, England.

Henning, F., and Heuse, W. (1923). *Z. Physik* **16**, 63.

Heusler, O. (1926). *Z. Anorg. Allgem. Chem.* **154**, 353.

Hill, N. A., and Cavin, O. B. (1964a). *J. Am. Ceram. Soc.* **47**, 360; also ORNL-3588, Oak Ridge National Laboratory, Oak Ridge, Tennessee.

Hill, N. A., and Cavin, O. B. (1964b). ORNL-3668, Oak Ridge National Lab., Oak Ridge, Tennessee.

Hilpert, S., and Ornstein, M. (1913). *Ber. Deut. Chem. Ges.* **46**, 1669.

Himmelstein, P., Leibmann, B., and Schäfer, L. (1963). *4th Uranium Carbide Meeting, East Hartford, Connecticut*; TID-7676. Technical Information Div., U.S.A.E.C.

Hoch, M. (1961). AD-261335 (work performed at Ohio State University Columbus, Ohio).

Hoch, M., and Johnston, H. L. (1961). *J. Phys. Chem.* **65**, 855.

Hoch, M., Blackburn, P., Dingledy, D., and Johnston, H. (1955). *J. Phys. Chem.* **59**, 97.

Hollahan, J. R., and Gregory, N. W. (1964). *J. Phys. Chem.* **68**, 2346; see also Hollahan, J. R. (1964). Ph.D. Thesis, University of Washington, Seattle, Washington.

Huber, E. J., Jr., and Holley, C. E., Jr. (1962). *In* "Thermodynamics of Nuclear Materials," p. 581. Intern. At. Energy Agency, Vienna.

Huber, E. J., Jr., Head, E. L., and Holley, C. E., Jr. (1963). *J. Phys. Chem.* **67**, 1730; see also Vienna Panel (1963).

Huber, E. J., Jr., and Holley, C. E., Jr. (1966). Am. Chem. Soc. Meeting, Albuquerque, New Mexico, Dec. 1966.

Huber, E. J., Jr., Head, E. L., Holley, C. E., Jr., Storms, E. K., and Krikorian, N. H. (1961). *J. Phys. Chem.* **65**, 1846.

Huber, E. J., Jr., Head, E. L., Holley, C. E., Jr., and Bowman, A. L. (1963). *J. Phys. Chem.* **67**, 793.

Huddle, R. U., Gough, J. R. C., and Beutler, H. (1962). *Proc. Symp. Battelle Mem. Inst.* See TID-7654, p. 349. Technical Information Div., U.S. Atomic Energy Commission.

Humphrey, G. L. (1951). *J. Am. Chem. Soc.* **73**, 2261.

Humphrey, G. L. (1953). *J. Am. Chem. Soc.* **75**, 2806.

Humphrey, G. L. (1954). *J. Am. Chem. Soc.* **76**, 978.

Hunt, E. B., and Rundle, R. E. (1951). *J. Am. Chem. Soc.* **73**, 4777.

Hüttig, G. F., Fattinger, V., and Kohla, K. (1950). *Powder Met. Bull.* **5**, 307.

Imai, Y., Ishizaki, T., and Yano, N. (1957). Japanese Patent 634.

Imoto, S., Sano, T., Takada, Y., Yamamoto, K., Watanabe, K., Isoda, T., and Uchikoshi, H. (1964). *In* "Carbides in Nuclear Energy, Vol. 1: Physical and Chemical Properties/Phase Diagrams" (L. E. Russell, ed.), p. 7. Macmillan, New York.

Jackson, D. D., Barton, G. W., Jr., Krikorian, O. H., and Newbury, R. S. (1962). *In* "Thermodynamics of Nuclear Materials," p. 529. Intern. At. Energy Agency, Vienna. See also (1962). UCRL-6701, University of California, Lawrence Radiation Laboratory, Livermore, California.

Jacobson, B., and Westgren, A. (1933). *Z. Physik. Chem.* **B20**, 361.

Jaeger, F. M., and Rosenbohm, E. (1932). *Rec. Trav. Chim.* **51**, 1.

Jaeger, F. M., and Veenstra, W. A. (1934). *Rec. Trav. Chim.* **53**, 677.

Jaffee, R. I., Ogden, H. R., and Maykuth, D. J. (1950). *Trans. AIME* **188**, 1261.

James, W. J., and Straumanis, M. E. (1961). *Z. Physik. Chem.* **29**, 134.

JANAF Tables. (1963). JANAF Thermochemical Tables, Dow Chemical Co., Midland, Michigan.

Johnson, T. R., White, G. D., Kruger, O. L., Steunenberg, R. K., and Handwerk, J. (1963). *4th Uranium Carbide Meeting, East Hartford, Connecticut*, TID-7676, Technical Information Div., U.S.A.E.C. See also (1962). ANL-6543 and ANL-6569, Argonne National Laboratory, Lemont, Illinois.

Joly, A. (1876). *Compt. Rend.* **82**, 1905.

Joly, A. (1877). *Ann. Sci. Ecole Norm. Super.* (*Paris*) **6**, 145.

Jones, T. (1956). TID-7567, Part I, pp. 32–45, Technical Information Div., U.S. Atomic Energy Commission.

Kachik, E. A., *et al.* (1946). Progress report on the metallurgical aspects of metal and metal ceramic bodies for use at high-temperature in jet and rocket engine surface. Report No. 5, School of Mineral Industries, Pennsylvania State University.

Kalish, H. S. (1960). *2nd Uranium Carbide Meeting, Battelle Memo. Inst., Columbus, Ohio*, TID-7589, p. 59. Technical Information Div., U.S. At. Energy Comm. See also (1961). TID-7614, pp. 93–111.

Karnaukhova, N. M. (1964). *Zh. Teckhn. Fiz.* **34**, 1906.

Katz, J. J., and Rabinowitch, E. (1951). "The Chemistry of Uranium," pp. 232–241. McGraw-Hill, New York.

Kaufman, L. (1962). *Trans. AIME* **224**, 1006.

Kaufman, L., and Sarney, A. (1964). *In* "International Symposium on Compounds of Interest in Nuclear Reactor Technology" (J. T. Waber, P. Chiotti, and W. N. Miner, eds.), p. 267. Met. Soc. Am. Inst. Mining, Met. Petrol. Engrs.

Kaye, G. (1962). *Nature* **195**, 1195.

Keller, D. L., Fackelmann, J. M., Speidel, E. O., and Paprocki, S. J. (1961). *In* "Powder Metallurgy in the Nuclear Age," (F. Benesovsky, ed.) Plansee Proceedings, p. 304.

Kelley, K. K. (1940a). *J. Chem. Phys.* **8**, 316.

Kelley, K. K. (1940b). *J. Am. Chem. Soc.* **62**, 818.

Kelley, K. K. (1944). *Ind. Eng. Chem.* **36**, 865.

Kelley, K. K., and King, E. G. (1961). *U.S. Bur. Mines, Bull.* **592**.

Kelley, K. K., Boericke, F. S., Moore, G. E., Huffman, E. H., and Bangert, W. M. (1944). *U.S. Bur. Mines, Tech. Paper* **662**.

Kempter, C. P. (1956). *J. Am. Chem. Soc.* **78**, 6209.

Kempter, C. P. (1962). *Inorg. Chem.* **1**, 975; see also *J. Less-Common Metals* **4**, 419–25.

Kempter, C. P., and Fries, R. J. (1960). *Anal. Chem.* **32**, 570.

Kempter, C. P., and Krikorian, N. H. (1962). *J. Less-Common Metals* **4**, 244.

Kempter, C. P., and Nadler, M. R. (1960). *J. Chem. Phys.* **32**, 1477.

Kempter, C. P., and Nadler, M. R. (1965). *J. Chem. Phys.* **43**, 1739.

Kempter, C. P., Storms, E. K., and Fries, R. J. (1960). *J. Chem. Phys.* **33**, 1873.

Kendall, E. G., Slaughter, J. I., and Riley, W. C. (1965). A65-23321; also SSD-TR-65-78, Ballistic Systems and Space Systems Divisions, Air Force Systems Command, Los Angeles Air Force Station, Los Angeles; also TDR-469(5250-10)-11 Aerospace Corporation, El Sequndo, California.

Kent, R. A. (1963). Ph.D. Thesis, Michigan State University, East Lansing, Michigan.

Kerr, W. (1963). NAA-SR-8943, North American Aviation, Inc.

Kibler, G. M., Lyon, T. F., Linevsky, J. J., and DeSantis, V. J. (1963). AD-403529, Flight Propulsion Laboratory Department, General Electric Co., Cincinnati, Ohio.

Kieffer, R., and Benesovsky, F. (1963). "Hartstoffe." Springer-Verlag, Vienna.

Kieffer, R., and Kölbl, F. (1949). *Powder Met. Bull.* **4**, 4.

Kimura, H., and Sasaki, Y. (1961). *Trans. Japan Inst. Metals* **2**, 98.

King, E. G. (1949). *J. Am. Chem. Soc.* **71**, 316.

Kingery, W. D., and Halden, F. A. (1955). *Am. Ceram. Soc. Bull.* **34**, 117.

Kirillin, V. A., Sheindlin, A. E., and Chekhovskoi, V. Ya. (1962). *Intern. J. Heat Mass Transfer* **5**, 1.

Kirillin, V. A., Sheindlin, A. E., Chekhovski, V. Ya., and Zhukova, I. A. (1965). *High Temp. (English Transl.)* **3**, 357.

Klopp, W. D., Maykuth, D. J., Ogden, H. R., and Jaffee, R. I. (1960). *Trans. AIME* **218**, 971.

Knapton, A. G., Savill, J., and Siddall, R. (1960). *J. Less-Common Metals* **2**, 357.

Kolchin, O. P., and Cheveluva, N. P. (1959). *Tsvetn. Metal.* **32**, 60.

Kopyleva, V. P. (1961). *Zh. Prikl. Khim.* **34**, 1936.

Korbitz, F. W., Jr. (1964). Ph.D. Thesis, Iowa State University, Ames, Iowa.

Kornilov, A. N., Leonidov, V. Ya., and Skuratov, S. N. (1962). *Moscow Univ., Vestnik Seriia Khim.* **17**, No. 6, 48.

Kornilov, A. N., Zaikin, I. D., Skuratov, S. M., Dubrovskaya, L. B., and Shveikin, G. P. (1964). *Zh. Fiz. Khim.* **38**, 702.

Kornilov, A. N., Zaikin, I. D., Skuratov, S. M., and Shveikin, G. P. (1966). *Zh. Fiz. Khim.* **40**, 1070.

Kosolapova, T. Ya., and Samsonov, G. V. (1959). *Zh. Prikl. Khim.* **32**, 1505.

Kosolapova, T. Ya., and Samsonov, G. V. (1961). *Russ. J. Phys. Chem. (English Transl.)* **35**, 363.

Kosolapova, T. Ya., and Samsonov, G. V. (1962). *Ukr. Khim. Zh.* **28**, 931.

Kotö, H. I., and Suzuki, K. (1948). *X-Sen* **5**, 15.

Kovalchenko, M. S., and Samsonov, G. V. (1961). *Dopovidi Adad. Nauk Ukr. RSR* **1961**, 478.

Koval'skii, A. E., and Makarenko, T. G. (1951). *Trans. Conf. Microhardness, 1951* p. 187. Acad. Sci. U.S.S.R. Press, Moscow.

Koval'skii, A. E., and Makarenko, T. G. (1953). *Zh. Tekn. Fiz.* **23**, 265.

Kraftmakher, Ya. A. (1963a). *Fiz. Tverd. Tela* **5**, 950.

Kraftmakher, Ya. A. (1963b). *Zh. Prikl. Mekhan. i Tekhn. Fiz.* **1963**, 158.

Krainer, H., and Konopicky, K. (1947). *Hüettenmaenn. Monatsh. Montan. Hochschule Leoben* **92**, 166.

Krauss, F. (1958). *Z. Metallk.* **49**, 386.
Krikorian, N. H. (1963). Private communication.
Krikorian, N. H. (1965). Private communication.
Krikorian, N. H., and Wallace, T. C. (1964a). *J. Electrochem. Soc.* **111**, 1431.
Krikorian, N. H., and Wallace, T. C. (1964b). Private communication to S. Langer (quoted in Langer *et al.*, 1964).
Krikorian, N. H., and Wallace, T. C. (1966). To be published.
Krikorian, N. H., Witteman, W. G., and Bowman, M. G. (1963). *J. Electrochem. Soc.* **110**, 560.
Krikorian, O. H. (1962). UCRL-6785, University of California, Lawrence Radiation Laboratory, Livermore, California.
Kruger, O. L. (1962). *J. Nucl. Mater.* **7**, 142; see also ANL-6330, Argonne National Laboratory, Lemont, Illinois.
Kruger, O. L. (1963). *J. Am. Ceram. Soc.* **46**, 80; See also (1962). ANL-FGF-343, Argonne National Laboratory, Lemont, Illinois.
Kruger, O. L. (1964). *In* "International Symposium on Compounds of Interest in Nuclear Reactor Technology" (J. T. Waber, P. Chiotti, and W. N. Miner, eds.), p. 387. Met. Soc. Am. Inst. Mining, Met. Petrol. Enginrs.
Kruger, O. L., and Savage, H. (1964). *J. Chem. Phys.* **40**, 3324.
Krupka, M. C. (1965). Reported by Storms (1966a).
Krupka, M. C. (1966). Private communication.
Kubaschevski, O., and Heymer, G. (1960). *Acta Met.* **8**, 416.
Kuo, K., and Hägg, G. (1952). *Nature* **170**, 245.
Kurnakov, N. N., and Troneva, M. Ya. (1962). *Russ. J. Inorg. Chem.* (*English Transl.*) **7**, 80.
Kusenko, F. G., and Gel'd, P. V. (1960). *Izv. Sibirsk. Otd. Akad. Nauk SSSR* **1960**(2), 46.
Kusenko, F. G., and Gel'd, P. V. (1961). *Izv. Vysshikh Uchebn. Zavendenii, Tsvetn. Met.* **4**, 43.
Kutsev, V. S., and Ormont, B. F. (1955). *Zh. Fiz. Khim.* **24**, 597.
Kutsev, V. S., Ormont, B. F., and Epel'baum, V. A. (1955). *Dokl. Akad. Nauk SSSR* **104**, 567.
Lander, J. J., and Germer, L. H. (1948). *Trans. AIME* **175**, 648.
Langer, S., Baldwin, N., Gantzel, P., Kester, F., and Hancock, C. (1964). *In* "International Symposium on Compounds of Interest in Nuclear Reactor Technology" (J. Waber, P. Chiotti, and W. N. Miner, eds.), p. 359. Met. Soc. Am. Inst. Mining, Met. Petrol. Engrs.
Larson, A. C., Roof, R. B., Jr., and Cromer, D. T. (1965). LA-3335, Los Alamos Scientific Laboratory, New Mexico.
Lautz, G., and Schneider, D. (1961). *Z. Naturforsch.* **16a**, 1368.
Lazareva, L., Kantor, P. B., and Kandyba, V. V. (1961). *Fiz. Metal. i Metalloved.* **11**, 628.
Leary, J. A. (1966). Private communication.
Leciejewicz, J. (1960). *Polish Acad. Sci., Inst. Nucl. Res., Rept.* **142/I-B**, (Translated in NP-9682); see also (1961). *Acta Cryst.* **14**, 200.
Lehman, G. W. (1960). WADD-TR-60-581, Wright Air Develop. Div., Wright-Patterson A.F.B., Ohio.
Leitnaker, J. M., and Witteman, W. G. (1962). *J. Chem. Phys.* **36**, 1445.
Lesser, R., and Brauer, G. (1958). *Z. Metallk.* **49**, 622.
Levinson, L. S. (1963a). *J. Chem. Phys.* **38**, 2105.
Levinson, L. S. (1963b). *J. Chem. Phys.* **39**, 1550; see also (1965). *ibid.* **42**, 3342.
Levinson, L. S. (1964a). *J. Chem. Phys.* **40**, 1437.
Levinson, L. S. (1964b). *J. Chem. Phys.* **40**, 3584.
Levinson, L. S. (1964c). *In* "Carbides in Nuclear Energy, Vol. 1: Physical and Chemical Properties/Phase Diagrams" (L. E. Russell, ed.), p. 429, Macmillan, New York.

Levinson, L. S. (1965). *J. Chem. Phys.* **42**, 2891.

Lewis, G. N., and Randall, M. (1961). "Thermodynamics." McGraw-Hill, New York (revised by K. S. Pitzer and L. Brewer).

Lichter, B. (1960). *Trans. AIME* **218**, 1015.

Litton, F. B. (1951). *J. Electrochem. Soc.* **98**, 488.

Litz, L. M., Garrett, A. B., and Croxton, F. C. (1948). *J. Am. Chem. Soc.* **70**, 1718; see also Litz, L. M. (1948). Ph.D. Thesis, Ohio State University, Columbus, Ohio.

Lofgren, N. L., and Krikorian, O. H. (1964). *In* "Carbides in Nuclear Energy, Vol. 1: Physical and Chemical Properties/Phase Diagrams" (L. E. Russell, ed.), p. 315. Macmillan, New York.

Lonsdale, H. K., and Graves, J. N. (1962). *In* "Thermodynamics of Nuclear Materials," p. 601. Intern. At. Energy Agency, Vienna. See also (1962). GA-3015, General Atomics Div., General Dynamics Corp., San Diego, California.

Lowell, C. E., and Williams, W. S. (1961). *Rev. Sci. Instr.* **32**, 1120.

Lowenthal, G. C. (1963). *Australian J. Phys.* **16**, 47.

Lyon, T. F. (1964). *Proc. Intern. Symp., Condensation Evaporation Solids, Dayton, Ohio, 1962* p. 435. See also Coffman *et al.* (1963).

McCabe, C. L., Hudson, R. G., and Paxton, H. W. (1958). *Trans. AIME* **212**, 102.

McCaldin, J. O., and Duwez, P. (1954). *J. Metals* **6**; *Trans. AIME* **200**, 619.

McClaine, L. A. (1963). ASD-TDR-62-204, Part II, Air Force Systems Command, Aeronautical Systems Div., Wright-Patterson A.F.B., Ohio.

McClaine, L. A. (1964). ASD-TDR-62-204, Part III, Air Force Systems Command, Aeronautical Systems Div., Wright-Patterson A.F.B., Ohio.

MacDonald, N. F., and Ransley, C. E. (1959). *Powder Met.* (*London*) **3**, 173.

McDonald, R. A., Oetting, F. L., and Prophet, H. (1964). *Proc. Meeting Interagency Chem. Rocket Propulsion Group Thermochem., New York, 1963*, CPIA-44, vol. 1, p. 213, Chemical Propulsion Information Agency, The Johns Hopkins Univ. Appl. Phys. Lab., Georgia Ave., Silver Spring, Maryland.

McGraw, L. D., Seltz, H., and Snyder, P. E. (1947). *J. Am. Chem. Soc.* **69**, 329.

McGuire, T. R., and Kriessman, C. J. (1952). *Phys. Rev.* **85**, 452.

McKenna, P. M. (1936). *Ind. Eng. Chem.* **28**, 767.

McMasters, O. D., and Larsen, W. L. (1961). *J. Less-Common Metals* **3**, 312.

McMullin, J. G., and Norton, J. T. (1953). *Trans. AIME* **197**, 1205.

McQuillan, A. D. (1951). *Proc. Roy. Soc.* **A204**, 309; see also (1950–1951). *J. Inst. Metals* **78**, 249.

Magnier, P., and Accary, A. (1964). *In* "Carbides in Nuclear Energy, Vol. 1: Physical and Chemical Properties/Phase Diagrams" (L. E. Russell, ed.), p. 22. Macmillan, New York.

Magnier, P., and Accary, A. (1965). Rept. CEA-R-2731, Documentation Française, Secrétariat Général du Gouvernement, Direction de la Documentation, 16, rue Lord Byron, Paris VIIIème.

Magnier, P., Collard, C., Tournarie, M., and Accary, A. (1964a). *In* "Carbides in Nuclear Energy, Vol. 1: Physical and Chemical Properties/Phase Diagrams" (L. E. Russell, ed.), p. 41. Macmillan, New York.

Magnier, P., Trouvé, J., and Accary, A. (1964b). *In* "Carbides in Nuclear Energy, Vol. 1: Physical and Chemical Properties/Phase Diagrams" (L. E. Russell, ed.), p. 95. Macmillan, New York.

Magnus, A., and Holzmann, H. (1929). *Ann. Phys.* (*Paris*) [10] **3**, 585.

Mah, A. D. (1954). *J. Am. Chem. Soc.* **76**, 3363.

Mah, A. D. (1963a). BM-RI-6177, Bureau of Mines (Reports of Investigations).

Mah, A. D. (1963b). BM-RI-6337, Bureau of Mines (Reports of Investigations).
Mah, A. D. (1964). BM-RI-6518, Bureau of Mines (Reports of Investigations).
Mah, A. D. (1965). BM-RI-6663, Bureau of Mines (Reports of Investigations).
Mah, A. D., and Boyle, B. J. (1955). *J. Am. Chem. Soc.* **77**, 6512.
Mah, A. D., Kelley, K. K., Gellert, N. L., King, E. G., and O'Brien, C. J. (1957). BM-RI-5316, Bureau of Mines (Reports of Investigations).
Maier, C. G., and Kelley, K. K. (1932). *J. Am. Chem. Soc.* **54**, 3243.
Mallett, M. W., Gerds, A. F., and Vaughn, D. A. (1951). *J. Electrochem. Soc.* **98**, 505; see also (1950). AECD-3060. Atomic Energy Commission Declassification number.
Mallett, M. W., Gerds, A. F., and Nelson, H. R. (1952). *J. Electrochem. Soc.* **99**, 197; see also (1951). AECD-3226. Atomic Energy Commission Declassification number.
Malter, L., and Langmuir, D. B. (1939). *Phys. Rev.* **55**, 743.
Marchal, M., and Accary, A. (1963). DP-Report-133. Documentation Française, Secrétariat Général du Gouvernement, Direction de la Documentation, 16, rue Lord Byron, Paris VIIIème.
Markovskii, L. Ya., Vekshina, N. V., and Shtrikhman, R. A. (1957). *Ogneupory* **22**, 42.
May, C. E., and Hoekstra, P. D. (1961). *NASA (Natl. Aeron. Space Admin.), Tech. Note* **TN-D-844**; see also NASA-memo-3-5-59E (1959).
Maykuth, D. J., Ogden, H. R., and Jaffee, R. I. (1953). *Trans. AIME* **197**, 231.
Meerson, G. A., and Krein, O. E. (1952). *J. Appl. Chem. USSR (English Transl.)* **25**, 143.
Meerson, G. A., and Krein, O. E. (1960a). *Zh. Neorgan. Khim.* **5**, 1164.
Meerson, G. A., and Krein, O. E. (1960b). *Zh. Neorgan. Khim.* **5**, 1924.
Meerson, G. A., and Samsonov, G. V. (1952). *J. Appl. Chem. USSR (English Transl.)* **25**, 823.
Meerson, G. A., and Umanskii, Ya. S. (1953). *Izv. Sektora Fiz.-Khim. Analiza, Inst. Obshch. Neorgan. Khim., Akad. Nauk SSSR* **22**, 104.
Meerson, G. A., Kotel'nikov, R. B., and Bashlykov, S. N. (1960). *At. Energ. (USSR)* **9**, 387–391.
Meinhardt, D., and Krisement, O. (1960). *Z. Naturforsch.* **15a**, 880.
Metcalfe, A. G. (1946). *J. Inst. Metals* **73**, 591.
Mersol, S. A., Vahldiek, F. W., and Lynch, C. T. (1966). *J. Less-Common Metals* **10**, 373.
Mezaki, R., Tilleux, E. W., Jambois, T. F., and Margrave, J. L. (1965). *3rd Symp. Thermophys. Properties, Papers, Lafayette, Ind.*, Thermophysical Properties at Extreme Temperatures and Pressures (S. Gratch, ed.) 1965. Am. Soc. Mech. Engrs. See also Margrave, J. L. (1962). ASD-TDR-62-204, Part I, Air Force Systems Command, Aeronautical Systems Div., Wright-Patterson A.F.B., Ohio.
Miccioli, B. R., and Shaffer, P. T. B. (1964). *J. Am. Ceram. Soc.* **47**, 351.
Mickelson, R., and Peterson, D. (1958). *Trans. Am. Soc. Metals* **50**, 340; see also Peterson, D., and Mickelson, R. (1954). ISC-463, Iowa State University, Ames, Iowa.
Moers, K. (1931). *Z. Anorg. Allgem. Chem.* **198**, 243.
Moissan, H. (1893a). *Compt. Rend.* **116**, 1222.
Moissan, H. (1893b). *Compt. Rend.* **116**, 1225.
Moissan, H. (1893c). *Compt. Rend.* **116**, 349.
Moissan, H. (1895a). *Compt. Rend.* **120**, 290.
Moissan, H. (1895b). *Compt. Rend.* **120**, 1320.
Moissan, H. (1896). *Compt. Rend.* **122**, 1297.
Moissan, H. (1897a). *Compt. Rend.* **125**, 839.
Moissan, H. (1897b). *Z. Anorg. Allgem. Chem.* **14**, 174.
Moissan, H., and Hoffmann, M. K. (1904). *Compt. Rend.* **138**, 1558.
Moore, G., and Kelley, K. K. (1957). *J. Am. Chem. Soc.* **69**, 2105.

Morette, A. (1938). *Bull. Soc. Chim. France* **5**, 1063.
Moser, J. B., and Kruger, O. L. (1965). *J. Nucl. Mater.* **17**, 153.
Mueller, M. H., and Hitterman, R. L. (1960). Reported by E. F. Sturcken in "Determination of Theoretical Diffraction Intensities for Alpha-uranium," Report NLCO-804, p. 49. U.S. At. Energy Comm.
Mukaibo, T., Naito, K., Sato, K., and Uchijima, T. (1962). *In* "Thermodynamics of Nuclear Materials," p. 645. Intern. At. Energy Agency, Vienna.
Mulford, R. N. R. (1966a). *In* "Thermodynamics," Vol. I, p. 231. Intern. At. Energy Agency, Vienna.
Mulford, R. N. R. (1966b). To be published.
Mulford, R. N. R., Ellinger, F. H., Hendrix, G. S., and Albrecht, E. D. (1960). *In* "Plutonium" (E. Grison, W. B. H. Lord, and R. D. Fowler, eds.), 1961, p. 301. Cleaver-Hume Press, London.
Mulford, R. N. R., Ford, J. O., and Hoffman, J. G. (1962). *In* "Thermodynamics of Nuclear Materials," p. 517. Intern. At. Energy Agency, Vienna.
Mulford, R. N. R., Ellinger, F. H., and Johnson, K. A. (1965). *J. Nucl. Mater.* **17**, 324.
Müller, L. (1930). *Ann. Physik* [5] **7**, 48.
Müller, S., and Dünner, P. (1965). *Z. Naturforsch.* **20a**, 1225.
Münster, A. (1959). *Z. Elektrochem.* **63**, 807.
Nadler, M. R., and Kempter, C. P. (1960). *J. Phys. Chem.* **64**, 1468.
Nakagawa, M. (1957). *Kogyo Kagaku Zasshi* **60**, 379.
Namba, S., Imoto, S., and Sano, T. (1962). *Technol. Rept. Osaka Univ.* **12**, 429.
Naylor, B. F. (1946). *J. Am. Chem. Soc.* **68**, 370.
Neel, D. S., Pears, C. D., and Oglesby, S., Jr. (1960). WADD-TR-60-924, Wright Air Develop. Div., Wright-Patterson A.F.B., Ohio (work done at Southern Research Institute).
Neshpor, V. S., and Ordan'yan, S. S. (1965). *Izv. Akad. Nauk SSSR, Neorgan. Materialy* **1**, 480.
Nesmeyanov, A., and Man, D. (1960). *Proc. Acad. Sci. USSR, Phys. Chem. Sect.* (*English Transl.*) **131**, 373.
Newkirk, A. E., and Aliferis, I. (1957). *J. Am. Chem. Soc.* **79**, 4629.
Newkirk, H. W., Jr., and Bates, J. L. (1959). HW-59468, General Electric Co., Hanford Atomic Products Operation, Richland, Washington.
Nikolaiski, E. (1960). *Z. Physik. Chem.* (*Frankfurt*) **24**, 405.
Nishimura, H., and Kimura, H. (1954). *Bull. Eng. Res. Inst. Kyoto Univ.* **6**, 19; see also *Nippon Kinzoku Gakkaish* **20**, 589 (1956).
Norman, J. H., and Winchell, P. (1964). *J. Phys. Chem.* **68**, 3802.
Norreys, J. J., Wheeler, M. J., and Gillam, E. (1964). *In* "Carbides in Nuclear Energy, Vol. 1: Physical and Chemical Properties/Phase Diagrams" (L. E. Russell, ed.), p.1. Macmillan, New York.
Norton, J. T., and Lewis, R. K. (1963). N63-18389, Advanced Metals Research Corp., Somerville, Massachusetts; see also NASA-CR-321, National Aeronautics and Space Administration, Washington 25, D.C.
Norton, J. T., and Lewis, R. K. (1964). NASA-CR-67380, Advanced Metals Research Corp., Somerville, Massachusetts; see also NASA-CR-58046 or N64-27289.
Nowotny, H., and Kieffer, R. (1952). *Z. Anorg. Allgem. Chem.* **267**, 261.
Nowotny, H., Parthé, E., Kieffer, R., and Benesovsky, F. (1954a). *Z. Metallk.* **45**, 97.
Nowotny, H., Parthé, E., Kieffer, R., and Benesovsky, F. (1954b). *Monatsh. Chem.* **85**, 255.

Nowotny, H., Kieffer, R., Benesovsky, F., and Brukl, C. (1959). *Monatsh. Chem.* **90**, 86.

Ogard, A. E., Pritchard, W. C., Douglass, R. M., and Leary, J. A. (1962). *In* "Powder Metallurgy in the Nuclear Age," (F. Benesovsky, ed.) Plansee Proceedings, p. 364. Springer, Vienna; see also (1962). *J. Inorg. Nucl. Chem.* **24**, 29.

Ogard, A. E., Land, C. C., and Leary, J. A. (1965). *J. Nucl. Mater.* **15**, 43.

Ogawa, K., and Bando, Y. (1959). *Funtai Oyobi Funmatsuyakin* **6**, 160.

Ogden, H. R., Schmidt, F. F., and Bartlett, E. S. (1963). *Trans. AIME* **227**, 1458.

Ohlinger, L. A. (1959a). *U.S. Govt. Res. Rept.* **32**, 83; PB 135661 or NEPA 735-NOR-51, Northrop Aircraft, Inc., Hawthorne.

Ohlinger, L. A. (1959b). *U.S. Govt. Res. Rept.* **32**, 82; PB 135682.

Oldham, S. E., and Fishel, W. P. (1932). *J. Am. Chem. Soc.* **54**, 3610.

Oriani, R. A., and Jones, T. S. (1954). *Rev. Sci. Instr.* **25**, 248.

Oriani, R. A., and Murphy, W. K. (1954). *J. Am. Chem. Soc.* **76**, 343.

Orton, G. W. (1961). Univ. Microfilms L. C. Card No. Mic 61-2839, *Dissertation Abstr.* **22**, 527; Ph.D. Thesis, Ohio State University, Columbus, Ohio.

Ôsawa, A., and Ôya, M. (1930). *Sci. Rept. Tohoku Univ., First Ser.* **19**, 95.

Osment, D. (1963). ASD-TDR-62-765, Air Force Systems Command, Aeronautical Systems Div., Wright-Patterson A.F.B., Ohio (work done at Southern Research Institute).

Owen, B. B., and Webber, R. T. (1948). *Trans. AIME* **175**, 693.

Palfreyman, M., and Keig, G. A. (1962). AERE-M 1106, Great Britain Atomic Energy Research Establishment, Harwell, Berkshire, England.

Palfreyman, M., and Potter, P. E. (1964). *In* "Carbides in Nuclear Energy, Vol. 1: Physical and Chemical Properties/Phase Diagrams" (L. E. Russell, ed.), p. 336. Macmillan, New York.

Palfreyman, M., and Russell, L. E. (1962). *In* "Powder Metallurgy in the Nuclear Age" (F. Benesovsky, ed.) Plansee Proceedings, p. 417. Springer, Vienna. See also Palfreyman and Keig (1962).

Pan, V. M. (1964). *Sb. Nauchn. Tr. Inst. Metallofiz., Akad. Nauk Ukr. SSR* **20**, 130.

Pankratz, L. B., Weller, W. W., and Kelley, K. K. (1964). BM-RI-6446, Bureau of Mines (Reports of Investigations).

Parke, R., and Bens, F. (1946). *Symp. Mater. Gas Turbines, 49th Meeting, Buffalo, N. Y., 1946* p. 80. Am. Soc. Testing Mater., Philadelphia, Pa.

Parrish, W. (1960). *Acta Cryst.* **13**, 838.

Parthé, E. (1961). AFOSR-1721, Office of Scientific Research, Baltimore, Maryland.

Parthé, E., and Sadagopan, V. (1963). *Acta Cryst.* **16**, 202; see also (1962). NP-11699.

Pascard, R. (1962). *In* "Powder Metallurgy in the Nuclear Age," (F. Benesovsky, ed.) Plansee Proceedings, p. 387. Springer, Vienna.

Pattoret, A., Smoes, S., and Drowart, J. (1966). *In* "Thermodynamics," Vol. 1, p. 377. Intern. At. Energy Agency, Vienna. See also (1965). EURATOM Report EUR 2458. f., translation available as Dounreay Translation 224, Dounreay Experimental Reactor Estab., Dounreay, Caithness, England.

Pemsler, J. P. (1961). *J. Electrochem. Soc.* **108**, 744.

Peterson, D. T. (1961). *Trans. Am. Soc. Metals* **53**, 765.

Phipps, T. E., Sears, G. W., Seifert, R. L. and Simpson, O. C. (1956). *Proc. U.N. Intern. Conf. Peaceful Uses At. Energy, Geneva 1955* Vol. 7, p. 382, U.N., New York.

Piazza, J. R., and Sinnott, M. J. (1962). *J. Chem. Eng. Data* **7**, 451–7.

Pirani, H. M., and Alterthum, H. (1923). *Z. Elektrochem.* **29**, 5.

Pochon, M. L., McKinsey, C. R., Perkins, R. A., and Forgeng, W. D. (1959). Metallurgical Society Conference, Vol. 2: "Reactive Metals," p. 327. Wiley (Interscience), New York.

Pollard, F. H., and Woodward, P. (1950). *Trans. Faraday Soc.* **46**, 190.

Pollock, B. D. (1961). *J. Phys. Chem.* **65**, 731.

Portnoĭ, K. I., Levinskiĭ, Yu. V., and Fadeeva, V. I. (1961). *Izv. Akad. Nauk SSSR, Otd. Tekhn. Nauk, Met. i Toplivo* **1961**(2), 147.

Powell, C. F., Campbell, I. E., and Gonser, B. W. (1955). "Vapor Plating." Wiley, New York.

Prescott, C. H., Jr. (1926). *J. Am. Chem. Soc.* **48**, 2534.

Prescott, C. H., Jr., and Hincke, W. B. (1927). *J. Am. Chem. Soc.* **49**, 2744.

Pring, J. N., and Fielding, W. (1909). *J. Chem. Soc.* **95**, 1497.

Pütz, P. (1906). *Metallurgie (Paris)* **3**, 649.

Quarterly Status Report. (1962). LAMPRE Program for Period Ending Nov. 20, LAMS-2815, Los Alamos Scientific Laboratory, New Mexico.

Ragone, D. V. (1951). B.S. Thesis, Department of Metallurgy, Massachusetts Institute of Technology, Cambridge, Massachusetts.

Raman, S., and Ramachandran, G. N. (1962). *Current Sci. (India)* **8**, 321.

Rand, M. H. (1962). *In* "Thermodynamics of Nuclear Materials," p. 71. Intern. At. Energy Agency, Vienna.

Rand, M. H., and Kubaschewski, O. (1960). AERE-R-3487, Great Britain Atomic Energy Research Establishment, Harwell, Berkshire, England. See also "Thermochemical Properties of Uranium Compounds." Wiley (Interscience), New York.

Rand, M. H., and Street, R. S. (1964). *In* "Carbides in Nuclear Energy, Vol. 1: Physical and Chemical Properties/Phase Diagrams" (L. E. Russell, ed.), p. 108. Macmillan, New York.

Rand, M. H., Fox, A. C., and Street, R. S. (1962). *Nature* **195**, 567.

Rasor, N. S., and McClelland, J. D. (1960). *Phys. Chem. Solids* **15**, 17; see also WADC-TR-56-400, Part 1. Wright Air Develop. Div., Wright-Patterson A.F.B., Ohio.

Rassaerts, H., Benesovsky, F., and Nowotny, H. (1966). *Planseeber. Pulvermet.* **14**, 23.

Rauh, E. G., and Thorn, R. J. (1954). *J. Chem. Phys.* **22**, 1414.

Read, M. H., and Altman, C. (1965). *Appl. Phys. Letters* **7**, 51.

Redfield, T. A., and Hill, J. H. (1951). ORNL-1087, Oak Ridge National Laboratory, Oak Ridge, Tennessee.

Reid, A. F., Wilmhurst, R. E., and Wylie, A. W. (1963). *J. Electrochem. Soc.* **110**, 429.

Rengstorff, P. W. (1947). M.S. Thesis, Department of Metallurgy, Massachusetts Institute of Technology, Cambridge, Massachusetts.

Rexer, J., and Peterson, D. T. (1964). AEC-39821, Rept. No. IS-875, Atomic Energy Commission.

Riley, B. (1964). *J. Sci. Instr.* **41**, 504.

Robins, D. A. (1959). *Natl. Phys. Lab., Gt. Brit., Proc. Symp.* **9**, 2.

Robinson, W. C., and Chiotti, P. (1964). IS-1061, Iowa State University, Ames, Iowa, TID-4500, Technical Information Div., U.S.A.E.C.

Robinson, W. C., and Chiotti, P. (1966). *J. Less-Common Metals* **10**, 190–199.

Romans, P. A., Paasche, O. G., and Kato, H. (1965). *J. Less-Common Metals* **8**, 213.

Rosen, S., Nevitt, M. V., and Mitcell, A. W. (1963). *J. Nucl. Mater.* **10**, 90.

Ross, R. G., and Hume-Rothery, W. (1963). *J. Less-Common Metals* **5**, 258.

Rostoker, W., and Yamamoto, A. (1954). *Trans. Am. Soc. Metals* **46**, 1136.

Rough, F. A., and Chubb, W. (1959). BMI-1370, Battelle Memorial Institute, Columbus, Ohio.

Rudy, E. (1965). AFML-TR-65-2, Part I, Volume IV, Air Force Materials Laboratory, Research and Technology Division, Air Force Systems Command, Wright-Patterson A.F.B., Ohio (work done at Aerojet-General Corporation.)

Rudy, E. (1966). Private communication.

Rudy, E., and Benesovsky, F. (1963). *Monatsh. Chem.* **94**, 204.

Rudy, E., and Brukl, C. (1966). *J. Am. Ceram. Soc.*, to be published.

Rudy, E., and Harmon, D. P. (1965). AFML-TR-65-2, Part I, Volume V, Air Force Materials Laboratory Research and Technology Division, Air Force Systems Command, Wright-Patterson A.F.B., Ohio.

Rudy, E., Benesovsky, F., and Sedlatschek, K. (1961). *Monatsh. Chem.* **92**, 841.

Rudy, E., Rudy, E., and Benesovsky, F. (1962a). *Monatsh. Chem.* **93**, 522.

Rudy, E., Rudy, E., and Benesovsky, F. (1962b). *Planseeber. Pulvermet.* **10**, 42.

Rudy, E., Rudy, E., and Benesovsky, F. (1962c). *Monatsh. Chem.* **93**, 1176.

Rudy, E., Harmon, D. P., and Brukl, C. E. (1965a). AFML-TR-65-2, Part I, Vol. II, Air Force Materials Laboratory, Research and Technology Division, Air Force Systems Command, Wright-Patterson, A.F.B., Ohio.

Rudy, E., Windisch, St. and Chang, Y. A. (1965b). AFML-TR-65-2, Part I, Vol. I, Air Force Materials Laboratory, Research and Technology Division, Air Force Systems Command, Wright-Patterson, A.F.B., Ohio.

Rudy, E., Windisch, St., and Hoffman, J. R. (1966). AFML-TR-65-2, Part I, Vol. VI, Air Force Materials Laboratory, Research and Technology Division, Air Force Systems Command, Wright-Patterson A.F.B., Ohio.

Ruff, O., and Martin, W. (1912). *Z. Angew. Chem.* **25**, 49.

Ruff, O., and Wunsch, R. (1914). *Z. Anorg. Allgem. Chem.* **85**, 292.

Rundle, R. E., Baenziger, N. C., Wilson, A. S., and McDonald, R. A. (1948). *J. Am. Chem. Soc.* **70**, 99; see also (1948). AECD-2247 and (1958). Report TID-5290, Technical Information Div., U.S. Atomic Energy Commission.

Rupert, G. (1963). *Rev. Sci. Instr.* **34**, 1183.

Samsonov, G. V. (1956). *Ukr. Khim. Zh.* **23**, 287 (English transl. in AEC-TR-3387).

Samsonov, G. V., and Golubeva, N. K. (1956). *Zh. Fiz. Khim.* **30**, 1258.

Samsonov, G. V., and Kosolapova, T. Ya. (1961). *Zh. Prikl. Khim.* **34**, 2780.

Samsonov, G. V., and Paderno, V. N. (1961). *Zh. Prikl. Khim.* **34**, 963.

Samsonov, G. V., and Rozinova, N. S. (1956). *Bull. Sect. Phys. Chem.* **34**, 963–969.

Samsonov, G. V., and Rukina, V. B. (1957). *Dopovidi Akad. Nauk Ukr. RSR* p. 247.

Samsonov, G. V., Kosolapova, T. Ya., and Paderno, V. N. (1960). *Zh. Prikl. Khim.* **33**, 1661.

Sandenaw, T. A., and Storms, E. K. (1965). LA-3331, Los Alamos Scientific Laboratory, New Mexico; see also Sandenaw, T. A., and Storms, E. K. (1966). *J. Phys. Chem. Solids* **27**, 217.

Sano, T., Imoto, S., and Takada, Y. (1960). *J. At. Energy Soc. Japan* **2**, 285.

Sano, T., Imoto, S., Namba, S., and Katsura, M. (1963). *Intern. At. Energy Agency Conf. New Nucl. Mater. Technol., Prague, 1963*, Vol. 1, p. 429, IAEA, Vienna.

Santoro, G. J. (1963). *Trans. AIME* **227**, 1361.

Santoro, G. J. (1965). *NASA* (*Natl. Aeron. Space Admin.*), *Tech. Note* **TN D-2638**.

Santoro, G. J., and Probst, H. B. (1965). *Advan. X-Ray Anal.* **7**, 126.

Sara, R. V. (1965a). *J. Am. Ceram. Soc.* **48**, 243.

Sara, R. V. (1965b). *Trans. AIME* **233**, 1683.

Sara, R. V. (1965c). *J. Am. Ceram. Soc.* **48**, 251.

Sara, R. V., and Lowell, C. E. (1964). WADD TDR-60-143, Part V, Wright Air Develop. Div., Wright-Patterson A.F.B., Ohio.

Sara, R. V., Lowell, C. E., and Dolloff, R. T. (1963). WADD TR 60-143, Part IV, Wright Air Develop. Div., Wright-Patterson A.F.B., Ohio.

Savage, H., and Seibel, R. D. (1963). ANL-6702, Argonne National Laboratory, Lemont, Illinois.

Scaife, D. E., and Wylie, A. W. (1958). *Australian At. Energy Symp., Proc. Sydney, 1958* p. 172. Melbourne Univ. Press, Victoria, Australia.

Schenck, R., Kurzen, F., and Wesselkock, H. (1931). *Z. Anorg. Allgem. Chem.* **203**, 159.

Schick, H. L. (1966). "Thermodynamics of Certain Refractory Compounds," Vol. II, Academic Press, New York, 1966.

Schmidt, F. F., Klopp, W. D., Albrecht, W. M., Holden, F. C., Ogden, H. R., and Jaffee, R. I. (1959). WADD-TR-59-13, Wright Air Develop. Div., Wright-Patterson A.F.B., Ohio.

Schofield, T. H. (1957). *J. Inst. Metals* **85**, 372.

Schofield, T. H., and Bacon, A. E. (1953). *J. Inst. Metals* **82**, 167.

Schönberg, N. (1954). *Acta Chem. Scand.* **8**, 624.

Schuler, D. (1952). Thesis, Tech. Hochschule, Zurich.

Schwarzkopf, P., and Kieffer, R. (1953). "Refractory Hard Metals." Macmillan, New York.

Sears, M. B., Ferris, L. M., and Gray, R. J. (1966). *J. Electrochem. Soc.* **113**, 269.

Seybolt, A. U. (1954). *J. Metals* **6**, 774.

Shaffer, P. T. B. (1963). *Am. Ceram. Soc.* **46**, 177.

Shimer, P. W. (1887). *Proc. Roy. Soc.* **42**, 89; see also (1887). *Chem. News* **55**, 156.

Shomate, C. H. (1944). *J. Am. Chem. Soc.* **66**, 928; see also (1954). *J. Phys. Chem.* **58**, 368.

Shomate, C. H., and Kelly, K. K. (1949). *J. Am. Chem. Soc.* **71**, 314.

Shveikin, G. P. (1958). *Tr. Inst. Khim., Akad. Nauk SSSR, Ural'sk. Filial* p. 51; see also *ibid.* No. 2, 45. Translated in AEC-TR-4303; *Sverdlorsk. Inst. Khim.* No. 2, 51 (translation); Shveikin, G. P., Gel'd, P. V., and Alyamovskii, S. I. (1963). *J. Inorg. Chem. USSR* **8**, 350.

Shveikin, G. P., and Gel'd, P. V. (1961). *Tsvetn. Metal.* **34**, 39.

Siemens, R. E., Babitzke, H. R., and Kato, H. (1964). *U.S. Bur. Mines, Rept. Invest.* **6492**(8).

Skaupy, F. (1927). *Z. Elektrochem.* **33**, 487.

Skavdahl, R. E. (1963). *Trans. Am. Nucl. Soc.* **6**, 393.

Skinner, G. B., Edwards, J. W., and Johnston, H. L. (1951). *J. Am. Chem. Soc.* **73**, 174.

Slade, R. E., and Higson, G. I. (1919). *J. Chem. Soc.* **115**, 205.

Smiley, W. G. (1955). *Anal. Chem.* **27**, 1098.

Smirnova, V. I., and Ormont, B. F. (1954). *Dokl. Akad. Nauk SSSR* **96**, 557 (Henry Brutcher Transl. No. 3376).

Smirnova, V. I., and Ormont, B. F. (1955). *Dokl. Akad. Nauk SSSR* **100**, 127 [UCRL Transl. No. 255 (L)].

Smirnova, V. I., and Ormont, B. F. (1956). *Zh. Fiz. Khim.* **30**, 1327.

Smith, D. K., and Cline, C. F. (1963). *J. Am. Ceram. Soc.* **46**, 566.

Smith, M. D., and Honeycombe, R. W. K. (1959). *J. Nucl. Mater.* **1**, 345.

Smith, M. E., Hansel, J. M., Johnson, R. B., and Waterbury, G. R. (1963). *Anal. Chem.* **35**, 1502.

Smith, W. H. (1957). *J. Metals* **9**, 47.

Smithells, C. J., and Williams, S. V. (1929). *Nature* **124**, 617.

Sowden, R. G., Hodge, N., Moreton-Smith, M. J., and White, D. B. (1964). *In* "Carbides in Nuclear Energy, Vol. I: Physical and Chemical Properties/Phase Diagrams" (L. E. Russell, ed.), p. 297. Macmillan, New York.

Speiser, R., Johnston, H. L., and Blackburn, P. (1950). *J. Am. Chem. Soc.* **72**, 4142.
Speiser, R., Spretnak, J. W., Few, W. E., and Parke, R. M. (1952). *J. Metals* **4**, 275.
Speiser, R., Blackburn, P., and Johnston, H. L. (1959). *J. Electrochem. Soc.* **106**, 52.
Stecher, P., Benesovsky, F., and Nowotny, H. (1964). *Planseeber. Pulvermet.* **12**, 89.
Stein, C., and Grant, N. J. (1955). *Trans. AIME* **203**, 127.
Sterrett, K. F., and Wallace, W. E. (1958). *J. Am. Chem. Soc.* **80**, 3176.
Stone, L., and Margolin, H. (1953). WAL-401/85-21, Watertown Arsenal Laboratory, Massachusetts.
Stone, P. L. (1962). Private communication.
Stoops, R. F., and Hamme, J. V. (1962). NSCS-2663-9, North Carolina State College, Raleigh, North Carolina.
Stoops, R. F., and Hamme, J. V. (1964). *J. Am. Ceram. Soc.* **47**, 59.
Storms, E. K. (1962). Private communication to Fries (1962).
Storms, E. K. (1964). LA-2942, Los Alamos Scientific Laboratory, New Mexico.
Storms, E. K. (1965). Unpublished observations.
Storms, E. K. (1966a). *In* "Thermodynamics," Vol. 1, p. 309. Intern. At. Energy Agency, Vienna.
Storms, E. K. (1966b). To be published.
Storms, E. K., and Fries, R. J. (1966). To be published.
Storms, E. K., and Huber, Jr., E. J. (1967). *J. Nucl. Mater.*, in press.
Storms, E. K., and Kempter, C. P. (1965). *J. Chem. Phys.* **42**, 2043.
Storms, E. K., and Krikorian, N. H. (1960). *J. Phys. Chem.* **64**, 1471.
Storms, E. K., and McNeal, R. J. (1962). *J. Phys. Chem.* **66**, 1401.
Storms, E. K., Witteman, W. G., and Krupka, M. C. (1966). To be published.
Stout, N. D. (1964). UCRL-12003, University of California, Lawrence Radiation Laboratory, Livermore, California.
Street, R. S., and Waters, T. N. (1962). AERE-M-1114, Great Britain Atomic Energy Research Establishment, Berkshire, England.
Stull, D. R., and Sinke, G. C. (1956). "Thermodynamic Properties of the Elements." Am. Chem. Soc., Washington, D.C.
Sykes, W. P. (1930). *Trans. Am. Soc. Steel Treating* **18**, 968.
Sykes, W. P., Van Horn, K. R., and Tucker, C. M. (1935). *Trans. AIME* **117**, 173.
Tadashi, K., and Tadashi, S. (1958). *Denki Shikensho Iho* **22**, 509.
Takahashi, Y., Westrum, E. F., Jr., and Kent, R. A. (1965). *J. Chem. Eng. Data* **10**, 128.
Takei, T. (1928). *Sci. Rept. Tohoku Univ., First Ser.* **17**, 939.
Takeuchi, S., Honma, T., Satow, T., and Hirai, T. (1966). *Trans. Japan Inst. Metals* **7**, 59.
Taylor, A., and Doyle, N. J. (1964). *J. Less-Common Metals* **7**, 37.
Taylor, A., Doyle, N. J., and Kagle, B. J. (1961). *J. Less-Common Metals* **3**, 265.
Taylor, A., Kagle, B. J., and Doyle, N. J. (1963). *J. Less-Common Metals* **5**, 26.
Taylor, B. L., Milner, G. W. C., Binks, F. T., and Prior, H. A. (1964). *In* "Carbides in Nuclear Energy, Vol. 1: Physical and Chemical Properties/Phase Diagrams" (L. E. Russell, ed.), p. 457. Macmillan, New York.
Taylor, K. M. (1960). TID-7589, p. 14, Technical Information Div., U.S. Atomic Energy Commission.
Taylor, R. E., and Finch, R. A. (1961). NAA-SR-6034, North American Aviation, Inc.
Taylor, R. E., and Nakata, M. M. (1962). NAA-AI-7034, North American Aviation, Inc.
Terao, N. (1964). *Japan J. Appl. Phys.* **3**, 104.
Thompson, J. G. (1933). *Metals & Alloys* **4**, 114.
Tofaute, W., Küttner, C., and Büttinghaus, A. (1935). *Arch. Eisenhuettenw.* **9**, 607.

Tripler, A. B., Jr., Snyder, M. J., and Duckworth, W. H. (1959). BMI-1313, Battelle Memorial Institute, Columbus, Ohio.

Troost, L. (1865). *Compte Rend.* **61**, 109.

Trulson, O. C., and Goldstein, H. W. (1965). *J. Phys. Chem.* **69**, 2531.

Tutiya, H. (1932). *Tokyo Inst. Phys. Chem. Res. Abstr.* **5**, 121.

Udy, M. C., and Boulger, F. W. (1954). *Trans. AIME* **200**, 207.

Umanskii, Ya. (1940). *Zh. Fiz. Khim.* **14**, 332; see also (1940–1941). *Struct. Rept.* **8**, 48.

Umanskii, Ya. (1943). *Acad. Sci. USSR, Phys.-Chem. Anal.* **26**, 127.

Vaughn, D. A., Melton, C. W., and Gerds, A. F. (1957). BMI-1175, Battelle Memorial Institute, Columbus, Ohio.

Vidale, G. L. (1961). Technical Information Series R61SD147, Space Sciences Laboratory, General Electric Co., King of Prussia, Pennsylvania.

Vienna Panel. (1963). "The Uranium-Carbon and Plutonium-Carbon Systems, A Thermochemical Assessment," Rept. No. 14, Intern. At. Energy Agency, Vienna.

Villagrana, R. E., and Thomas, G. (1965). *Phys. Status Solidi* **9**, 499; see also Villagrana, R. E. (1965). UCRL-11782; Villagrana, R. E., and Thomas, G. (1965). *Appl. Phys. Letters* **6**, 61.

Vintaikin, E. Z. (1959). *Proc. Acad. Sci. USSR, Phys. Chem. Sect.* (*English Transl.*) **129**, 951.

Vintaikin, E. Z. (1963). *Fiz. Metal. i Metalloved.* **16**, 144.

Volkova, N. M., and Gel'd, P. V. (1963). *Izv. Vysshikh Uchebn. Zavedenii, Tsvetn. Met.* p. 89.

Volkova, N. M., and Gel'd, P. V. (1965). *Izv. Vysshikh Uchebn. Zavedenii, Tsvetn. Met.* p. 77.

Volkova, N. M., Alyamovskii, S. I., and Gel'd, P. V. (1963). *Izv. Akad. Nauk SSSR, Otd. Tekhn. Nauk, Met. i Gorn. Delo* p. 134.

Volkova, N. M., Gel'd, P. V., and Alyamovskii, S. I. (1965). *Zh. Neorgan. Khim.* **10**, 1768.

von Stackelberg, M. (1930). *Z. Physik. Chem.* (*Frankfurt*) **9B**, 437.

Vozzella, P. A., and DeCrescente, M. A. (1965). PWAC-478, Pratt and Whitney Aircraft, Middletown, Connecticut.

Vozzella, P. A., Miller, A. D., and DeCrescente, M. A. (1963). *4th Uranium Carbide Meeting, East Hartford, Connecticut*, TID-7676, Technical Information Div., U.S.A.E.C. See also (1962). PWAC-378, Pratt and Whitney Aircraft, Middletown, Connecticut.

Wagner, F. C., Bocur, E. J., and Steinberg, M. A. (1956). *Trans. Am. Soc. Metals* **48**, 742.

Wallace, T. C. (1966a). To be published.

Wallace, T. C. (1966b). Private communication.

Wallace, T. C., and Bowman, A. L. (1966). To be published.

Wallace, T. C., Gutierrez, C. P., and Stone, P. L. (1963). *J. Phys. Chem.* **67**, 796.

Wallace, T. C., Krikorian, N. H., and Stone, P. L. (1964). *J. Electrochem. Soc.* **111**, 1404.

Webb, W. W., Norton, J. T., and Wagner, C. (1956). *J. Electrochem. Soc.* **103**, 112.

Weiss, G. (1946). *Ann. Chim.* (*Paris*) [12] **1**, 446.

Westbrook, J. (1957). *J. Metals* **9**, 898.

Westgren, A. (1930). *Metallwirtschaft* **9**, 921.

Westgren, A. (1933). *Jernkontorets Ann.* **117**, 501.

Westgren, A., and Phragmén, G. (1926). *Z. Anorg. Allgem. Chem.* **156**, 27.

Westrum, E. F., Jr., and Feick, G. (1963). *J. Chem. Eng. Data* **8**, 176.

Westrum, E. F., Jr., Suits, E., and Lonsdale, H. K. (1965). *3rd Symp. Thermophys. Properties, Papers, Lafayette, Ind., 1965* Thermophysical Properties at Extreme Temperatures and Pressures (S. Gratch, ed.) p. 156. Am. Soc. Mech. Engrs.

Wilhelm, H. A., and Chiotti, P. (1950). *Trans. Am. Soc. Metals* **42**, 1295; see also (1950). AECD-3072.

Wilhelm, H. A., Chiotti, P., Snow, A. I., and Daane, A. H. (1949). *J. Chem. Soc.* Suppl. Issue No. 2, p. S318.

Wilhelm, H. A., Carlson, O. N., and Dickinson, J. M. (1954). *J. Metals* **6**, 915.

Willens, R. H., and Buehler, E. (1965). *Appl. Phys. Letters* **7**, 25.

Williams, J. T. (1955). *Trans. AIME* **203**, 345.

Williams, J. T., and Sambell, R. A. J. (1959). *J. Less-Common Metals* **1**, 217.

Williams, J. T., Sambell, R. A. J., and Wilkinson, D. (1960). AERE-M-625, Great Britain Atomic Energy Research Establishment, Harwell, Berkshire, England; see also (1960). *J. Less-Common Metals* **2**, 352.

Williams, R. O. (1958). *Trans. AIME* **209**, 1257.

Williams, W. S. (1961). *J. Appl. Phys.* **32**, 552.

Williams, W. S., and Lye, R. G. (1964). ML-TDR-64-25, Part I, Air Force Materials Laboratory, Research and Technology Div., Air Force Systems Command, Wright-Patterson A.F.B., Ohio.

Wilson, W. B. (1960). *J. Am. Ceram. Soc.* **43**, 77.

Witteman, W. G. (1963). Private communication.

Witteman, W. G. (1966). Private communication.

Witteman, W. G., and Bowman, M. G. (1963). *4th Uranium Carbide Meeting, East Hartford, Connecticut*, TID-7676, Technical Information Div., U.S.A.E.C.

Witteman, W. G., and Wallace, T. C. (1966). To be published.

Witteman, W. G., Leitnaker, J. M., and Bowman, M. G. (1958). LA-2159, Los Alamos Scientific Laboratory, New Mexico.

Wood, R. M. (1962). *Proc. Phys. Soc.* (*London*) **80**, 783.

Worrell, W. L., and Chipman, J. (1964). *J. Phys. Chem.* **68**, 860.

Worthing, A. G. (1924). *Z. Physik* **22**, 9.

Worthing, A. G. (1925). *Phys. Rev.* **25**, 846.

Yvon, K., Reiger, W., and Nowotny, H. (1966). *Monatsh. Chem.* **97**, 689.

Zachariasen, W. H. (1952). *Acta Cryst.* **5**, 17.

Zachariasen, W. H., and Ellinger, F. H. (1955). *Acta Cryst.* **8**, 431.

Zachariasen, W. H., and Ellinger, F. H. (1963a). *Acta Cryst.* **16**, 777.

Zachariasen, W. H., and Ellinger, F. H. (1963b). *Acta Cryst.* **16**, 369.

Zalabak, C. F. (1961). *NASA* (*Natl. Aeron. Space Admin.*), *Tech. Note* **TN D-761**.

Zaplatynsky, I. (1966). *J. Am. Ceram. Soc.* **49**, 109.

Zelikman, A. N., and Govorit, N. N. (1950). *J. Appl. Chem. USSR* (*English Transl.*) **23**, 727.

Zhelankin, V. I., and Kutsev, V. S. (1964). *Zh. Fiz. Khim.* **38**, 562.

Zhelankin, V. I., Kutsev, V. S., and Ormont, B. F. (1958). *Zh. Neorgan Khim.* **3**, 1237.

Zhelankin, V. I., Kutsev, V. S., and Ormont, B. F. (1961). *Zh. Fiz. Khim.* **35**, 1288; see also *Zh. Fiz. Khim.* **33**, 1988 (1959).

Ziegler, G. W., Jr. (1950). Ph.D. Thesis, Ohio State University, Columbus, Ohio.

AUTHOR INDEX

Numbers in italics indicate the pages on which the complete references are listed.

C

I

J

SUBJECT INDEX